CONTROL VALVE HANDBOOK

Third Edition

FISHER CONTROLS INTERNATIONAL, INC

Marshalltown, Iowa 50158 U.S.A.
Cernay 68700 France
Sao Paulo 05424 Brazil
Singapore 128461

Preface to Third Edition

Control valves are an increasingly vital component of modern manufacturing around the world. Well–selected and maintained control valves increase efficiency, safety, profitability, and ecology.

The *Control Valve Handbook* has been a primary reference for more than 30 years. This third edition is a complete revision and update that includes vital information on control valve performance and the latest technologies.

- Chapter 1 offers an introduction to control valves including definitions for common control valve and instrumentation terminology.
- Chapter 2 develops the vital topic of control valve performance.
- Chapter 3 covers valve and actuator types.
- Chapter 4 describes digital valve controllers, analog positioners, boosters, and other control valve accessories.
- Chapter 5 is a comprehensive guide to selecting the best control valve for an application.
- Chapter 6 covers the selection and use of special control valves.
- Chapter 7 covers desuperheaters, steam conditioning valves, and turbine bypass systems.
- Chapter 8 offers typical control valve installation and maintenance procedures.
- Chapter 9 includes information on control valve standards and approval agencies throughout the world.
- Chapter 10 offers useful tables of engineering reference data.
- Chapter 11 includes piping reference data.
- Chapter 12 is a handy resource for common conversions.

The *Control Valve Handbook* is both a textbook and a reference on the strongest link in the control loop: the control valve and its accessories. This book includes extensive and proven knowledge from leading experts in the process control field including contributions from the ISA and the Crane Company.

Table of Contents

Table of Contents

Chapter 1

Introduction to Control Valves

What Is A Control Valve?

Process plants consist of hundreds, or even thousands, of control loops all networked together to produce a product to be offered for sale. Each of these control loops is designed to keep some important process variable such as pressure, flow, level, temperature, etc. within a required operating range to ensure the quality of the end product. Each of these loops receives and internally creates disturbances that detrimentally affect the process variable, and interaction from other loops in the network provides disturbances that influence the process variable.

To reduce the effect of these load disturbances, sensors and transmitters collect information about the process variable and its relationship to some desired set point. A controller then processes this information and de-cides what must be done to get the process variable back to where it should be after a load disturbance occurs. When all the measuring, comparing, and calculating are done, some type of final control element must implement the strategy selected by the controller.

The most common final control element in the process control industries is the control valve. The control valve manipulates a flowing fluid, such as gas, steam, water, or chemical compounds, to compensate for the load disturbance and keep the regulated process variable as close as possible to the desired set point.

Many people who talk about control valves or valves are really referring to a control valve assembly. The control valve assembly typically consists of the valve body, the internal trim parts, an actuator to provide the motive power to operate the valve, and a variety of additional valve accessories, which can include positioners, transducers, supply pressure regulators, manual operators, snubbers, or limit switches. Other chapters of this handbook supply more detail about each of these control valve assembly components.

Whether it is called a valve, control valve or a control valve assembly, is not as important as recognizing that the control valve is a critical part of the control loop. It is not accurate to say that the control valve is the most important part of the loop. It is useful to think of a control loop as an instrumentation chain. Like any other chain, the whole chain is only as good as its weakest link. It is important to ensure that the control valve is not the weakest link.

Following are definitions for process control, sliding-stem control valve, rotary-shaft control valve, and other control valve functions and characteristics terminology.

NOTE:

Definitions with an asterisk (*) are from the ISA Control Valve Terminology draft standard S75.05 dated October, 1996, used with permission.

Process Control Terminology

Accessory: A device that is mounted on the actuator to complement the actuator's function and make it a complete operating unit. Examples include positioners, supply pressure regulators, solenoids, and limit switches.

Actuator*: A pneumatic, hydraulic, or electrically powered device that supplies force and motion to open or close a valve.

Actuator Assembly: An actuator, including all the pertinent accessories that make it a complete operating unit.

Backlash: The general name given to a form of dead band that results from a temporary discontinuity between the input and output of a device when the input of the device changes direction. Slack, or looseness of a mechanical connection is a typical example.

Capacity* (Valve): The rate of flow through a valve under stated conditions.

Closed Loop: The interconnection of process control components such that information regarding the process variable is continuously fed back to the controller set point to provide continuous, automatic corrections to the process variable.

Controller: A device that operates automatically by use of some established algorithm to regulate a controlled variable. The controller input receives information about the status of the process variable and then provides an appropriate output signal to the final control element.

Control Loop: (See Closed Loop.)

Control Range: The range of valve travel over which a control valve can maintain the installed valve gain between the normalized values of 0.5 and 2.0.

Control Valve: (See Control Valve Assembly.)

Control Valve Assembly: Includes all components normally mounted on the valve: the valve body assembly, actuator, positioner, air sets, transducers, limit switches, etc.

Dead Band: The range through which an input signal can be varied, upon reversal of direction, without initiating an observable change in the output signal. Dead band is the name given to a general phenomenon that can apply to any device. For the valve

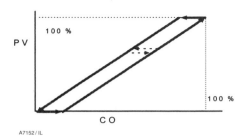

PV

100 %

100 %

CO

A7152 / IL

Figure 1-1. Process Dead Band

assembly, the controller output (CO) is the input to the valve assembly and the process variable (PV) is the output as shown in figure 1-1. When the term Dead Band is used, it is essential that both the input and output variables are identified, and that any tests to measure dead band be under fully loaded conditions. Dead band is typically expressed as a percent of the input span.

Dead Time: The time interval (Td) in which no response of the system is detected following a small (usually 0.25% - 5%) step input. It is measured from the time the step input is initiated to the first detectable response of the system being tested. Dead Time can apply to a valve assembly or to the entire process. (See T$_{63}$.)

Disk: A valve trim element used to modulate the flow rate with either linear or rotary motion. Can also be referred to as a valve plug or closure member.

Equal Percentage Characteristic*: An inherent flow characteristic that, for equal increments of rated travel, will ideally give equal percentage changes of the flow coefficient (C$_v$) (figure 1-2).

Final Control Element: The device that implements the control strategy determined by the output of the controller. While the final control element can be a damper, a variable speed drive pump, or an on-off switching de-

vice, the most common final control element in the process control industries is the control valve assembly. The control valve manipulates a flowing fluid, such as gasses, steam, water, or chemical compounds, to compensate for the load disturbance and keep the regulated process variable as close as possible to the desired set point.

First-Order: A term that refers to the dynamic relationship between the input and output of a device. A first-order system or device is one that has only one energy storage device and whose dynamic transient relationship between the input and output is characterized by an exponential behavior.

Friction: A force that tends to oppose the relative motion between two surfaces that are in contact with each other. The friction force is a function of the normal force holding these two surfaces together and the characteristic nature of the two surfaces. Friction has two components: static friction and dynamic friction. Static friction is the force that must be overcome before there is any relative motion between the two surfaces. Once relative movement has begun, dynamic friction is the force that must be overcome to maintain the relative motion. Running or sliding friction are colloquial terms that are sometimes used to describe dynamic friction. Stick/slip or "stiction" are colloquial terms that are sometimes used to describe static friction. Static friction is one of the major causes of dead band in a valve assembly.

Gain: An all-purpose term that can be used in many situations. In its most general sense, gain is the ratio of the magnitude of the output change of a given system or device to the magnitude of the input change that caused the output change. Gain has two components: static gain and dynamic gain. Static gain is the gain relationship between the input and output and is an indicator of the ease with which the input can initiate a change in the

3

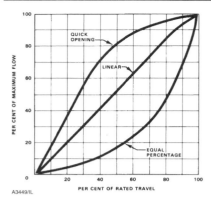

A3449/IL

Figure 1-2. Inherent Valve Characteristics

output when the system or device is in a steady-state condition. Sensitivity is sometimes used to mean static gain. Dynamic gain is the gain relationship between the input and output when the system is in a state of movement or flux. Dynamic gain is a function of frequency or rate of change of the input.

Hysteresis*: The maximum difference in output value for any single input value during a calibration cycle, excluding errors due to dead band.

Inherent Characteristic*: The relationship between the flow coefficient and the closure member (disk) travel as it is moved from the closed position to rated travel with constant pressure drop across the valve.

Typically these characteristics are plotted on a curve where the horizontal axis is labeled in percent travel and the vertical axis is labeled as percent flow (or C_v) (figure 1-2). Because valve flow is a function of both the valve travel and the pressure drop across the valve, conducting flow characteristic tests at a constant pressure drop provides a systematic way of comparing one valve characteristic design to another. Typical valve characteristics conducted in this manner

are named Linear, Equal-Percentage, and Quick Opening (figure 1-2).

Inherent Valve Gain: The magnitude ratio of the change in flow through the valve to the change in valve travel under conditions of constant pressure drop. Inherent valve gain is an inherent function of the valve design. It is equal to the slope of the inherent characteristic curve at any travel point and is a function of valve travel.

Installed Characteristic*: The relationship between the flow rate and the closure member (disk) travel as it is moved from the closed position to rated travel as the pressure drop across the valve is influenced by the varying process conditions. (See Valve Type and Characterization in Chapter 2 for more details on how the installed characteristic is determined.)

Installed Valve Gain: The magnitude ratio of the change in flow through the valve to the change in valve travel under actual process conditions. Installed valve gain is the valve gain relationship that occurs when the valve is installed in a specific system and the pressure drop is allowed to change naturally according to the dictates of the overall system. The installed valve gain is equal to the slope of the installed characteristic curve, and is a function of valve travel. (See Valve Type and Characterization in Chapter 2 for more details on how the installed gain is determined.)

I/P: Shorthand for current-to-pressure (I-to-P). Typically applied to input transducer modules.

Linearity*: The closeness to which a curve relating to two variables approximates a straight line. (Linearity also means that the same straight line will apply for both upscale and downscale directions. Thus, dead band as defined above, would typically be considered a non-linearity.)

Linear Characteristic*: An inherent flow characteristic that can be repre-

4

sented by a straight line on a rectangular plot of flow coefficient (C_v) versus rated travel. Therefore equal increments of travel provide equal increments of flow coefficient, C_v (figure 1-2).

Loop: (See Closed Loop.)

Loop Gain: The combined gain of all the components in the loop when viewed in series around the loop. Sometimes referred to as open-loop gain. It must be clearly specified whether referring to the static loop gain or the dynamic loop gain at some frequency.

Manual Control: (See Open Loop.)

Open Loop: The condition where the interconnection of process control components is interrupted such that information from the process variable is no longer fed back to the controller set point so that corrections to the process variable are no longer provided. This is typically accomplished by placing the controller in the manual operating position.

Packing: A part of the valve assembly used to seal against leakage around the valve disk or stem.

Positioner*: A position controller (servomechanism) that is mechanically connected to a moving part of a final control element or its actuator and that automatically adjusts its output to the actuator to maintain a desired position in proportion to the input signal.

Process: All the combined elements in the control loop, except the controller. The process typically includes the control valve assembly, the pressure vessel or heat exchanger that is being controlled, as well as sensors, pumps, and transmitters.

Process Gain: The ratio of the change in the controlled process variable to a corresponding change in the output of the controller.

Process Variability: A precise statistical measure of how tightly the process is being controlled about the set point. Process variability is defined in percent as typically (2s/m), where m is the set point or mean value of the measured process variable and s is the standard deviation of the process variable.

Quick Opening Characteristic*: An inherent flow characteristic in which a maximum flow coefficient is achieved with minimal closure member travel (figure 1-2).

Relay: A device that acts as a power amplifier. It takes an electrical, pneumatic, or mechanical input signal and produces an output of a large volume flow of air or hydraulic fluid to the actuator. The relay can be an internal component of the positioner or a separate valve accessory.

Resolution: The minimum possible change in input required to produce a detectable change in the output when no reversal of the input takes place. Resolution is typically expressed as a percent of the input span.

Response Time: Usually measured by a parameter that includes both dead time and time constant. (See T_{63}, Dead Time, and Time Constant.) When applied to the valve, it includes the entire valve assembly.

Second-Order: A term that refers to the dynamic relationship between the input and output of a device. A second-order system or device is one that has two energy storage devices that can transfer kinetic and potential energy back and forth between themselves, thus introducing the possibility of oscillatory behavior and overshoot.

Sensor: A device that senses the value of the process variable and provides a corresponding output signal to a transmitter. The sensor can be an integral part of the transmitter, or it may be a separate component.

5

Set Point: A reference value representing the desired value of the process variable being controlled.

Shaft Wind-Up: A phenomenon where one end of a valve shaft turns and the other does not. This typically occurs in rotary style valves where the actuator is connected to the valve closure member by a relatively long shaft. While seal friction in the valve holds one end of the shaft in place, rotation of the shaft at the actuator end is absorbed by twisting of the shaft until the actuator input transmits enough force to overcome the friction.

Sizing (Valve): A systematic procedure designed to ensure the correct valve capacity for a set of specified process conditions.

Stiction: (See Friction.)

T$_{63}$ (Tee-63): A measure of device response. It is measured by applying a small (usually 1-5%) step input to the system. T$_{63}$ is measured from the time the step input is initiated to the time when the system output reaches 63% of the final steady-state value. It is the combined total of the system Dead Time (T$_d$) and the system Time Constant (t). (See Dead Time and Time Constant.)

Time Constant: A time parameter that normally applies to a first-order element. It is the time interval measured from the first detectable response of the system to a small (usually 0.25% - 5%) step input until the system output reaches 63% of its final steady-state value. (See T$_{63}$.) When applied to an open-loop process, the time constant is usually designated as τ (Tau). When applied to a closed-loop system, the time constant is usually designated as λ (Lambda).

Transmitter: A device that senses the value of the process variable and transmits a corresponding output signal to the controller for comparison with the set point.

Travel*: The movement of the closure member from the closed position to an intermediate or rated full open position.

Travel Indicator: A pointer and scale used to externally show the position of the closure member typically with units of opening percent of travel or degrees of rotation.

Trim*: The internal components of a valve that modulate the flow of the controlled fluid.

Valve: (See Control Valve Assembly.)

Volume Booster: A stand-alone relay is often referred to as a volume booster or simply booster because it boosts, or amplifies, the volume of air supplied to the actuator. (See Relay.)

Sliding-Stem Control Valve Terminology

The following terminology applies to the physical and operating characteristics of standard sliding-stem control valves with diaphragm or piston actuators. Some of the terms, particularly those pertaining to actuators, are also appropriate for rotary-shaft control valves. Many of the definitions presented are in accordance with ISA S75.05, Control Valve Terminology, although other popular terms are also included. Additional explanation is provided for some of the more complex terms. Component part names are called out on accompanying figures 1-3 through 1-6. Separate sections follow that define specific rotary-shaft control valve terminology, control valve functions and characteristics terminology, and other process control terminology.

Actuator Spring: A spring, or group of springs, enclosed in the yoke or actuator casing that moves the actuator stem in a direction opposite to that created by diaphragm pressure.

Actuator Stem: The part that connects the actuator to the valve stem

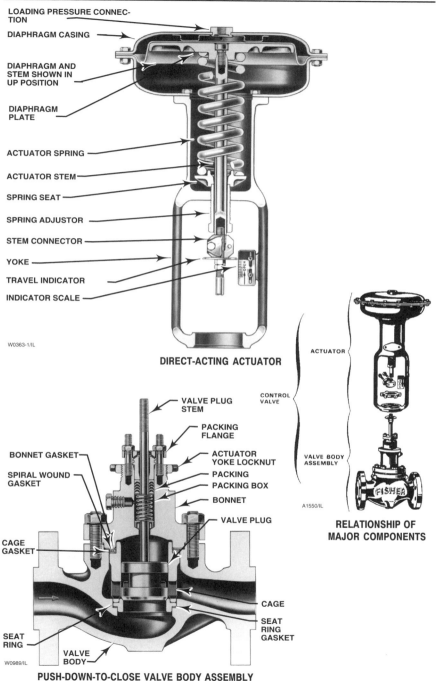

LOADING PRESSURE CONNEC-
TION

DIAPHRAGM CASING

DIAPHRAGM AND
STEM SHOWN IN
UP POSITION

DIAPHRAGM
PLATE

ACTUATOR SPRING

ACTUATOR STEM

SPRING SEAT

SPRING ADJUSTOR

STEM CONNECTOR

YOKE

TRAVEL INDICATOR

INDICATOR SCALE

W0363-1/IL

DIRECT-ACTING ACTUATOR

ACTUATOR

CONTROL
VALVE

VALVE PLUG
STEM

PACKING
FLANGE

BONNET GASKET

ACTUATOR
YOKE LOCKNUT

SPIRAL WOUND
GASKET

PACKING

PACKING BOX

BONNET

VALVE BODY
ASSEMBLY

A1550/IL

VALVE PLUG

CAGE
GASKET

**RELATIONSHIP OF
MAJOR COMPONENTS**

CAGE

SEAT
RING
GASKET

SEAT
RING

VALVE
BODY

W0989/IL

PUSH-DOWN-TO-CLOSE VALVE BODY ASSEMBLY

Figure 1-3. Major Components of Typical Sliding Stem Control Valve Assembly

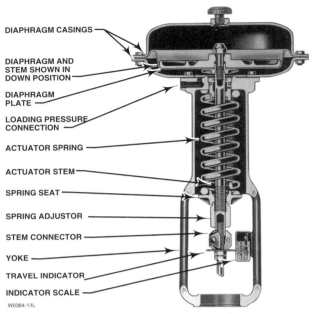

DIAPHRAGM CASINGS

DIAPHRAGM AND
STEM SHOWN IN
DOWN POSITION

DIAPHRAGM
PLATE

LOADING PRESSURE
CONNECTION

ACTUATOR SPRING

ACTUATOR STEM

SPRING SEAT

SPRING ADJUSTOR

STEM CONNECTOR

YOKE

TRAVEL INDICATOR

INDICATOR SCALE

W0364-1/IL

*Figure 1-4. Typical Reverse-Acting
Diaphragm Actuator*

W0667/IL

Figure 1-5. Extension Bonnet

W6434/IL

Figure 1-6. Bellows Seal Bonnet

and transmits motion (force) from the actuator to the valve.

Actuator Stem Extension: An extension of the piston actuator stem to provide a means of transmitting piston

motion to the valve positioner (figure 1-7).

Actuator Stem Force: The net force from an actuator that is available for actual positioning of the valve plug.

8

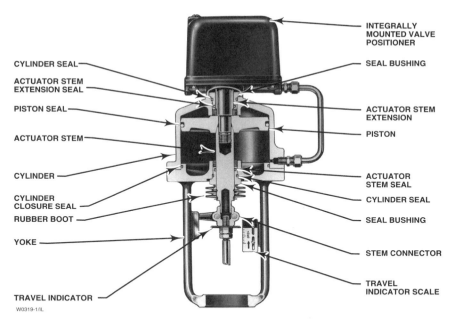

INTEGRALLY
MOUNTED VALVE
POSITIONER

CYLINDER SEAL

ACTUATOR STEM
EXTENSION SEAL

PISTON SEAL

ACTUATOR STEM

CYLINDER

CYLINDER
CLOSURE SEAL

RUBBER BOOT

YOKE

TRAVEL INDICATOR

W0319-1/IL

SEAL BUSHING

ACTUATOR STEM
EXTENSION

PISTON

ACTUATOR
STEM SEAL

CYLINDER SEAL

SEAL BUSHING

STEM CONNECTOR

TRAVEL
INDICATOR SCALE

Figure 1-7. Typical Double-Acting Piston Actuator

Angle Valve: A valve design in which one port is co-linear with the valve stem or actuator, and the other port is at a right angle to the valve stem. (See also Globe Valve.)

Bellows Seal Bonnet: A bonnet that uses a bellows for sealing against leakage around the closure member stem (figure 1–6).

Bonnet: The portion of the valve that contains the packing box and stem seal and can guide the stem. It provides the principal opening to the body cavity for assembly of internal parts or it can be an integral part of the valve body. It can also provide for the attachment of the actuator to the valve body. Typical bonnets are bolted, threaded, welded, pressure-seals, or integral with the body. (This term is often used in referring to the bonnet and its included packing parts. More properly, this group of component parts should be called the bonnet assembly.)

Bonnet Assembly: (Commonly Bonnet, more properly Bonnet Assembly): An assembly including the part through which a valve stem moves and a means for sealing against leakage along the stem. It usually provides a means for mounting the actuator and loading the packing assembly.

Bottom Flange: A part that closes a valve body opening opposite the bonnet opening. It can include a guide bushing and/or serve to allow reversal of the valve action.

Bushing: A device that supports and/or guides moving parts such as valve stems.

Cage: A part of a valve trim that surrounds the closure member and can provide flow characterization and/or a seating surface. It also provides stability, guiding, balance, and alignment, and facilitates assembly of other parts of the valve trim. The walls of the cage contain openings that usually determine the flow characteristic of

9

W0958/IL W0959/IL W0957/IL

QUICK OPENING　　　　**LINEAR**　　　　**EQUAL PERCENTAGE**

Figure 1-8. Characterized Cages for Globe-Style Valve Bodies

the control valve. Various cage styles are shown in figure 1-8.

Closure Member: The movable part of the valve that is positioned in the flow path to modify the rate of flow through the valve.

Closure Member Guide: That portion of a closure member that aligns its movement in either a cage, seat ring, bonnet, bottom flange, or any two of these.

Cylinder: The chamber of a piston actuator in which the piston moves (figure 1-7).

Cylinder Closure Seal: The sealing element at the connection of the piston actuator cylinder to the yoke.

Diaphragm: A flexible, pressure responsive element that transmits force to the diaphragm plate and actuator stem.

Diaphragm Actuator: A fluid powered device in which the fluid acts upon a flexible component, the diaphragm.

Diaphragm Case: A housing, consisting of top and bottom section, used for supporting a diaphragm and establishing one or two pressure chambers.

Diaphragm Plate: A plate concentric with the diaphragm for transmitting force to the actuator stem.

Direct Actuator: A diaphragm actuator in which the actuator stem extends with increasing diaphragm pressure.

Extension Bonnet: A bonnet with greater dimension between the packing box and bonnet flange for hot or cold service.

Globe Valve: A valve with a linear motion closure member, one or more ports, and a body distinguished by a globular shaped cavity around the port region. Globe valves can be further classified as: two-way single-ported; two-way double-ported (figure 1-9); angle-style (figure 1-10); three-way (figure 1-11); unbalanced cage-guided (figure 1-3); and balance cage-guided (figure 1-12).

Lower Valve Body: A half housing for internal valve parts having one flow connection. The seat ring is normally clamped between the upper valve body and the lower valve body in split valve constructions.

Offset Valve: A valve construction having inlet and outlet line connections on different planes but 180 degrees opposite each other.

Packing Box (Assembly): The part of the bonnet assembly used to seal against leakage around the closure

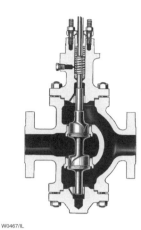

Figure 1-9. Reverse Double-Ported Globe-Style Valve Body

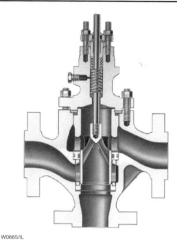

Figure 1-11. Three-Way Valve with Balanced Valve Plug

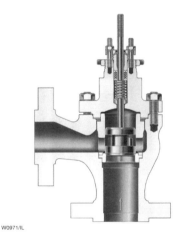

Figure 1-10. Flanged Angle-Style Control Valve Body

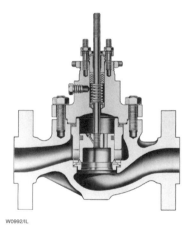

Figure 1-12. Valve Body with Cage-Style Trim, Balanced Valve Plug, and Soft Seat

member stem. Included in the complete packing box assembly are various combinations of some or all of the following component parts: packing, packing follower, packing nut, lantern ring, packing spring, packing flange, packing flange studs or bolts, packing flange nuts, packing ring, packing wiper ring, felt wiper ring, belleville springs, anti-extrusion ring. Individual

packing parts are shown in figure 1-13.

Piston: A movable pressure responsive element that transmits force to the piston actuator stem (figure 1-7).

Piston Type Actuator: A fluid powered device in which the fluid acts upon a movable piston to provide motion to the actuator stem. Piston type actuators (figure 1-7) are classified as either double-acting, so that full power

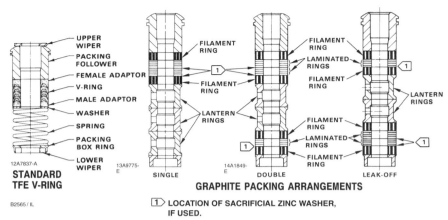

12A7837-A
**STANDARD
TFE V-RING**

B2565 / IL

13A9775-E
SINGLE

14A1849-E
DOUBLE

LEAK-OFF

GRAPHITE PACKING ARRANGEMENTS

1️⃣ LOCATION OF SACRIFICIAL ZINC WASHER,
IF USED.

*Figure 1-13. Comprehensive Packing Material Arrangements
for Globe-Style Valve Bodies*

can be developed in either direction, or as spring-fail so that upon loss of supply power, the actuator moves the valve in the required direction of travel.

Plug: A term frequently used to refer to the closure member.

Port: The flow control orifice of a control valve.

Retaining Ring: A split ring that is used to retain a separable flange on a valve body.

Reverse Actuator: A diaphragm actuator in which the actuator stem retracts with increasing diaphragm pressure. Reverse actuators have a seal bushing (figure 1-4) installed in the upper end of the yoke to prevent leakage of the diaphragm pressure along the actuator stem.

Rubber Boot: A protective device to prevent entrance of damaging foreign material into the piston actuator seal bushing.

Seal Bushing: Top and bottom bushings that provide a means of sealing

the piston actuator cylinder against leakage. Synthetic rubber O-rings are used in the bushings to seal the cylinder, the actuator stem, and the actuator stem extension (figure 1-7).

Seat: The area of contact between the closure member and its mating surface that establishes valve shut-off.

Seat Load: The net contact force between the closure member and seat with stated static conditions. In practice, the selection of an actuator for a given control valve will be based on how much force is required to overcome static, stem, and dynamic unbalance with an allowance made for seat load.

Seat Ring: A part of the valve body assembly that provides a seating surface for the closure member and can provide part of the flow control orifice.

Separable Flange: A flange that fits over a valve body flow connection. It is generally held in place by means of a retaining ring.

Spring Adjustor: A fitting, usually threaded on the actuator stem or into the yoke, to adjust the spring compression.

Spring Seat: A plate to hold the spring in position and to provide a flat surface for the spring adjustor to contact.

Static Unbalance: The net force produced on the valve stem by the fluid pressure acting on the closure member and stem with the fluid at rest and with stated pressure conditions.

Stem Connector: The device that connects the actuator stem to the valve stem.

Trim: The internal components of a valve that modulate the flow of the controlled fluid. In a globe valve body, trim would typically include closure member, seat ring, cage, stem, and stem pin.

Trim, Soft-Seated: Valve trim with an elastomeric, plastic or other readily deformable material used either in the closure component or seat ring to provide tight shutoff with minimal actuator forces.

Upper Valve Body: A half housing for internal valve parts and having one flow connection. It usually includes a means for sealing against leakage along the stem and provides a means for mounting the actuator on the split valve body.

Valve Body: The main pressure boundary of the valve that also provides the pipe connecting ends, the fluid flow passageway, and supports the seating surfaces and the valve closure member. Among the most common valve body constructions are: a) single-ported valve bodies having one port and one valve plug; b) double-ported valve bodies having two ports and one valve plug; c) two-way valve bodies having two flow connections, one inlet and one outlet; d) three-way valve bodies having three flow connections, two of which can be inlets with one outlet (for converging or mixing flows), or one inlet and two outlets (for diverging or diverting flows). The term valve body, or even just body, frequently is used in referring to the valve body together with its bonnet assembly and included trim parts. More properly, this group of components should be called the valve body assembly.

Valve Body Assembly (Commonly Valve Body or Valve, more properly Valve Body Assembly)**:** An assembly of a valve, bonnet assembly, bottom flange (if used), and trim elements. The trim includes the closure member, which opens, closes, or partially obstructs one or more ports.

Valve Plug: A term frequently interchanged with plug in reference to the closure member.

Valve Stem: In a linear motion valve, the part that connects the actuator stem with the closure member.

Yoke: The structure that rigidly connects the actuator power unit to the valve.

Rotary-Shaft Control Valve Terminology

The definitions that follow apply specifically to rotary-shaft control valves.

Actuator Lever: Arm attached to rotary valve shaft to convert linear actuator stem motion to rotary force to position disk or ball of rotary-shaft valve. The lever normally is positively connected to the rotary shaft by close tolerance splines or other means to minimize play and lost motion.

Ball, Full: The flow-controlling member of rotary-shaft control valves using a complete sphere with a flow passage through it. The flow passage equals or matches the pipe diameter.

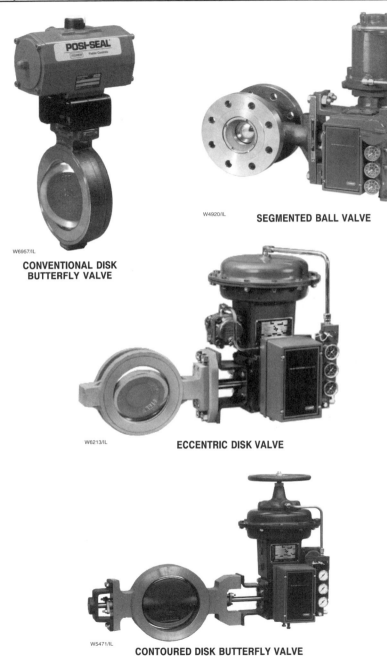

W4920/IL

SEGMENTED BALL VALVE

W6957/IL

**CONVENTIONAL DISK
BUTTERFLY VALVE**

W6213/IL

ECCENTRIC DISK VALVE

W5471/IL

CONTOURED DISK BUTTERFLY VALVE

Figure 1-14. Typical Rotary-Shaft Control Valve Constructions

Ball, Segmented: The flow–controlling member of rotary shaft control valves using a partial sphere with a flow passage through it.

Ball, V-notch: The most common type of segmented ball control valve. The V-notch ball includes a polished or plated partial-sphere surface that rotates against the seal ring throughout the travel range. The V-shaped notch in the ball permits wide rangeability and produces an equal percentage flow characteristic.

Note:

The balls mentioned above, and the disks which follow, perform a function comparable to the valve plug in a globe-style control valve. That is, as they rotate they vary the size and shape of the flowstream by opening more or less of the seal area to the flowing fluid.

Disk, Conventional: The symmetrical flow-controlling member used in the most common varieties of butterfly rotary valves. High dynamic torques normally limit conventional disks to 60 degrees maximum rotation in throttling service.

Disk, Dynamically Designed: A butterfly valve disk contoured to reduce dynamic torque at large increments of rotation, thereby making it suitable for throttling service with up to 90 degrees of disk rotation.

Disk, Eccentric: Common name for valve design in which the positioning of the valve shaft/disk connections causes the disk to take a slightly eccentric path on opening. This allows the disk to be swung out of contact with the seal as soon as it is opened, thereby reducing friction and wear.

Flangeless Valve: Valve style common to rotary-shaft control valves. Flangeless valves are held between ANSI-class flanges by long through-bolts (sometimes also called wafer-style valve bodies).

Plug, Eccentric: Style of rotary control valve with an eccentrically rotating plug which cams into and out of the seat, which reduces friction and wear. This style of valve has been well suited for erosive applications.

Reverse Flow: Flow from the shaft side over the back of the disk, ball, or plug. Some rotary-shaft control valves are capable of handling flow equally well in either direction. Other rotary designs might require modification of actuator linkage to handle reverse flow.

Rod End Bearing: The connection often used between actuator stem and actuator lever to facilitate conversion of linear actuator thrust to rotary force with minimum of lost motion. Use of a standard reciprocating actuator on a rotary-shaft valve body commonly requires linkage with two rod end bearings. However, selection of an actuator specifically designed for rotary-shaft valve service requires only one such bearing and thereby reduces lost motion.

Rotary-Shaft Control Valve: A valve style in which the flow closure member (full ball, partial ball, disk or plug) is rotated in the flowstream to control the capacity of the valve (figure 1-14).

Seal Ring: The portion of a rotary-shaft control valve assembly corresponding to the seat ring of a globe valve. Positioning of the disk or ball relative to the seal ring determines the flow area and capacity of the unit at that particular increment of rotational travel. As indicated above, some seal ring designs permit bi-directional flow.

Shaft: The portion of a rotary-shaft control valve assembly corresponding to the valve stem of a globe valve. Rotation of the shaft positions the disk or ball in the flowstream and thereby controls capacity of the valve.

Sliding Seal: The lower cylinder seal in a pneumatic piston-style actuator designed for rotary valve service. This seal permits the actuator stem to move both vertically and laterally without leakage of lower cylinder pressure.

Standard Flow: For those rotary-shaft control valves having a separate seal ring or flow ring, the flow direction in which fluid enters the valve body through the pipeline adjacent to the seal ring and exits from the side opposite the seal ring. Sometimes called forward flow. (See also Reverse Flow.)

Trunnion Mounting: A style of mounting the disk or ball on the valve shaft or stub shaft with two bearings diametrically opposed.

Control Valve Functions and Characteristics Terminology

Bench Set: The calibration of the actuator spring range of a control valve to account for the in-service process forces.

Capacity: Rate of flow through a valve under stated conditions.

Clearance Flow: That flow below the minimum controllable flow with the closure member not seated.

Diaphragm Pressure Span: Difference between the high and low values of the diaphragm pressure range. This can be stated as an inherent or installed characteristic.

Double-Acting Actuator: An actuator in which power is supplied in either direction.

Dynamic Unbalance: The net force produced on the valve plug in any stated open position by the fluid pressure acting upon it.

Effective Area: In a diaphragm actuator, the effective area is that part of the diaphragm area that is effective in producing a stem force. The effective

area of a diaphragm might change as it is stroked, usually being a maximum at the start and a minimum at the end of the travel range. Molded diaphragms have less change in effective area than flat sheet diaphragms; thus, molded diaphragms are recommended.

Equal Percentage Flow Characteristic: (See Process Control Terminology: Equal Percentage Flow Characteristic.)

Fail-Closed: A condition wherein the valve closure member moves to a closed position when the actuating energy source fails.

Fail-Open: A condition wherein the valve closure member moves to an open position when the actuating energy source fails.

Fail-Safe: A characteristic of a valve and its actuator, which upon loss of actuating energy supply, will cause a valve closure member to be fully closed, fully open, or remain in the last position, whichever position is defined as necessary to protect the process. Fail-safe action can involve the use of auxiliary controls connected to the actuator.

Flow Characteristic: Relationship between flow through the valve and percent rated travel as the latter is varied from 0 to 100 percent. This term should always be designated as either inherent flow characteristic or installed flow characteristic.

Flow Coefficient (C_v): A constant (C_v) related to the geometry of a valve, for a given travel, that can be used to establish flow capacity. It is the number of U.S. gallons per minute of $60°F$ water that will flow through a valve with a one pound per square inch pressure drop.

High-Recovery Valve: A valve design that dissipates relatively little flow-stream energy due to streamlined internal contours and minimal flow turbulence. Therefore, pressure down-

. stream of the valve vena contracta re- covers to a high percentage of its inlet value. Straight-through flow valves, such as rotary-shaft ball valves, are typically high-recovery valves.

Inherent Diaphragm Pressure Range: The high and low values of pressure applied to the diaphragm to produce rated valve plug travel with atmospheric pressure in the valve body. This range is often referred to as a bench set range because it will be the range over which the valve will stroke when it is set on the work bench.

Inherent Flow Characteristic: The relationship between the flow rate and the closure member travel as it is moved from the closed position to rated travel with constant pressure drop across the valve.

Installed Diaphragm Pressure Range: The high and low values of pressure applied to the diaphragm to produce rated travel with stated conditions in the valve body. It is because of the forces acting on the closure member that the inherent diaphragm pressure range can differ from the installed diaphragm pressure range.

Installed Flow Characteristic: The relationship between the flow rate and the closure member travel as it is moved from the closed position to rated travel as the pressure drop across the valve is influenced by the varying process conditions.

Leakage: (See Seat Leakage.)

Linear Flow Characteristic: (See Process Control Terminology: Linear Characteristic.)

Low-Recovery Valve: A valve design that dissipates a considerable amount of flowstream energy due to turbulence created by the contours of the flowpath. Consequently, pressure downstream of the valve vena contracta recovers to a lesser percentage of its inlet value than is the case with

a valve having a more streamlined flowpath. Although individual designs vary, conventional globe-style valves generally have low pressure recovery capability.

Modified Parabolic Flow Characteristic: An inherent flow characteristic that provides equal percent characteristic at low closure member travel and approximately a linear characteristic for upper portions of closure member travel.

Normally Closed Valve: (See Fail-Closed.)

Normally Open Valve: (See Fail-Open.)

Push-Down-to-Close Construction: A globe-style valve construction in which the closure member is located between the actuator and the seat ring, such that extension of the actuator stem moves the closure member toward the seat ring, finally closing the valve (figure 1-3). The term can also be applied to rotary-shaft valve constructions where linear extension of the actuator stem moves the ball or disk toward the closed position. (Also called direct acting.)

Push-Down-to-Open Construction: A globe-style valve construction in which the seat ring is located between the actuator and the closure member, so that extension of the actuator stem moves the closure member from the seat ring, opening the valve. The term can also be applied to rotary-shaft valve constructions where linear extension of the actuator stem moves the ball or disk toward the open position. (Also called reverse acting.)

Quick Opening Flow Characteristic: (See Process Control Terminology: Quick Opening Characteristic.)

Rangeability: The ratio of the largest flow coefficient (C_v) to the smallest flow coefficient (C_v) within which the deviation from the specified flow characteristic does not exceed the stated limits. A control valve that still does a good job of controlling when flow increases to 100 times the minimum controllable flow has a rangeability of 100 to 1. Rangeability can also be expressed as the ratio of the maximum to minimum controllable flow rates.

Rated Flow Coefficient (C$_v$): The flow coefficient (C$_v$) of the valve at rated travel.

Rated Travel: The distance of movement of the closure member from the closed position to the rated full-open position. The rated full-open position is the maximum opening recommended by the manufacturers.

Relative Flow Coefficient: The ratio of the flow coefficient (C$_v$) at a stated travel to the flow coefficient (C$_v$) at rated travel.

Seat Leakage: The quantity of fluid passing through a valve when the valve is in the fully closed position with pressure differential and temperature as specified. (ANSI leakage classifications are outlined in Chapter 5.)

Spring Rate: The force change per unit change in length of a spring. In diaphragm control valves, the spring rate is usually stated in pounds force per inch compression.

Stem Unbalance: The net force produced on the valve stem in any position by the fluid pressure acting upon it.

Vena Contracta: The portion of a flow stream where fluid velocity is at its maximum and fluid static pressure and the cross-sectional area are at their minimum. In a control valve, the vena contracta normally occurs just downstream of the actual physical restriction.

Other Process Control Terminology

The following terms and definitions not previously defined are frequently encountered by people associated

with control valves, instrumentation, and accessories. Some of the terms (indicated with an asterisk) are quoted from the ISA standard, Process Instrumentation Terminology, ISA 51.1-1976. Others included are also popularly used throughout the control valve industry.

ANSI: Abbreviation for American National Standards Institute.

API: Abbreviation for American Petroleum Institute.

ASME: Abbreviation for American Society of Mechanical Engineers.

ASTM: Abbreviation for American Society for Testing and Materials.

Automatic Control System*: A control system that operates without human intervention.

Bode Diagram*: A plot of log amplitude ratio and phase angle values on a log frequency base for a transfer function (figure– 1-15). It is the most common form of graphically presenting frequency response data.

Calibration Curve*: A graphical representation of the calibration report (figure 1-15). Steady state output of a device plotted as a function of its steady state input. The curve is usually shown as percent output span versus percent input span.

Calibration Cycle*: The application of known values of the measured variable and the recording of corresponding values of output readings, over the range of the instrument, in ascending and descending directions (figure 1-15). A calibration curve obtained by varying the input of a device in both increasing and decreasing directions. It is usually shown as percent output span versus percent input span and provides a measurement of hysteresis.

Clearance Flow: That flow below the minimum controllable flow with the closure general member not seated.

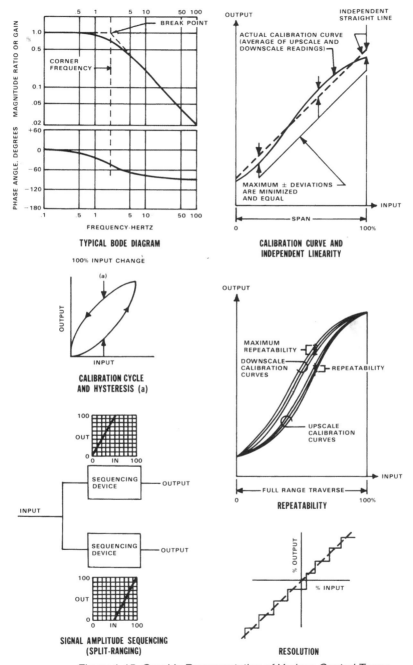

Figure 1-15. Graphic Representation of Various Control Terms

Controller*: A device that operates automatically to regulate a controlled variable.

Enthalpy: A thermodynamic quantity that is the sum of the internal energy of a body and the product of its volume multiplied by the pressure: $H = U + pV$. (Also called the heat content.)

Entropy: The theoretical measure of energy that cannot be transformed into mechanical work in a thermodynamic system.

Feedback Signal*: The return signal that results from a measurement of the directly controlled variable. For a control valve with a positioner, the return signal is usually a mechanical indication of closure member stem position that is fed back into the positioner.

FCI: Abbreviation for Fluid Controls Institute.

Frequency Response Characteristic*: The frequency-dependent relation, in both amplitude and phase, between steady-state sinusoidal inputs and the resulting fundamental sinusoidal outputs. Output amplitude and phase shift are observed as functions of the input test frequency and used to describe the dynamic behavior of the control device.

Hardness: Resistance of metal to plastic deformation, usually by indentation. Resistance of plastics and rubber to penetration of an indentor point into its surface.

Hunting*: An undesirable oscillation of appreciable magnitude, prolonged after external stimuli disappear. Sometimes called cycling or limit cycle, hunting is evidence of operation at or near the stability limit. In control valve applications, hunting would appear as an oscillation in the loading pressure to the actuator caused by instability in the control system or the valve positioner.

ISA: Abbreviation for the Instrument Society of America. Now recognized as the International Society for Measurement and Control.

Instrument Pressure: The output pressure from an automatic controller that is used to operate a control valve.

Loading Pressure: The pressure employed to position a pneumatic actuator. This is the pressure that actually works on the actuator diaphragm or piston and it can be the instrument pressure if a valve positioner is not used.

NACE: Used to stand for National Association of Corrosion Engineers. As the scope of the organization became international, the name was changed to NACE International. NACE is no longer an abbreviation.

OSHA: Abbreviation for Occupational Safety and Health Act. (U.S.A.)

Operating Medium: This is the fluid, generally air or gas, used to supply the power for operation of valve positioner or automatic controller.

Operative Limits*: The range of operating conditions to which a device can be subjected without permanent impairment of operating characteristics.

Range: The region between the limits within which a quantity is measured, received, or transmitted, expressed by stating the lower and upper range values (for example: 3 to 15 psi; -40 to +212°F; -40 to +100°C).

Repeatability*: The closeness of agreement among a number of consecutive measurements of the output for the same value of the input under the same operating conditions, approaching from the same direction, for full range traverses. It is usually measured as a non-repeatability and expressed as repeatability in percent of span. It does not include hyesteresis (figure 1-15).

Sensitivity*: The ratio of the change in output magnitude to the change of the input that causes it after the steady-state has been reached.

Signal*: A physical variable, one or more parameters of which carry information about another variable the signal represents.

Signal Amplitude Sequencing (Split Ranging)*: Action in which two or more signals are generated or two or more final controlling elements are actuated by and input signal, each one responding consecutively, with or without overlap, to the magnitude of that input signal (figure 1-15).

Span*: The algebraic difference between the upper and lower range values (for example: Range = 0 to 150°F; Span = 150°F; Range = 3 to 15 psig, Span = 12 psig).

Supply Pressure*: The pressure at the supply port of a device. Common values of control valve supply pressure are 20 psig for a 3 to 15 psig range and 35 psig for a 6 to 30 psig range.

Zero Error*: Error of a device operating under specified conditions of use when the input is at the lower range value. It is usually expressed as percent of ideal span.

Chapter 2

Control Valve Performance

In today's dynamic business environment, manufacturers are under extreme economic pressures. Market globalization is resulting in intense pressures to reduce manufacturing costs to compete with lower wages and raw material costs of emerging countries. Competition exists between international companies to provide the highest quality products and to maximize plant throughputs with fewer resources, although meeting ever changing customer needs. These marketing challenges must be met although fully complying with public and regulatory policies.

Process Variability

To deliver acceptable returns to their shareholders, international industry leaders are realizing they must reduce raw material and scrap costs while increasing productivity. Reducing process variability in the manufacturing processes through the application of process control technology is recognized as an effective method to improve financial returns and meet global competitive pressures.

The basic objective of a company is to make a profit through the production of a quality product. A quality product conforms to a set of specifications. Any deviation from the established specification means lost profit due to excessive material use, reprocessing costs, or wasted product. Thus, a large financial impact is obtained through improving process control. Reducing process variability through better process control allows optimization of the process and the production of products right the first time.

The non-uniformity inherent in the raw materials and processes of production are common causes of variation that produce a variation of the process

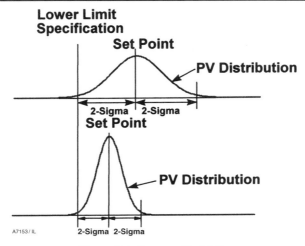

Figure 2-1. Process Variability

variable both above and below the set point. A process that is in control, with only the common causes of variation present, typically follows a bell-shaped normal distribution (figure 2-1).

A statistically derived band of values on this distribution, called the +/-2 sigma band, describes the spread of process variable deviations from the set point. This band is the variability of the process. It is a measure of how tightly the process is being controlled. Process Variability (see definition in Chapter 1) is a precise measure of tightness of control and is expressed as a percentage of the set point.

If a product must meet a certain lower-limit specification, for example, the set point needs to be established at a 2 sigma value above this lower limit. Doing so will ensure that all the product produced at values to the right of the lower limit will meet the quality specification.

The problem, however, is that money and resources are being wasted by making a large percentage of the product to a level much greater than required by the specification (see upper distribution in figure 2-1).

The most desirable solution is to reduce the spread of the deviation about the set point by going to a control valve that can produce a smaller sigma (see lower distribution in figure 2-1).

Reducing process variability is a key to achieving business goals. Most companies realize this, and it is not uncommon for them to spend hundreds of thousands of dollars on instrumentation to address the problem of process variability reduction.

Unfortunately, the control valve is often overlooked in this effort because its impact on dynamic performance is not realized. Extensive studies of control loops indicate as many as 80% of the loops did not do an adequate job of reducing process variability. Furthermore, the control valve was found to be a major contributor to this problem for a variety of reasons.

To verify performance, manufacturers must test their products under dynamic process conditions. These are typically performed in a flow lab in actual closed-loop control (figure 2-2). Evaluating control valve assemblies under closed-loop conditions provides the only true measure of variability performance. Closed-loop performance data proves significant reductions in pro-

Figure 2-2. Performance Test Loop

cess variability can be achieved by choosing the right control valve for the application.

The ability of control valves to reduce process variability depends upon many factors. More than one isolated parameter must be considered. Research within the industry has found the particular design features of the final control element, including the valve, actuator, and positioner, are very important in achieving good process control under dynamic conditions. Most importantly, the control valve assembly must be optimized or developed as a unit. Valve components not designed as a complete assembly typically do not yield the best dynamic performance. Some of the most important design considerations include:

- Dead band

- Actuator/positioner design

- Valve response time

- Valve type and sizing

Each of these design features will be considered in this chapter to provide insight into what constitutes a superior valve design.

Dead Band

Dead band is a major contributor to excess process variability, and control valve assemblies can be a primary source of dead band in an instrumentation loop due to a variety of causes such as friction, backlash, shaft wind-up, relay or spool valve dead zone, etc..

Dead band is a general phenomenon where a range or band of controller output (CO) values fails to produce a change in the measured process variable (PV) when the input signal reverses direction. (See definitions of these terms in Chapter 1.) When a load disturbance occurs, the process variable (PV) deviates from the set point. This deviation initiates a corrective action through the controller and back through the process. However, an initial change in controller output can produce no corresponding corrective change in the process variable. Only when the controller output has changed enough to progress through the dead band does a corresponding change in the process variable occur.

Any time the controller output reverses direction, the controller signal must pass through the dead band before any corrective change in the process variable will occur. The presence of dead band in the process ensures the process variable deviation from the set point will have to increase until it is big enough to get through the dead band. Only then can a corrective action occur.

Dead band has many causes, but friction and backlash in the control valve, along with shaft wind-up in rotary valves, and relay dead zone are some of the more common forms. Because most control actions for regulatory control consist of small changes (1% or less), a control valve with excessive dead band might not even respond to many of these small changes. A well-engineered valve should respond to signals of 1% or less to provide effective reduction in process variability. However, it is not uncommon for some valves to exhibit dead band as great as 5% or more. In a recent plant audit, 30% of the valves had dead bands in excess of 4%. Over 65% of the loops audited had dead bands greater than 2%.

Figure 2-3 shows just how dramatic the combined effects of dead band can be. This diagram represents an open-loop test of three different control valves under normal process conditions. The valves are subjected to a series of step inputs which range from 0.5% to 10%. Step tests under flowing conditions such as these are essential because they allow the performance of the entire valve assembly to be evaluated, rather than just the valve actuator assembly as would be the

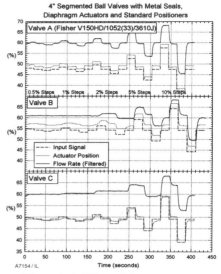

Figure 2–3. Effect of Dead Band on Valve Performance

case under most bench test conditions.

Some performance tests on a valve assembly compare only the actuator stem travel versus the input signal. This is misleading because it ignores the performance of the valve itself.

It is critical to measure dynamic performance of a valve under flowing conditions so the change in process variable can be compared to the change in valve assembly input signal. It matters little if only the valve stem changes in response to a change in valve input because if there is no corresponding change in the controlled variable, there will be no correction to the process variable.

In all three valve tests (figure 2-3), the actuator stem motion changes fairly faithfully in response to the input signal changes. On the other hand, there is a dramatic difference in each of these valve's ability to change the flow in response to an input signal change.

For Valve A the process variable (flow rate) responds well to input signals as low as 0.5. Valve B requires input signal changes as great as 5% before it begins responding faithfully to each of the input signal steps. Valve C is considerably worse, requiring signal changes as great as 10% before it begins to respond faithfully to each of the input signal steps. The ability of either Valve B or C to improve process variability is very poor.

Friction is a major cause of dead band in control valves. Rotary valves are often very susceptible to friction caused by the high seat loads required to obtain shut-off with some seal designs. Because of the high seal friction and poor drive train stiffness, the valve shaft winds up and does not translate motion to the control element. As a result, an improperly designed rotary valve can exhibit significant dead band that clearly has a detrimental effect on process variability.

Manufacturers usually lubricate rotary valve seals during manufacture, but after only a few hundred cycles this lubrication wears off. In addition, pressure-induced loads also cause seal wear. As a result, the valve friction can increase by 400% or more for some valve designs. This illustrates the misleading performance conclusions that can result from evaluating products using bench type data before the torque has stabilized. Valves B and C (figure 2-3) show the devastating effect these higher friction torque factors can have on a valve's performance.

Packing friction is the primary source of friction in sliding stem valves. In these types of valves, the measured friction can vary significantly between valve styles and packing arrangements.

Actuator style also has a profound impact on control valve assembly friction. Generally, spring-and-diaphragm actuators contribute less friction to the control valve assembly than piston actuators. An additional advantage of spring-and-diaphragm actuators is that their frictional characteristics are more uniform with age. Piston actuator friction probably will increase significantly with use as guide surfaces and the O-rings wear, lubrication fails, and the elastomer degrades. Thus, to ensure continued good performance, maintenance is required more often for piston actuators than for spring-and-diaphragm actuators. If that maintenance is not performed, process variability can suffer dramatically without the operator's knowledge.

Backlash (see definition in Chapter 1) is the name given to slack, or looseness of a mechanical connection. This slack results in a discontinuity of motion when the device changes direction. Backlash commonly occurs in gear drives of various configurations. Rack-and-pinion actuators are particularly prone to dead band due to backlash. Some valve shaft connections also exhibit dead band effects. Spline connections generally have much less dead band than keyed shafts or double-D designs.

While friction can be reduced significantly through good valve design, it is a difficult phenomenon to eliminate entirely. A well-engineered control valve should be able to virtually eliminate dead band due to backlash and shaft wind-up.

For best performance in reducing process variability, the total dead band for the entire valve assembly should be 1% or less. Ideally, it should be as low as 0.25%.

Actuator-Positioner Design

Actuator and positioner design must be considered together. The combination of these two pieces of equipment greatly affects the static performance (dead band), as well as the dynamic response of the control valve assembly and the overall air consumption of the valve instrumentation.

Positioners are used with the majority of control valve applications specified today. Positioners allow for precise positioning accuracy and faster response to process upsets when used with a conventional digital control system. With the increasing emphasis upon economic performance of process control, positioners should be considered for every valve application where process optimization is important.

The most important characteristic of a good positioner for process variability reduction is that it be a high gain device. Positioner gain is composed of two parts: the static gain and the dynamic gain.

Static gain is related to the sensitivity of the device to the detection of small (0.125% or less) changes of the input signal. Unless the device is sensitive to these small signal changes, it cannot respond to minor upsets in the process variable. This high static gain of the positioner is obtained through a preamplifier, similar in function to the preamplifier contained in high fidelity sound systems. In many pneumatic positioners, a nozzle-flapper or similar device serves as this high static gain preamplifier.

Once a change in the process variable has been detected by the high static gain positioner preamplifier, the positioner must then be capable of making the valve closure member move rapidly to provide a timely corrective action to the process variable. This requires much power to make the actuator and valve assembly move quickly to a new position. In other words, the positioner must rapidly supply a large volume of air to the actuator to make it respond promptly. The ability to do this comes from the high dynamic gain of the positioner. Although the positioner preamplifier can have high static gain, it typically has little ability to supply the power needed. Thus, the preamplifier function must be supplemented by a high dynamic gain power amplifier that supplies the required air flow as rapid-

ly as needed. This power amplifier function is typically provided by a relay or a spool valve.

Spool valve positioners are relatively popular because of their simplicity. Unfortunately, many spool valve positioners achieve this simplicity by omitting the high gain preamplifier from the design. The input stage of these positioners is often a low static gain transducer module that changes the input signal (electric or pneumatic) into movement of the spool valve, but this type of device generally has low sensitivity to small signal changes. The result is increased dead time and overall response time of the control valve assembly.

Some manufacturers attempt to compensate for the lower performance of these devices by using spool valves with enlarged ports and reduced overlap of the ports. This increases the dynamic power gain of the device, which helps performance to some extent if it is well matched to the actuator, but it also dramatically increases the air consumption of these high gain spool valves. Many high gain spool valve positioners have static instrument air consumption five times greater than typical high performance two-stage positioners.

Typical two-stage positioners use pneumatic relays at the power amplifier stage. Relays are preferred because they can provide high power gain that gives excellent dynamic performance with minimal steady-state air consumption. In addition, they are less subject to fluid contamination.

Positioner designs are changing dramatically, with microprocessor devices becoming increasingly popular (see Chapter 4). These microprocessor-based positioners provide dynamic performance equal to the best conventional two-stage pneumatic positioners. They also provide valve monitoring and diagnostic capabilities to help ensure that initial good performance does not degrade with use.

In summary, high-performance positioners with both high static and dynamic gain provide the best overall process variability performance for any given valve assembly.

Valve Response Time

For optimum control of many processes, it is important that the valve reach a specific position quickly. A quick response to small signal changes (1% or less) is one of the most important factors in providing optimum process control. In automatic, regulatory control, the bulk of the signal changes received from the controller are for small changes in position. If a control valve assembly can quickly respond to these small changes, process variability will be improved.

Valve response time is measured by a parameter called T_{63} (Tee-63); (see definitions in Chapter 1). T_{63} is the time measured from initiation of the input signal change to when the output reaches 63% of the corresponding change. It includes both the valve assembly dead time, which is a static time, and the dynamic time of the valve assembly. The dynamic time is a measure of how long the actuator takes to get to the 63% point once it starts moving.

Dead band, whether it comes from friction in the valve body and actuator or from the positioner, can significantly affect the dead time of the valve assembly. It is important to keep the dead time as small as possible. Generally dead time should be no more than one-third of the overall valve response time. However, the relative relationship between the dead time and the process time constant is critical. If the valve assembly is in a fast loop where the process time constant approaches the dead time, the dead time can dramatically affect loop performance. On these fast loops, it is critical to select control equipment with dead time as small as possible.

Also, from a loop tuning point of view, it is important that the dead time be relatively consistent in both stroking directions of the valve. Some valve assembly designs can have dead times that are three to five times longer in one stroking direction than the other. This type of behavior is typically induced by the asymmetric behavior of the positioner design, and it can severely limit the ability to tune the loop for best overall performance.

Once the dead time has passed and the valve begins to respond, the remainder of the valve response time comes from the dynamic time of the valve assembly. This dynamic time will be determined primarily by the dynamic characteristics of the positioner and actuator combination. These two components must be carefully matched to minimize the total valve response time. In a pneumatic valve assembly, for example, the positioner must have a high dynamic gain to minimize the dynamic time of the valve assembly. This dynamic gain comes mainly from the power amplifier stage in the positioner. In other words, the faster the positioner relay or spool valve can supply a large volume of air to the actuator, the faster the valve response time will be. However, this high dynamic gain power amplifier will have little effect on the dead time unless it has some intentional dead band designed into it to reduce static air consumption. Of course, the design of the actuator significantly affects the dynamic time. For example, the greater the volume of the actuator air chamber to be filled, the slower the valve response time.

At first, it might appear that the solution would be to minimize the actuator volume and maximize the positioner dynamic power gain, but it is really not that easy. This can be a dangerous combination of factors from a stability point of view. Recognizing that the positioner/actuator combination is its own feedback loop, it is possible to make the positioner/actuator loop gain too high for the actuator design being used, causing the valve assembly to go into an unstable oscillation. In addition, reducing the actuator volume has an adverse affect on the thrust-to-friction ratio, which increases the valve assembly dead band resulting in increased dead time.

If the overall thrust-to-friction ratio is not adequate for a given application, one option is to increase the thrust capability of the actuator by using the next size actuator or by increasing the pressure to the actuator. This higher thrust-to-friction ratio reduces dead band, which should help to reduce the dead time of the assembly. However, both of these alternatives mean that a greater volume of air needs to be supplied to the actuator. The tradeoff is a possible detrimental effect on the valve response time through increased dynamic time.

One way to reduce the actuator air chamber volume is to use a piston actuator rather than a spring-and-diaphragm actuator, but this is not a panacea. Piston actuators usually have higher thrust capability than spring-and-diaphragm actuators, but they also have higher friction, which can contribute to problems with valve response time. To obtain the required thrust with a piston actuator, it is usually necessary to use a higher air pressure than with a diaphragm actuator, because the piston typically has a smaller area. This means that a larger volume of air needs to be supplied with its attendant ill effects on the dynamic time. In addition, piston actuators, with their greater number of guide surfaces, tend to have higher friction due to inherent difficulties in alignment, as well as friction from the O-ring. These friction problems also tend to increase over time. Regardless of how good the O-rings are initially, these elastomeric materials will degrade with time due to wear and other environmental conditions. Likewise wear on the guide surfaces will increase the friction, and depletion of

the lubrication will occur. These friction problems result in a greater piston actuator dead band, which will increase the valve response time through increased dead time.

Instrument supply pressure can also have a significant impact on dynamic performance of the valve assembly. For example, it can dramatically affect the positioner gain, as well as overall air consumption.

Fixed-gain positioners have generally been optimized for a particular supply pressure. This gain, however, can vary by a factor of two or more over a small range of supply pressures. For example, a positioner that has been optimized for a supply pressure of 20 psig might find its gain cut in half when the supply pressure is boosted to 35 psig.

Supply pressure also affects the volume of air delivered to the actuator, which in turn determines stroking speed. It is also directly linked to air consumption. Again, high-gain spool valve positioners can consume up to five times the amount of air required for more efficient high-performance, two-stage positioners that use relays for the power amplification stage.

To minimize the valve assembly dead time, minimize the dead band of the valve assembly, whether it comes from friction in the valve seal design, packing friction, shaft wind-up, actuator, or positioner design. As indicated, friction is a major cause of dead band in control valves. On rotary valve styles, shaft wind-up (see definition in Chapter 1) can also contribute significantly to dead band. Actuator style also has a profound impact on control valve assembly friction. Generally, spring-and-diaphragm actuators contribute less friction to the control valve assembly than piston actuators over an extended time. As mentioned, this is caused by the increasing friction from the piston O-ring, misalignment problems, and failed lubrication.

Having a positioner design with a high static gain preamplifier can make a significant difference in reducing dead band. This can also make a significant improvement in the valve assembly resolution (see definition in Chapter 1). Valve assemblies with dead band and resolution of 1% or less are no longer adequate for many process variability reduction needs. Many processes require the valve assembly to have dead band and resolution as low as 0.25%, especially where the valve assembly is installed in a fast process loop.

One of the surprising things to come out of many industry studies on valve response time has been the change in thinking about spring-and-diaphragm actuators versus piston actuators. It has long been a misconception in the process industry that piston actuators are faster than spring-and-diaphragm actuators. Research has shown this to be untrue for small signal changes.

This mistaken belief arose from many years of experience with testing valves for stroking time. A stroking time test is normally conducted by subjecting the valve assembly to a 100% step change in the input signal and measuring the time it takes the valve assembly to complete its full stroke in either direction.

Although piston-actuated valves usually do have faster stroking times than most spring-and-diaphragm actuated valves, this test does not indicate valve performance in an actual process control situation. In normal process control applications, the valve is rarely required to stroke through its full operating range. Typically, the valve is only required to respond within a range of 0.25% to 2% change in valve position. Extensive testing of

valves has shown that spring-and-diaphragm valve assemblies consistently outperform piston actuated valves on small signal changes, which are more representative of regulatory process control applications. Higher friction in the piston actuator is one factor that plays a role in making them less responsive to small signals than spring-and-diaphragm actuators.

Selecting the proper valve, actuator, positioner combination is not easy. It is not simply a matter of finding a combination that is physically compatible. Good engineering judgment must go into the practice of valve assembly sizing and selection to achieve the best dynamic performance from the loop.

Figure 2-4 shows the dramatic differences in dead time and overall T_{63} response time caused by differences in valve assembly design.

Valve Type And Characterization

The style of valve used and the sizing of the valve can have a large impact on the performance of the control valve assembly in the system. While a valve must be of sufficient size to pass the required flow under all possible contingencies, a valve that is too large for the application is a detriment to process optimization.

Flow capacity of the valve is also related to the style of valve through the inherent characteristic of the valve. The inherent characteristic (see definition in Chapter 1) is the relationship between the valve flow capacity and the valve travel when the differential pressure drop across the valve is held constant.

VALVE RESPONSE TIME			
	STEP SIZE	T(d) SEC.	T63 SEC.
ENTECH SPEC. 4" VALVE SIZE	%	≤0.2	≤0.6
Valve A (Fisher V150HD/1052(33)/3610J)			
VALVE ACTION / OPENING	2	0.25	0.34
VALVE ACTION / CLOSING	–2	0.50	0.74
VALVE ACTION / OPENING	5	0.16	0.26
VALVE ACTION / CLOSING	–5	0.22	0.42
VALVE ACTION / OPENING	10	0.19	0.33
VALVE ACTION / CLOSING	–10	0.23	0.46
Valve B			
VALVE ACTION / OPENING	2	5.61	7.74
VALVE ACTION / CLOSING	–2	0.46	1.67
VALVE ACTION / OPENING	5	1.14	2.31
VALVE ACTION / CLOSING	–5	1.04	2
VALVE ACTION / OPENING	10	0.42	1.14
VALVE ACTION / CLOSING	–10	0.41	1.14
Valve C			
VALVE ACTION / OPENING	2	4.4	5.49
VALVE ACTION / CLOSING	–2	NR	NR
VALVE ACTION / OPENING	5	5.58	7.06
VALVE ACTION / CLOSING	–5	2.16	3.9
VALVE ACTION / OPENING	10	0.69	1.63
VALVE ACTION / CLOSING	–10	0.53	1.25
NR = No Response			

Figure 2–4. Valve Response Time Summary

Typically, these characteristics are plotted on a curve where the horizontal axis is labeled in percent travel although the vertical axis is labeled as percent flow (or C_v). Since valve flow is a function of both the valve travel and the pressure drop across the valve, it is traditional to conduct inherent valve characteristic tests at a constant pressure drop. This is not a normal situation in practice, but it provides a systematic way of comparing one valve characteristic design to another.

Under the specific conditions of constant pressure drop, the valve flow becomes only a function of the valve travel and the inherent design of the valve trim. These characteristics are called the inherent flow characteristic of the valve. Typical valve characteris-

tics conducted in this manner are named linear, equal percentage, and quick opening. (See Conventional Characterized Valve Plugs in Chapter 3 for a complete description.)

The ratio of the incremental change in valve flow (output) to the corresponding increment of valve travel (input) which caused the flow change is defined as the valve gain; that is,

Inherent Valve Gain = (change in flow)/(change in travel) = slope of the inherent characteristic curve

The linear characteristic has a constant inherent valve gain throughout its range, and the quick-opening characteristic has an inherent valve gain that is the greatest at the lower end of the travel range. The greatest inherent valve gain for the equal per-

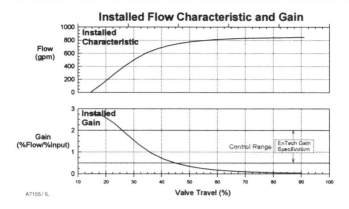

Figure 2-5. Installed Flow Characteristic and Gain

centage valve is at the largest valve opening.

Inherent valve characteristic is an inherent function of the valve flow passage geometry and does not change as long as the pressure drop is held constant. Many valve designs, particularly rotary ball valves, butterfly valves, and eccentric plug valves, have inherent characteristics, which cannot be easily changed; however, most globe valves have a selection of valve cages or plugs that can be interchanged to modify the inherent flow characteristic.

Knowledge of the inherent valve characteristic is useful, but the more important characteristic for purposes of process optimization is the installed flow characteristic of the entire process, including the valve and all other equipment in the loop. The installed flow characteristic is defined as the relationship between the flow through the valve and the valve assembly input when the valve is installed in a specific system, and the pressure drop across the valve is allowed to change naturally, rather than being held constant. An illustration of such an installed flow characteristic is shown in the upper curve of figure

2-5. The flow in this figure is related to the more familiar valve travel rather than valve assembly input.

Installed gain, shown in the lower curve of figure 2-5, is a plot of the slope of the upper curve at each point. Installed flow characteristic curves such as this can be obtained under laboratory conditions by placing the entire loop in operation at some nominal set point and with no load disturbances. The loop is placed in manual operation, and the flow is then measured and recorded as the input to the control valve assembly is manually driven through its full travel range. A plot of the results is the installed flow characteristic curve shown in the upper part of figure 2-5. The slope of this flow curve is then evaluated at each point on the curve and plotted as the installed gain as shown in the lower part of figure 2-5.

Field measurements of the installed process gain can also be made at a single operating point using open-loop step tests (figure 2-3). The installed process gain at any operating condition is simply the ratio of the percent change in output (flow) to the percent change in valve assembly input signal.

The reason for characterizing inherent valve gain through various valve trim designs is to provide compensation for other gain changes in the control loop. The end goal is to maintain a loop gain, which is reasonably uniform over the entire operating range, to maintain a relatively linear installed flow characteristic for the process (see definition in Chapter 1). Because of the way it is measured, as defined above, the installed flow characteristic and installed gain represented in figure 2-5 are really the installed gain and flow characteristic for the entire process.

Typically, the gain of the unit being controlled changes with flow. For example, the gain of a pressure vessel tends to decrease with throughput. In this case, the process control engineer would then likely want to use an equal percentage valve that has an increasing gain with flow. Ideally, these two inverse relationships should balance out to provide a more linear installed flow characteristic for the entire process.

Theoretically, a loop has been tuned for optimum performance at some set point flow condition. As the flow varies about that set point, it is desirable to keep the loop gain as constant as possible to maintain optimum performance. If the loop gain change due to the inherent valve characteristic does not exactly compensate for the changing gain of the unit being controlled, then there will be a variation in the loop gain due to variation in the installed process gain. As a result, process optimization becomes more difficult. There is also a danger that the loop gain might change enough to cause instability, limit cycling, or other dynamic difficulties.

Loop gain should not vary more than a 4-to-1 ratio; otherwise, the dynamic performance of the loop suffers unacceptably. There is nothing magic about this specific ratio; it is simply one which many control practitioners

agree produces an acceptable range of gain margins in most process control loops.

This guideline forms the basis for the following EnTech gain limit specification (From *Control Valve Dynamic Specification*, Version 2.1, March 1994, EnTech Control Inc., Toronto, Ontario, Canada):

> Loop Process Gain = 1.0 (% of transmitter span)/(% controller output)
>
> Nominal Range: 0.5 - 2.0 (Note 4-to-1 ratio)

Note that this definition of the loop process includes all the devices in the loop configuration except the controller. In other words, the product of the gains of such devices as the control valve assembly, the heat exchanger, pressure vessel, or other system being controlled, the pump, the transmitter, etc. is the process gain. Because the valve is part of the loop process as defined here, it is important to select a valve style and size that will produce an installed flow characteristic that is sufficiently linear to stay within the specified gain limits over the operating range of the system. If too much gain variation occurs in the control valve itself, it leaves less flexibility in adjusting the controller. It is good practice to keep as much of the loop gain in the controller as possible.

Although the 4-to-1 ratio of gain change in the loop is widely accepted, not everyone agrees with the 0.5 to 2.0 gain limits. Some industry experts have made a case for using loop process gain limits from 0.2 to 0.8, which is still a 4-to-1 ratio. The potential danger inherent in using this reduced gain range is that the low end of the gain range could result in large valve swings during normal operation. It is good operating practice to keep valve swings below about 5%. However, there is also a danger in letting the gain get too large. The loop can become oscillatory or even unstable if the loop gain gets too high at some

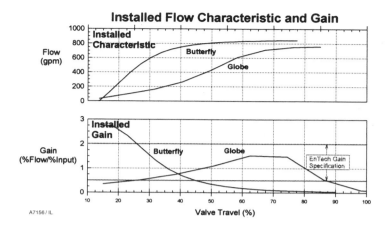

Figure 2-6. Effect of Valve Style on Control Range

point in the travel. To ensure good dynamic performance and loop stability over a wide range of operating conditions, industry experts recommend that loop equipment be engineered so the process gain remains within the range of 0.5 to 2.0.

Process optimization requires a valve style and size be chosen that will keep the process gain within the selected gain limit range over the widest possible set of operating conditions. Because minimizing process variability is so dependent on maintaining a uniform installed gain, the range over which a valve can operate within the acceptable gain specification limits is known as the control range of the valve.

The control range of a valve varies dramatically with valve style. Figure 2-6 shows a line-size butterfly valve compared to a line-size globe valve. The globe valve has a much wider control range than the butterfly valve. Other valve styles, such as V-notch ball valves and eccentric plug valves generally fall somewhere between these two ranges.

Because butterfly valves typically have the narrowest control range, they are generally best suited for fixed-load applications. In addition, they must be carefully sized for optimal performance at fixed loads.

If the inherent characteristic of a valve could be selected to exactly compensate for the system gain change with flow, one would expect the installed process gain (lower curve) to be essentially a straight line at a value of 1.0.

Unfortunately, such a precise gain match is seldom possible due to the logistical limitations of providing an infinite variety of inherent valve trim characteristics. In addition, some valve styles, such as butterfly and ball valves, do not offer trim alternatives that allow easy change of the inherent valve characteristic.

This condition can be alleviated by changing the inherent characteristics of the valve assembly with nonlinear cams in the feedback mechanism of the positioner. The nonlinear feedback cam changes the relationship between the valve input signal and the valve stem position to achieve a desired inherent valve characteristic for

35

the entire valve assembly, rather than simply relying upon a change in the design of the valve trim.

Although the use of positioner cams does affect modifying the valve characteristic and can sometimes be useful, the effect of using characterized cams is limited in most cases. This is because the cam also dramatically changes the positioner loop gain, which severely limits the dynamic response of the positioner. Using cams to characterize the valve is usually not as effective as characterizing the valve trim, but it is always better than no characterization at all, which is often the only other choice with rotary valves.

Some electronic devices attempt to produce valve characterization by electronically shaping the I/P positioner input signal ahead of the positioner loop. This technique recalibrates the valve input signal by taking the linear 4-20 mA controller signal and using a pre-programmed table of values to produce the valve input required to achieve the desired valve characteristic. This technique is sometimes referred to as forward path or set point characterization.

Because this characterization occurs outside the positioner feedback loop, this type of forward path or set point characterization has an advantage over characterized positioner cams. It avoids the problem of changes in the positioner loop gain. This method, however, also has its dynamic limitations. For example, there can be places in a valve range where a 1.0% process signal change might be narrowed through this characterization process to only a 0.1% signal change to the valve (that is, in the flat regions of the characterizing curve). Many control valves are unable to respond to signal changes this small.

The best process performance occurs when the required flow characteristic is obtained through changes in the valve trim rather than through use of

cams or other methods. Proper selection of a control valve designed to produce a reasonably linear installed flow characteristic over the operating range of the system is a critical step in ensuring optimum process performance.

Valve Sizing

Oversizing of valves sometimes occurs when trying to optimize process performance through a reduction of process variability. This results from using line-size valves, especially with high-capacity rotary valves, as well as the conservative addition of multiple safety factors at different stages in the process design.

Oversizing the valve hurts process variability in two ways. First, the oversized valve puts too much gain in the valve, leaving less flexibility in adjusting the controller. Best performance results when most loop gain comes from the controller.

Notice in the gain curve of figure 2-5, the process gain gets quite high in the region below about 25% valve travel. If the valve is oversized, making it more likely to operate in or near this region, this high gain can likely mean that the controller gain will need to be reduced to avoid instability problems with the loop. This, of course, will mean a penalty of increased process variability.

The second way oversized valves hurt process variability is that an oversized valve is likely to operate more frequently at lower valve openings where seal friction can be greater, particularly in rotary valves. Because an oversized valve produces a disproportionately large flow change for a given increment of valve travel, this phenomenon can greatly exaggerate the process variability associated with dead band due to friction.

Regardless of its actual inherent valve characteristic, a severely oversized valve tends to act more like a quick-opening valve, which results in high installed process gain in the lower lift regions (figure 2-5). In addition, when the valve is oversized, the valve tends to reach system capacity at relatively low travel, making the flow curve flatten out at higher valve travels (figure 2-5). For valve travels above about 50 degrees, this valve has become totally ineffective for control purposes because the process gain is approaching zero and the valve must undergo wide changes in travel with very little resulting changes in flow. Consequently, there is little hope of achieving acceptable process variability in this region.

The valve shown in figure 2-5 is totally misapplied in this application because it has such a narrow control range (approximately 25 degrees to 45 degrees). This situation came about because a line-sized butterfly valve was chosen, primarily due to its low cost, and no consideration was given to the lost profit that results from sacrificing process variability through poor dynamic performance of the control valve.

Unfortunately, this situation is often repeated. Process control studies show that, for some industries, the majority of valves currently in process control loops are oversized for the application. While it might seem counterintuitive, it often makes economic sense to select a control valve for present conditions and then replace the valve when conditions change.

When selecting a valve, it is important to consider the valve style, inherent characteristic, and valve size that will provide the broadest possible control range for the application.

Economic Results

Consideration of the factors discussed in this chapter can have a dramatic impact on the economic results of an operating plant. More and more control valve users focus on dynamic per-

formance parameters such as dead band, response times, and installed gain (under actual process load conditions) as a means to improve process-loop performance. Although it is possible to measure many of these dynamic performance parameters in an open-loop situation, the impact these parameters have becomes clear when closed-loop performance is measured. The closed-loop test results shown in figure 2-7 demonstrate the ability of three different valves to reduce process variability over different tuning conditions.

This diagram plots process variability as a percent of the set point variable versus the closed-loop time constant, which is a measure of loop tuning. The horizontal line labeled Manual, shows how much variability is inherent in the loop when no attempt is made to control it (open-loop). The line sloping downward to the left marked Minimum Variability represents the calculated dynamic performance of an ideal valve assembly (one with no non-linearities). All real valve assemblies should normally fall somewhere between these two conditions.

Not all valves provide the same dynamic performance even though they all theoretically meet static performance purchase specifications and are considered to be equivalent valves (figure 2-7). Valve A in figure 2-7 does a good job of following the trend of the minimum variability line over a wide range of controller tunings. This valve shows excellent dynamic performance with minimum variability. In contrast, Valves B and C designs fare less well and increase in variability as the system is tuned more aggressively for decreasing closed-loop time constants.

All three valve designs are capable of controlling the process and reducing the variability, but two designs do it less well. Consider what would happen if the poorer performing Valve B was replaced with the best performing Valve A, and the system was tuned to

Closed-Loop Random Load Disturbance Summary

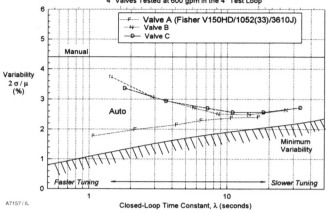

Figure 2-7. Closed-Loop Performance

a 2.0 second closed-loop time constant.

The test data shows this would result in a 1.4% improvement in process variability. This might not seem like much, but the results over a time can be impressive. A valve that can provide this much improvement every minute of every day can save significant dollars over a single year.

By maintaining closer adherence to the set point, it is possible to achieve a reduction in raw materials by moving the set point closer to the lower specification limit. This 1.4% improvement in this example converts to a raw material savings of 12,096 U.S. gallons per day. Assuming a material cost of US $0.25 per gallon, the best valve would contribute an additional US $3,024 per day directly to profits. This adds up to an impressive US $1,103,760 per year.

The excellent performance of the better valve in this example provides strong evidence that a superior control valve assembly can have a profound economic impact. This example is

only one way a control valve can increase profits through tighter control. Decreased energy costs, increased throughput, less reprocessing cost for out-of-spec product, and so on are all ways a good control valve can increase economic results through tighter control. While the initial cost might be higher for the best control valve, the few extra dollars spent on a well-engineered control valve can dramatically increase the return on investment. Often the extra initial cost of the valve can be paid for in a matter of days.

As a result of studies such as these, the process industries have become increasingly aware that control valve assemblies play an important role in loop/unit/plant performance. They have also realized that traditional methods of specifying a valve assembly are no longer adequate to ensure the benefits of process optimization. While important, such static performance indicators as flow capacity, leakage, materials compatibility, and bench performance data are not sufficiently adequate to deal with the dynamic characteristics of process control loops.

Summary

The control valve assembly plays an extremely important role in producing the best possible performance from the control loop. Process optimization means optimizing the entire process, not just the control algorithms used in the control room equipment. The valve is called the final control element because the control valve assembly is where process control is implemented. It makes no sense to install an elaborate process control strategy and hardware instrumentation system capable of achieving 0.5% or better process control and then to implement that control strategy with a 5% or worse control valve. Audits performed on thousands of process control loops have provided strong proof that the final control element plays a significant role in achieving true process optimization. Profitability in-

creases when a control valve has been properly engineered for its application.

Control valves are sophisticated, high-tech products and should not be treated as a commodity. Although traditional valve specifications play an important role, valve specifications must also address real dynamic performance characteristics if true process optimization is to be achieved. It is imperative that these specifications include such parameters as dead band, dead time, response time, etc.

Finally, process optimization begins and ends with optimization of the entire loop. Parts of the loop cannot be treated individually to achieve coordinated loop performance. Likewise, performance of any part of the loop cannot be evaluated in isolation. Isolated tests under non-loaded, bench-type conditions will not provide performance information that is obtained from testing the hardware under actual process conditions.

Chapter 3

Valve and Actuator Types

Control Valves

The control valve regulates the rate of fluid flow as the position of the valve plug or disk is changed by force from the actuator. To do this, the valve must:

• Contain the fluid without external leakage;

• Have adequate capacity for the intended service;

• Be capable of withstanding the erosive, corrosive, and temperature influences of the process; and

• Incorporate appropriate end connections to mate with adjacent pipelines and actuator attachment means to permit transmission of actuator thrust to the valve plug stem or rotary shaft.

Many styles of control valve bodies have been developed through the years. Some have found wide application; others meet specific service conditions and are used less frequently. The following summary describes some popular control valve body styles in use today.

Globe Valves

Single-Port Valve Bodies

• Single port is the most common valve body style and is simple in construction.

• Single-port valves are available in various forms, such as globe, angle, bar stock, forged, and split constructions.

• Generally single-port valves are specified for applications with stringent shutoff requirements. They use metal-to-metal seating surfaces or soft-seating with PTFE or other composition materials forming the seal. Single-port valves can handle most service requirements.

● Because high-pressure fluid is normally loading the entire area of the port, the unbalance force created must be considered in selecting actuators for single-port control valve bodies.

● Although most popular in the smaller sizes, single-port valves can often be used in 4-inch to 8-inch sizes with high-thrust actuators.

● Many modern single-seated valve bodies use cage or retainer-style construction to retain the seat-ring cage, provide valve-plug guiding, and provide a means for establishing particular valve flow characteristics. Retainer-style trim also offers ease of maintenance with flow characteristics altered by changing the plug.

● Cage or retainer-style single-seated valve bodies can also be easily modified by change of trim parts to provide reduced-capacity flow, noise attenuation, or reduction or elimination of cavitation.

Figure 3-1 shows two of the more popular styles of single-ported or single-seated globe-type control valve bodies. They are widely used in process control applications, particularly in sizes from 1-inch through 4-inch. Normal flow direction is most often up through the seat ring.

Angle valves are nearly always single ported (figure 3-2). They are commonly used in boiler feedwater and heater drain service and in piping schemes where space is at a premium and the valve can also serve as an elbow. The valve shown has cage-style construction. Others might have screwed-in seat rings, expanded outlet connections, restricted trim, and outlet liners for reduction of erosion damage.

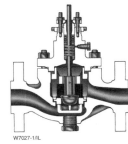

Figure 3-1. Popular Single-Ported Globe-Style Valve Bodies

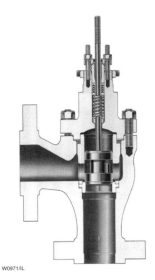

Figure 3-2. Flanged Angle-Style Control Valve Body

Bar-stock valve bodies are often specified for corrosive applications in the chemical industry (figure 3-3). They can be machined from any metallic

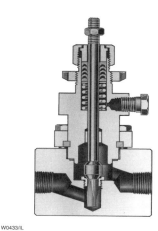

W0433/IL

Figure 3-3. Bar Stock Valve Bodies

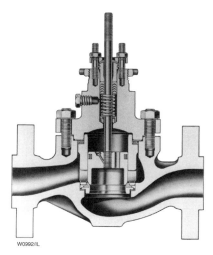

W0992/IL

Figure 3-5. Valve Body with Cage-Style Trim, Balanced Valve Plug, and Soft Seat

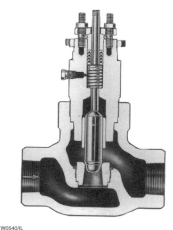

W0540/IL

Figure 3-4. High Pressure Globe-Style Control Valve Body

bar-stock material and from some plastics. When exotic metal alloys are required for corrosion resistance, a bar-stock valve body is normally less expensive than a valve body produced from a casting.

High-pressure single-ported globe valves are often used in production of gas and oil (figure 3-4). Variations available include cage-guided trim, bolted body-to-bonnet connection,

and self-draining angle versions. Flanged versions are available with ratings to Class 2500.

Balanced-Plug Cage-Style Valve Bodies

This popular valve body style, single-ported in the sense that only one seat ring is used, provides the advantages of a balanced valve plug often associated only with double-ported valve bodies (figure 3-5). Cage-style trim provides valve plug guiding, seat ring retention, and flow characterization. In addition a sliding piston ring-type seal between the upper portion of the valve plug and the wall of the cage cylinder virtually eliminates leakage of the upstream high pressure fluid into the lower pressure downstream system. Downstream pressure acts on both the top and bottom sides of the valve plug, thereby nullifying most of the static unbalance force. Reduced unbalance force permits operation of the valve with smaller actuators than those necessary for conventional single-ported valve bodies. Interchangeability of trim permits choice of several flow characteristics or of noise attenuation or anti-cavitation components. For most

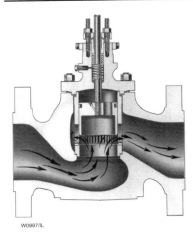

W0997/IL

Figure 3-6. High Capacity Valve Body with Cage-Style Noise Abatement Trim

available trim designs, the standard direction of flow is in through the cage openings and down through the seat ring. These are available in various material combinations, sizes through 20-inch, and pressure ratings to Class 2500.

High Capacity, Cage-Guided Valve Bodies

This adaptation of the cage-guided bodies mentioned above was designed for noise applications such as high pressure gas reducing stations where sonic gas velocities are often encountered at the outlet of conventional valve bodies (figure 3-6). The design incorporates oversize end connections with a streamlined flow path and the ease of trim maintenance inherent with cage-style constructions. Use of noise abatement trim reduces overall noise levels by as much as 35 decibels. Also available in cageless versions with bolted seat ring, end connection sizes through 20-inch, Class 600, and versions for liquid service. Flow direction depends on the intended service and trim selection, with unbalanced constructions normally flowing up and balanced constructions normally flowing down.

Port-Guided Single-Port Valve Bodies

● These bodies are usually limited to 150 psi (10 bar) maximum pressure drop.

● They are susceptible to velocity-induced vibration.

● Port-guided single-port valve bodies are typically provided with screwed in seat rings which might be difficult to remove after use.

Double-Ported Valve Bodies

● Dynamic force on plug tends to be balanced as flow tends to open one port and close the other.

● Reduced dynamic forces acting on plug might permit choosing a smaller actuator than would be necessary for a single-ported valve body with similar capacity.

● Bodies are usually furnished only in the larger sizes—4-inch or larger.

● Bodies normally have higher capacity than single-ported valves of the same line size.

● Many double-ported bodies reverse, so the valve plug can be installed as either push-down-to-open or push-down-to-close (figure 3-7).

● Metal-to-metal seating usually provides only Class II shutoff capability, although Class III capability is also possible.

● Port-guided valve plugs are often used for on-off or low–pressure throttling service. Top-and-bottom-guided valve plugs furnish stable operation for severe service conditions.

The control valve body shown in figure 3–7 is assembled for push-down-to-open valve plug action. The valve plug is essentially balanced and a relatively small amount of actuator force is required to operate the valve.

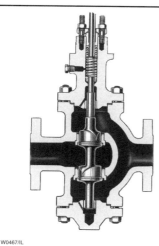

W0467/IL

Figure 3-7. Reverse–Acting Double-Ported Globe-Style Valve Body

Double ported designs are typically used in refineries on highly viscous fluids or where there is a concern about dirt, contaminants, or process deposits on the trim.

Three-Way Valve Bodies

• Three pipeline connections provide general converging (flow-mixing) or diverging (flow-splitting) service.

• Best designs use cage-style trim for positive valve plug guiding and ease of maintenance.

• Variations include trim materials selected for high temperature service. Standard end connections (flanged, screwed, butt weld, etc.) can be specified to mate with most any piping scheme.

• Actuator selection demands careful consideration, particularly for constructions with unbalanced valve plug.

Balanced valve plug style three-way valve body is shown with cylindrical valve plug in the down position (figure 3-8). This position opens the bottom common port to the right-hand port and shuts off the left-hand port. The

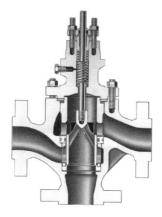

W0665/IL

Figure 3-8. Three Way Valve with Balanced Valve Plug

W4081/IL

Figure 3-9. Typical Butterfly Control Valve

construction can be used for throttling mid-travel position control of either converging or diverging fluids.

Rotary Valves

Butterfly Valve Bodies

• Bodies require minimum space for installation (figure 3-9).

• They provide high capacity with low pressure loss through the valves.

• Butterfly valve bodies offer economy, particularly in larger sizes and in

45

terms of flow capacity per investment dollar.

- Conventional contoured disks provide throttling control for up to 60-degree disk rotation. Patented, dynamically streamlined disks suit applications requiring 90-degree disk rotation.

- Bodies mate with standard raised-face pipeline flanges.

- Butterfly valve bodies might require high-output or large actuators if the valve is big or the pressure drop is high, because operating torques might be quite large.

- Units are available for service in nuclear power plant applications with very stringent leakage requirements.

- Standard liner can provide good shutoff and corrosion protection with nitrile or PTFE liner.

- Standard butterfly valves are available in sizes through 72-inch for miscellaneous control valve applications. Smaller sizes can use versions of traditional diaphragm or piston pneumatic actuators, including the modern rotary actuator styles. Larger sizes might require high-output electric or long-stroke pneumatic cylinder actuators. Butterfly valves exhibit an approximately equal percentage flow characteristic. They can be used for throttling service or for on-off control. Soft-seat construction can be obtained by using a liner or by including an adjustable soft ring in the body or on the face of the disk.

- A dynamically contoured disk, such as the **Fishtail**® disk shown, permits control through full 90 degrees of disk rotation, although conventional disks are usually limited to rotation of 60 degrees.

W5978/IL

Figure 3-10. Rotary-Shaft Control Valve with V-Notch Ball

V-Notch Ball Control Valve Bodies

This construction is similar to a conventional ball valve, but with patented, contoured V-notch in the ball (figure 3-10). The V-notch produces an equal-percentage flow characteristic. These control valves have good rangeability, control, and shutoff capability. The paper industry, chemical plants, sewage treatment plants, the power industry, and petroleum refineries use such valve bodies.

- Straight-through flow design produces little pressure drop.

- V-notch ball control valve bodies are suited to control of erosive or viscous fluids, paper stock, or other slurries containing entrained solids or fibers.

- They use standard diaphragm or piston rotary actuators.

- Ball remains in contact with seal during rotation, which produces a shearing effect as the ball closes and minimizes clogging.

- Bodies are available with either heavy-duty or PTFE-filled composition ball seal ring to provide excellent rangeability in excess of 300:1.

- V-notch ball control valve bodies are available in flangeless or flanged-

W4170/IL

Figure 3–12. Eccentric–Plug Control Valve

W2770/IL

Figure 3-11. Eccentric-Disk Rotary-Shaft Control Valve

body end connections. Both flanged and flangeless valves mate with Class 150, 300, or 600 flanges or DIN flanges.

Eccentric-Disk Control Valve Bodies

• Bodies offer effective throttling control.

• Eccentric-disk control valve bodies provide linear flow characteristic through 90 degrees of disk rotation (figure 3-11).

• Eccentric mounting of disk pulls it away from seal after it begins to open, minimizing seal wear.

• Eccentric-disk control valve bodies are available in sizes through 24-inch compatible with standard ASME flanges.

• They use standard pneumatic diaphragm or piston rotary actuators.

• Standard flow direction is dependent on seal design; reverse flow results in reduced capacity.

Eccentric disk rotary shaft control valves are intended for general service applications not requiring precision throttling control. They are frequently applied in applications requiring large sizes and high temperatures due to their lower cost relative to other styles of control valves. The control range for this style of valve is approximately one third as large as a ball or globe style valves. Consequently, additional care is required in sizing and applying this style of valve to eliminate control problems associated with process load changes. They work quite well for constant process load applications.

Eccentric-Plug Control Valve Bodies

• Valve assembly combats erosion. The rugged body and trim design handle temperatures to 800°F (427°C) and shutoff pressure drops to 1500 psi (103 bar).

• Path of eccentric plug minimizes contact with the seat ring when opening, reducing seat wear and friction, prolonging seat life, and improving throttling performance (figure 3–12)..

• Self-centering seat ring and rugged plug allow forward or reverse flow with tight shutoff in either direction. Plug, seat ring and retainer are available in hardened materials, in-

cluding ceramics, for selection of erosion resistance.

• Designs offering a segmented
V-notch ball in place of the plug for
higher capacity requirements are
available.

This style of rotary control valve suits
erosive, coking and other hard-to-handle fluids, providing either throttling or
on-off operation. The flanged or
flangeless valves feature streamlined
flow passages and rugged metal-trim
components for dependable service in
slurry applications. Mining, petroleum
refining, power, and pulp and paper
industries use these valves.

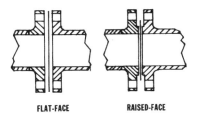

FLAT-FACE   RAISED-FACE

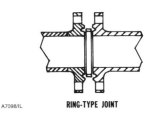

A7098/IL   RING-TYPE JOINT

Control Valve End Connections

*Figure 3-13. Popular Varieties of
Bolted Flange Connections*

The three common methods of installing control valves in pipelines are by
means of screwed pipe threads,
bolted gasketed flanges, and welded
end connections.

Screwed Pipe Threads

Screwed end connections, popular in
small control valves, offer more economy than flanged ends. The threads
usually specified are tapered female
NPT (National Pipe Thread) on the
valve body. They form a metal-to-metal seal by wedging over the mating
male threads on the pipeline ends.
This connection style, usually limited
to valves not larger than 2-inch, is not
recommended for elevated temperature service. Valve maintenance might
be complicated by screwed end connections if it is necessary to take the
body out of the pipeline because the
valve cannot be removed without
breaking a flanged joint or union connection to permit unscrewing the valve
body from the pipeline.

Bolted Gasketed Flanges

Flanged end valves are easily removed from the piping and are suit-

able for use through the range of
working pressures for which most
control valves are manufactured (figure 3-13). Flanged end connections
can be used in a temperature range
from absolute zero to approximately
1500°F (815°C). They are used on all
valve sizes. The most common
flanged end connections include flat
face, raised face, and ring type joint.

The flat face variety allows the matching flanges to be in full face contact
with the gasket clamped between
them. This construction is commonly
used in low pressure, cast iron and
brass valves and minimizes flange
stresses caused by initial bolting-up
force.

The raised face flange features a circular raised face with inside diameter
the same as the valve opening and
with the outside diameter something
less than the bolt circle diameter. The
raised face is finished with concentric
circular grooves for good sealing and
resistance to gasket blowout. This
kind of flange is used with a variety of
gasket materials and flange materials
for pressures through the 6000 psig
(414 bar) pressure range and for temperatures through 1500°F (815°C).

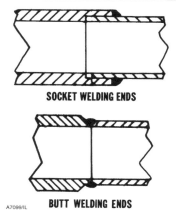

SOCKET WELDING ENDS

A7099/IL **BUTT WELDING ENDS**

Figure 3-14. Common Welded End Connections

This style of flanging is normally standard on Class 250 cast iron bodies and all steel and alloy steel bodies.

The ring-type joint flange looks like the raised-face flange except that a U-shaped groove is cut in the raised face concentric with the valve opening. The gasket consists of a metal ring with either an elliptical or octagonal cross section. When the flange bolts are tightened, the gasket is wedged into the groove of the mating flange and a tight seal is made. The gasket is generally soft iron or Monel (Trademark of Inco Alloys International) but is available in almost any metal. This makes an excellent joint at high pressure and is used up to 15,000 psig (1034 bar), but is generally not used at high temperatures. It is furnished only on steel and alloy valve bodies when specified.

Welding End Connections

Welding ends on control valves are leak tight at all pressures and temperatures and are economical in first cost (figure 3-13). Welding end valves are more difficult to take from the line and are obviously limited to weldable materials. Welding ends come in two

styles, socket welding and buttwelding.

The socket welding ends are prepared by boring in each end of the valve a socket with an inside diameter slightly larger than the pipe outside diameter. The pipe slips into the socket where it butts against a shoulder and then joins to the valve with a fillet weld. Socket welding ends in a given size are dimensionally the same regardless of pipe schedule. They are usually furnished in sizes through 2-inch.

The buttwelding ends are prepared by beveling each end of the valve to match a similar bevel on the pipe. The two ends are then butted to the pipeline and joined with a full penetration weld. This type of joint is used on all valve styles and the end preparation must be different for each schedule of pipe. These are generally furnished for control valves in sizes 2-1/2-inch and larger. Care must be exercised when welding valve bodies in the pipeline to prevent excessive heat transmitted to valve trim parts. Trims with low-temperature composition materials must be removed before welding.

Valve Body Bonnets

The bonnet of a control valve is that part of the body assembly through which the valve plug stem or rotary shaft moves. On globe or angle bodies, it is the pressure retaining component for one end of the valve body. The bonnet normally provides a means of mounting the actuator to the body and houses the packing box. Generally rotary valves do not have bonnets. (On some rotary-shaft valves, the packing is housed within an extension of the valve body itself, or the packing box is a separate component bolted between the valve body and bonnet.)

On a typical globe-style control valve body, the bonnet is made of the same material as the valve body or is an equivalent forged material because it

49

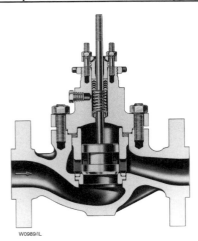

W0989/IL

*Figure 3-15. Typical Bonnet,
Flange, and Stud Bolts*

is a pressure-containing member subject to the same temperature and corrosion effects as the body. Several styles of valve body-to-bonnet connections are illustrated. The most common is the bolted flange type shown in figure 3-15 showing a bonnet with an integral flange and figure 3-3 showing a bonnet with a separable, slip-on flange held in place with a split ring. The bonnet used on the high pressure globe valve body in figure 3-4 is screwed into the valve body. Figure 3-9 is typical of rotary-shaft control valves where the packing is housed within the valve body and a bonnet is not used. The actuator linkage housing is not a pressure-containing part and is intended to enclose the linkage for safety and environmental protection.

On control valve bodies with cage- or retainer-style trim, the bonnet furnishes loading force to prevent leakage between the bonnet flange and the valve body and also between the seat ring and the valve body. The tightening of the body-bonnet bolting compresses a flat sheet gasket to seal the body-bonnet joint, compresses a spiral-wound gasket on top of the cage, and compresses another flat

50

sheet gasket below the seat ring to provide the seat ring-body seal. The bonnet also provides alignment for the cage, which in turn guides the valve plug, to ensure proper valve plug stem alignment with the packing.

As mentioned, the conventional bonnet on a globe-type control valve houses the packing. The packing is most often retained by a packing follower held in place by a flange on the yoke boss area of the bonnet (figure 3-15). An alternate packing retention means is where the packing follower is held in place by a screwed gland (figure 3-3). This alternate is compact, so it is often used on small control valves; however, the user cannot always be sure of thread engagement. Therefore, caution should be used in adjusting packing compression when the control valve is in service.

Most bolted-flange bonnets have an area on the side of the packing box which can be drilled and tapped. This opening is closed with a standard pipe plug unless one of the following conditions exists:

● It is necessary to purge the valve body and bonnet of process fluid, in which case the opening can be used as a purge connection.

● The bonnet opening is being used to detect leakage from the first set of packing or from a failed bellows seal.

Extension Bonnets

Extension bonnets are used for either high or low temperature service to protect valve stem packing from extreme process temperatures. Standard PTFE valve stem packing is useful for most applications up to 450°F (232°C). However, it is susceptible to damage at low process temperatures if frost forms on the valve stem. The frost crystals can cut grooves in the PTFE, forming leakage paths for process fluid along the stem. Extension bonnets remove the packing box of

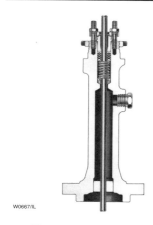

W0667/IL

Figure 3-16. Extension Bonnet

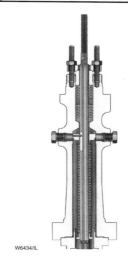

W6434/IL

Figure 3-18. Bellows Seal Bonnet

W1416IL

Figure 3-17. Valve Body with Fabricated Extension Bonnet

the bonnet far enough from the extreme temperature of the process that the packing temperature remains within the recommended range.

Extension bonnets are either cast (figure 3-16) or fabricated (figure 3-17). Cast extensions offer better high-temperature service because of greater heat emissivity, which provides better cooling effect. Conversely, smooth surfaces, such as can be fabricated from stainless steel tubing, are preferred for cold service because heat

influx is normally the major concern. In either case, extension wall thickness should be minimized to cut down heat transfer. Stainless steel is usually preferable to carbon steel because of its lower coefficient of thermal conductivity. On cold service applications, insulation can be added around the extension to protect further against heat influx.

Bellows Seal Bonnets

Bellows seal bonnets (figure 3-18) are used when no leakage (less than 1×10^{-6} cc/sec of helium) along the stem can be tolerated. They are often used when the process fluid is toxic, volatile, radioactive, or highly expensive. This special bonnet construction protects both the stem and the valve packing from contact with the process fluid. Standard or environmental packing box constructions above the bellows seal unit will prevent catastrophic failure in case of rupture or failure of the bellows.

As with other control valve pressure/temperature limitations, these pressure ratings decrease with increasing temperature. Selection of a bellows seal design should be carefully considered and particular attention should

51

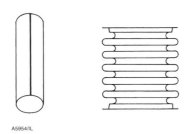

A5954/IL

Figure 3-19. Mechanically Formed Bellows

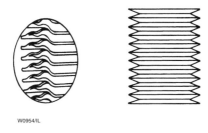

W0954/IL

Figure 3-20. Welded Leaf Bellows

be paid to proper inspection and maintenance after installation. The bellows material should be carefully considered to ensure the maximum cycle life.

Two types of bellows seal designs are used for control valves. These are mechanically formed and welded leaf bellows (figure 3-19 and figure 3-20 respectively). The welded-leaf design offers a shorter total package height. Due to its method of manufacture and inherent design, service life may be limited. The mechanically formed bellows is taller in comparison and is produced with a more repeatable manufacturing process.

Control Valve Packing

Most control valves use packing boxes with the packing retained and adjusted by a flange and stud bolts (figure 3-15). Several packing materials can be used depending on the service conditions expected and whether the application requires compliance to environmental regulations. Brief descriptions and service condition guidelines follow for several popular materials and typical packing material arrangements are shown in figure 3-21.

PTFE V-Ring

• Plastic material with inherent ability to minimize friction.

• Molded in V-shaped rings that are spring loaded and self-adjusting in the packing box. Packing lubrication not required.

• Resistant to most known chemicals except molten alkali metals.

• Requires extremely smooth (2 to 4 micro-inches RMS) stem finish to seal properly. Will leak if stem or packing surface is damaged.

• Recommended temperature limits: −40 to +450°F (−40 to +232°C)

• Not suitable for nuclear service because PTFE is easily destroyed by radiation.

Laminated and Filament Graphite

• Suitable for high temperature nuclear service or where low chloride content is desirable (Grade GTN).

• Provides leak-free operation, high thermal conductivity, and long service life, but produces high stem friction and resultant hysteresis.

• Impervious to most hard-to-handle fluids and high radiation.

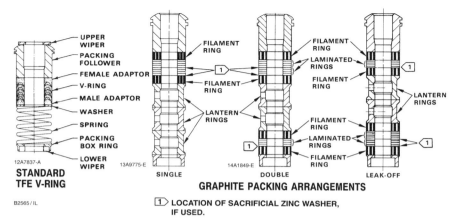

Figure 3-21. Comprehensive Packing Material Arrangements
for Globe-Style Valve Bodies

- Suitable temperature range: Cryogenic temperatures to 1200°F (649°C)

- Lubrication not required, but an extension bonnet or steel yoke should be used when packing box temperature exceeds 800°F (427°C).

USA Regulatory Requirements for Fugitive Emissions

Fugitive emissions are non-point source volatile organic emissions which result from process equipment leaks. Equipment leaks in the United States have been estimated at over 400 million pounds per year. Strict government regulations, developed by the US, dictate leak detection and repair programs (LDAR). Valves and pumps have been identified as key sources of fugitive emissions. For valves, this is the leakage to atmosphere due to packing seal or gasket failures.

The LDAR programs require industry to monitor all valves (control and non-control) at an interval that is deter-

mined by the percentage of valves found to be leaking above a threshold level of 500 ppmv (some cities use a 100 ppmv criteria). This leakage level is so slight you cannot see or hear it. The use of sophisticated portable monitoring equipment is required for detection. Dectection occurs by sniffing the valve packing area for leakage using an Environmental Protection Agency (EPA) protocol. This is a costly and burdensome process for industry.

The regulations do allow for the extension of the monitoring period for up to one year if the facility can demonstrate a very low ongoing percentage of leaking valves (less than 0.5% of the total valve population). The opportunity to extend the measurement frequency is shown in figure 3-22. New packing technologies extend packing-seal life and performance to support an annual monitoring objective.

ENVIRO–SEAL® packing system is one example of this new generation of packing seals. Enhanced seals incorporate four key design principles. These are the containment of the pliable seal material through an anti-ex-

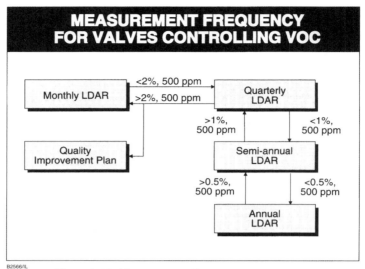

B2566/IL

*Figure 3-22. Measurement Frequency for Valves
Controlling Volatile Organic Chemicals (VOC)*

trusion component, proper alignment of the valve stem or shaft within the bonnet bore, applying a constant packing stress through belleville springs and minimizing the number of seal rings to reduce consolidation, friction, and thermal expansion.

The traditional valve selection process entails selecting a valve for the application based on pressure and temperature requirements, flow characteristics, and material compatibility. An additional factor—packing selection—is now involved in the valve engineering process.

In the past, packing selection was primarily based on process temperature; that is, PTFE was selected for temperatures below 450°F (232°C) and graphite was selected for temperatures above 450°F (232°C). Considerations now include the effect of packing friction on process control, seal performance (pressure/temperature/ppmv sealing capabilities), and service life. Given the variety of process applications, these variables are difficult to quantify. A relative packing performance comparison provides an engineered approach to the packing selection process.

The following table provides a comparison of various sliding-stem packing selections and a relative ranking of seal performance, service life, and packing friction for environmental applications. Braided graphite filament and double PTFE are not acceptable environmental sealing solutions.

Sliding Stem Environmental Packing Selection

Packing System	Maximum Pressure & Temperature Limits for 500 PPM Service[1]		Seal Performance Index	Service Life Index	Packing Friction
	Customary US	Metric			
Single PTFE V-Ring	300 psi 0 to 200°F	20.7 bar -18 to 93°C	Better	Long	Very Low
ENVIRO-SEAL PTFE	See Fig. 3–25 -50 to 450°F	See Fig. 3–25 -46 to 232°C	Superior	Very Long	Low
ENVIRO-SEAL Duplex	750 psi -50 to 450°F	51.7 bar -46 to 232°C	Superior	Very Long	Low
ENVIRO-SEAL Graphite	1500 psi 20 to 600°F	103 bar -18 to 315°C	Superior	Very Long	High
(1) The values shown are only guidelines. These guidelines can be exceeded, but shortened packing life or increased leakage might result. The temperature ratings apply to the actual packing temperature, not to the process temperature.					

The following applies to rotary valves. In the case of rotary valves, single PTFE and graphite ribbon packing arrangements do not perform well as fugitive emission sealing solutions.

Rotary Environmental Packing Selection

Packing System	Maximum Pressure & Temperature Limits for 500 PPM Service[1]		Seal Performance Index	Service Life Index	Packing Friction
	Customary US	Metric			
ENVIRO-SEAL PTFE	1500 psig -50 to 450°F	103 bar -46 to 232°C	Superior	Very Long	Low
ENVIRO-SEAL Graphite	1500 psig 20 to 600°F	103 bar -18 to 315°C	Superior	Very Long	Moderate
(1) The values shown are only guidelines. These guidelines can be exceeded, but shortened packing life or increased leakage might result. The temperature ratings apply to the actual packing temperature, not to the process temperature.					

Cross-sections of these packing designs for globe and rotary valves are shown in figures 3- 23, 3-24, 3-25, and 3-26.

When selecting a packing-seal technology for fugitive emission service, it is important to ask the following questions to help ensure long term performance. Detailed answers based on test data should be available from the valve manufacturer.

• Was the packing system tested within the valve style to be used?

• Was the packing system subjected to multiple operating cycles?

• Was the packing system subjected to multiple thermal cycles?

• Were packing adjustments made during the performance test?

• Was the packing system tested at or above the service conditions of the planned application?

• Did testing of packing systems for rotary valves include deflection of the valve shaft?

• Was stem leakage monitored using EPA Method 21 or another industry accepted practice?

• Were the packing components examined for wear after the completion of each test?

• Was the compression load on the packing measured as the test progressed?

• Are the test results documented and available for review?

The control of valve fugitive emissions and a reduction in industry's cost of

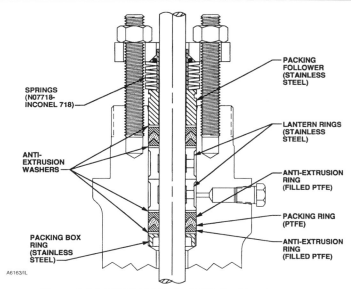

Figure 3-24. PTFE ENVIRO–SEAL Packing System

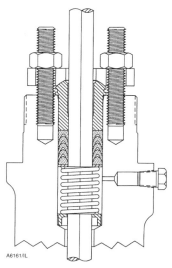

Figure 3-23. Single PTFE V–Ring Packing

regulatory compliance can be achieved through these new stem sealing technologies. Over the next several years, regulatory authorities

will probably generate additional regulations for all industries that have volatile organics in the process stream.

While these new packing sealing systems have been designed specifically for fugitive emission applications, these technologies should be considered for any application where seal performance and seal life have been an ongoing concern or maintenance cost issue.

Characterization of Cage-Guided Valve Bodies

In valve bodies with cage-guided trim, the shape of the flow openings or windows in the wall of the cylindrical cage determines flow characterization. As the valve plug is moved away from the seat ring, the cage windows are opened to permit flow through the valve. Standard cages have been designed to produce linear, equal–percentage, and quick–opening inherent flow characteristics. Note the differ-

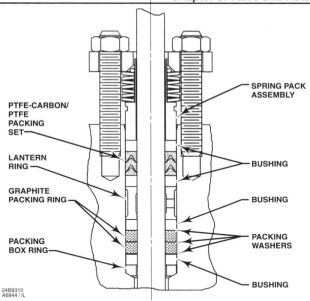

PTFE-CARBON/
PTFE
PACKING
SET

LANTERN
RING

GRAPHITE
PACKING RING

PACKING
BOX RING

SPRING PACK
ASSEMBLY

BUSHING

BUSHING

PACKING
WASHERS

BUSHING

24B9310
A6844 / IL

Figure 3-25. Duplex (PTFE and Graphite)
ENVIRO–SEAL Packing System

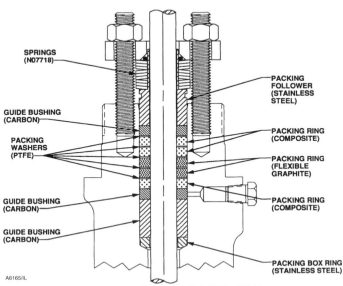

SPRINGS
(N07718)

GUIDE BUSHING
(CARBON)

PACKING
WASHERS
(PTFE)

GUIDE BUSHING
(CARBON)

GUIDE BUSHING
(CARBON)

PACKING
FOLLOWER
(STAINLESS
STEEL)

PACKING RING
(COMPOSITE)

PACKING RING
(FLEXIBLE
GRAPHITE)

PACKING RING
(COMPOSITE)

PACKING BOX RING
(STAINLESS STEEL)

A6165/IL

Figure 3-26. Graphite ENVIRO–SEAL
Packing System

ences in the shapes of the cage windows shown in figure 3-27. The flow
rate/travel relationship provided by

valves using these cages is equivalent
to the linear, quick–opening, and

W0958/IL

QUICK OPENING

W0959/IL

LINEAR

W0957/IL

EQUAL PERCENTAGE

Figure 3-27. Characterized Cages for Globe-Style Valve Bodies

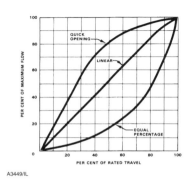

A3449/IL

Figure 3-28. Inherent Flow Characteristics Curves

equal–percentage curves shown for contoured valve plugs (figure 3-28).

Cage-guided trim in a control valve provides a distinct advantage over conventional valve body assemblies in that maintenance and replacement of internal parts is much simplified. The inherent flow characteristic of the valve can be easily changed by installing a different cage. Interchange of cages to provide a different inherent flow characteristic does not require changing valve plug or seat ring. The standard cages shown can be used with either balanced or unbalanced trim constructions. Soft seating, when required, is available as a retained insert in the seat ring and is independent of cage or valve plug selection.

Cage interchangeability can be extended to specialized cage designs that provide noise attenuation or combat cavitation. These cages furnish a modified linear inherent flow characteristic, but require flow to be in a specific direction through the cage openings. Therefore, it could be necessary to reverse the valve body in the pipeline to obtain proper flow direction.

Characterized Valve Plugs

The valve plug, the movable part of a globe-style control valve assembly, provides a variable restriction to fluid flow. Valve plug styles are each designed to provide a specific flow characteristic, permit a specified manner of guiding or alignment with the seat ring, or have a particular shutoff or damage-resistance capability.

Valve plugs are designed for either two-position or throttling control. In two-position applications, the valve plug is positioned by the actuator at either of two points within the travel range of the assembly. In throttling control, the valve plug can be positioned at any point within the travel range as dictated by the process requirements.

The contour of the valve plug surface next to the seat ring is instrumental in determining the inherent flow characteristic of a conventional globe-style control valve. As the actuator moves

58

the valve plug through its travel range, the unobstructed flow area changes in size and shape depending on the contour of the valve plug. When a constant pressure differential is maintained across the valve, the changing relationship between percentage of maximum flow capacity and percentage of total travel range can be portrayed (figure 3-28), and is designated as the inherent flow characteristic of the valve.

Commonly specified inherent flow characteristics include:

Linear Flow Characteristic—A valve with an ideal linear inherent flow characteristic produces flow rate directly proportional to the amount of valve plug travel, throughout the travel range. For instance, at 50% of rated travel, flow rate is 50% of maximum flow; at 80% of rated travel, flow rate is 80% of maximum; etc. Change of flow rate is constant with respect to valve plug travel. Valves with a linear characteristic are often specified for liquid level control and for flow control applications requiring constant gain.

Equal-Percentage Flow Characteristic—Ideally, for equal increments of valve plug travel, the change in flow rate regarding travel may be expressed as a constant percent of the flow rate at the time of the change. The change in flow rate observed regarding travel will be relatively small when the valve plug is near its seat and relatively high when the valve plug is nearly wide open. Therefore, a valve with an inherent equal-percentage flow characteristic provides precise throttling control through the lower portion of the travel range and rapidly increasing capacity as the valve plug nears the wide-open position. Valves with equal-percentage flow characteristics are used on pressure control applications, on applications where a large percentage of the pressure drop is normally absorbed by the system itself with only a relatively

small percentage available at the control valve and on applications where highly varying pressure drop conditions can be expected. In most physical systems, the inlet pressure decreases as the rate of flow increases, and an equal percentage characteristic is appropriate. For this reason, equal percentage is the most common valve characteristic.

Quick-Opening Flow Characteristic—A valve with a quick opening flow characteristic provides a maximum change in flow rate at low travels. The curve is basically linear through the first 40 percent of valve plug travel, then flattens out noticeably to indicate little increase in flow rate as travel approaches the wide-open position. Control valves with quick-opening flow characteristics are often used for on/off applications where significant flow rate must be established quickly as the valve begins to open. Consequently, they are often used in relief valve applications. Quick-opening valves can also be selected for many of the same applications for which linear flow characteristics are recommended, because the quick-opening characteristic is linear up to about 70 percent of maximum flow rate. Linearity decreases sharply after flow area generated by valve plug travel equals the flow area of the port. For a typical quick-opening valve (figure 3-29), this occurs when valve plug travel equals one-fourth of port diameter.

Valve Plug Guiding

Accurate guiding of the valve plug is necessary for proper alignment with the seat ring and efficient control of the process fluid. The common methods used are listed below and their names are generally self descriptive.

Cage Guiding: The outside diameter of the valve plug is close to the inside wall surface of the cylindrical cage throughout the travel range. Since bonnet, cage, and seat ring are self-aligning on assembly, correct valve

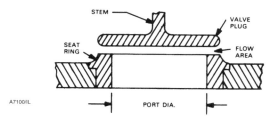

Figure 3-29. Typical Construction to Provide Quick-Opening Flow Characteristic

plug/seat ring alignment is assured when valve closes (figure 3-15).

Top Guiding: Valve plug is aligned by a single guide bushing in the bonnet or valve body (figure 3-4), or by packing arrangement.

Stem Guiding: Valve plug is aligned with the seat ring by a guide bushing in the bonnet that acts on the valve plug stem (figure 3-3, left view).

Top-and-Bottom Guiding: Valve plug is aligned by guide bushings in the bonnet and bottom flange (figure 3-7).

Port Guiding: Valve plug is aligned by the valve body port. This construction is typical for control valves using small-diameter valve plugs with fluted skirt projections to control low flow rates (figure 3-3, right view).

Restricted-Capacity Control Valve Trim

Most control valve manufacturers can provide valves with reduced- or restricted-capacity trim parts. The reduced flow rate might be desirable for any of the following reasons:

● Restricted capacity trim may make it possible to select a valve body large enough for increased future flow requirements, but with trim capacity properly sized for present needs.

● Valves can be selected for adequate structural strength, yet retain

reasonable travel/capacity relationship.

● Large bodies with restricted capacity trim can be used to reduce inlet and outlet fluid velocities.

● Purchase of expensive pipeline reducers can be avoided.

● Over-sizing errors can be corrected by use of restricted capacity trim parts.

Conventional globe-style valve bodies can be fitted with seat rings with smaller port size than normal and valve plugs sized to fit those smaller ports. Valves with cage-guided trim often achieve the reduced capacity effect by using valve plug, cage, and seat ring parts from a smaller valve size of similar construction and adapter pieces above the cage and below the seat ring to mate those smaller parts with the valve body (figure 3-30). Because reduced capacity service is not unusual, leading manufacturers provide readily available trim part combinations to perform the required function. Many restricted capacity trim combinations are designed to furnish approximately 40% of full-size trim capacity.

Actuators

Pneumatically operated control valve actuators are the most popular type in use, but electric, hydraulic, and manual actuators are also widely used. The spring-and-diaphragm pneumatic actuator is most commonly specified due to its dependability and simplicity of

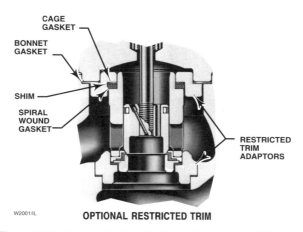

W2001/IL   **OPTIONAL RESTRICTED TRIM**

Figure 3-30. Adaptor Method for Providing Reduced Flow Capacity

design. Pneumatically operated piston actuators provide high stem force output for demanding service conditions. Adaptations of both spring-and-diaphragm and pneumatic piston actuators are available for direct installation on rotary-shaft control valves.

Electric and electro-hydraulic actuators are more complex and more expensive than pneumatic actuators. They offer advantages where no air supply source is available, where low ambient temperatures could freeze condensed water in pneumatic supply lines, or where unusually large stem forces are needed. A summary follows, discussing the design and characteristics of popular actuator styles.

Diaphragm Actuators

● Pneumatically operated diaphragm actuators use air supply from controller, positioner, or other source.

● Various styles include: direct-acting (increasing air pressure pushes down diaphragm and extends actuator stem, figure 3-31); reverse-acting (increasing air pressure pushes up diaphragm and retracts actuator stem, figure 3-31); reversible (actuators that can be assembled for either direct or

reverse action, figure 3-32); direct-acting unit for rotary valves (increasing air pressure pushes down on diaphragm, which may either open or close the valve, depending on orientation of the actuator lever on the valve shaft, figure 3–33).

● Net output thrust is the difference between diaphragm force and opposing spring force.

● Molded diaphragms provide linear performance and increased travels.

● Output thrust required and supply air pressure available dictate size.

● Diaphragm actuators are simple, dependable, and economical.

Piston Actuators

● Piston actuators are pneumatically operated using high–pressure plant air to 150 psig, often eliminating the need for supply pressure regulator.

● Piston actuators furnish maximum thrust output and fast stroking speeds.

● Piston actuators are double acting to give maximum force in both di-

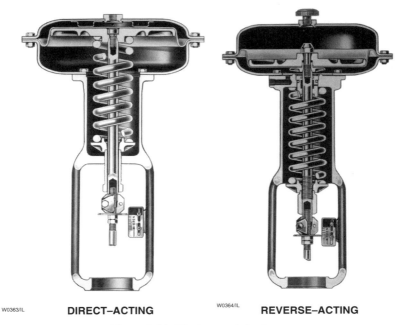

W0363/IL **DIRECT–ACTING**   W0364/IL **REVERSE–ACTING**

Figure 3-31. Diaphragm Actuators

W6655*A/IL

Figure 3-32. Reversible
Power Module

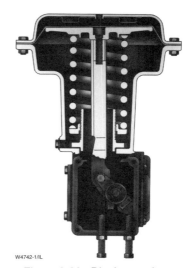

W4742-1/IL

Figure 3-33. Diaphragm Actuator for Rotary Shaft Valves

rections, or spring return to provide
fail-open or fail-closed operation(figure 3-34).

● Various accessories can be in-
corporated to position a double-acting

W0320-1/IL

Figure 3-34. Control Valve with Double-Acting Piston Actuator

W2286/IL

Figure 3-35. Control Valve with Double-Acting Electrohydraulic Actuator and Handwheel

piston in the event of supply pressure failure. These include pneumatic trip valves and lock-up systems.

● Also available are hydraulic snubbers, handwheels, and units without yokes, which can be used to operate butterfly valves, louvers, and similar industrial equipment.

● Other versions for service on rotary-shaft control valves include a sliding seal in the lower end of the cylinder. This permits the actuator stem to move laterally as well as up and down without leakage of cylinder pressure. This feature permits direct connection of the actuator stem to the actuator lever mounted on the rotary valve shaft, thereby eliminating one joint or source of lost motion.

Electrohydraulic Actuators

● Electrohydraulic actuators require only electrical power to the mo-

tor and an electrical input signal from the controller (figure 3-35).

● Electrohydraulic actuators are ideal for isolated locations where pneumatic supply pressure is not available but where precise control of valve plug position is needed.

● Units are normally reversible by making minor adjustments and might be self-contained, including motor, pump, and double-acting hydraulically operated piston within a weatherproof or explosion-proof casing.

Manual Actuators

● Manual actuators are useful where automatic control is not required, but where ease of operation and good manual control is still necessary (figure 3–36). They are often used to actuate the bypass valve in a three-valve bypass loop around control valves for manual control of the process during maintenance or shutdown of the automatic system.

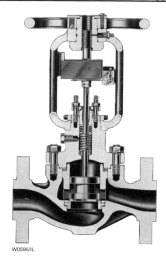

W0595/IL

W2583/IL

FOR SLIDING-STEM VALVES   **FOR ROTARY-SHAFT VALVES**

Figure 3-36. Typical Manual Actuators

• Manual actuators are available in various sizes for both globe-style valves and rotary-shaft valves.

• Dial-indicating devices are available for some models to permit accurate repositioning of the valve plug or disk.

• Manual actuators are much less expensive than automatic actuators.

Rack and Pinion Actuators

Rack and pinion designs provide a compact and economical solution for rotary shaft valves (figure 3-37). Because of backlash, they are typically used for on–off applications or where process variability is not a concern.

Electric Actuators

Traditional electric actuator designs use an electric motor and some form of gear reduction to move the valve. Through adaptation, these mechanisms have been used for continuous control with varying degrees of suc-

W6957/IL

Figure 3-37. Typical Rack and Pinion Actuator

cess. To date, electric actuators have been much more expensive than pneumatic for the same performance levels. This is an area of rapid technological change, and future designs may cause a shift towards greater use of electric actuators.

64

Chapter 4

Control Valve Accessories

This chapter offers information on digital valve controllers, analog positioners, boosters, and other control valve accessories.

Positioners

Pneumatically operated valves depend on a positioner to take an input signal from a process controller and convert it to valve travel. These instruments are available in three configurations:

1. Pneumatic—A pneumatic signal (usually 3-15 psig) is supplied to the positioner. The positioner translates this to a required valve position and supplies the valve actuator with the required air pressure to move the valve to the correct position.

2. Analog I/P—This positioner performs the same function as the one above, but uses electrical current

(usually 4-20 mA) instead of air as the input signal.

3. Digital—Although this positioner functions very much as the Analog I/P described above, it differs in that the electronic signal conversion is digital rather than analog. The digital products cover three categories.

- Digital Non-Communicating—A current signal (4-20 mA) is supplied to the positioner, which both powers the electronics and controls the output.

- HART—This is the same as the digital non-communicating but is also capable of two-way digital communication over the same wires used for the analog signal.

- Fieldbus—This type receives digitally based signals and positions the valve using digital electronic circuitry coupled to mechanical components. An all-digital control signal replaces the analog control signal. Additionally, two-way digital communication is possible over the same wires. The shift in field communications technology towards a fieldbus technology benefit the end user by enabling improved control architecture, product capability and reduced wiring.

A shift toward the use of analog I/P positioners, one instrument, instead of a combination of pneumatic positioner and transducer, two instruments, has been taking place for many years. This shift results from lower installed cost for the single instrument approach and the gradual acceptance of electronic instruments for valve service. This trend combines with a move toward HART and fieldbus products to change the instrument mix away from transducers, pneumatic positioners and to analog I/P positioners and digital valve controllers (figure 4-1).

The ability to embed software commands into the memory of the device represents the real difference between digital and analog I/P segments. This allows automatic configuration and setup of the valve. Most importantly, it allows two-way communication for process, valve, and instrument diagnostics.

W6848/IL

Figure 4-1. Modern Control Valve Utilizing a Digital Valve Controller

A general trend moves toward higher positioner use on control valves because of greater use of DCS systems and customer focus on valve accuracy. Users purchase digital valve controllers for several reasons:

- Reduced cost of loop commissioning, including installation and calibration.

- Use of diagnostics to maintain loop performance levels.

- Improved process control through reduced process variability.

- Offset the decreasing mechanical skill base of instrument technicians.

Two aspects of digital valve controllers make them particularly attractive:

- Automatic calibration and configuration. Considerable time savings are realized over traditional zero and spanning.

- Valve diagnostics. Through the Distributed Control System (DCS), PC software tools, or handheld communicators, users can diagnose the health of the valve while it is in the line.

FIELDVUE® instruments enable new diagnostic capabilities that can be accessed remotely. This single element requires a look at the potential impact of the technology as it applies to control valves.

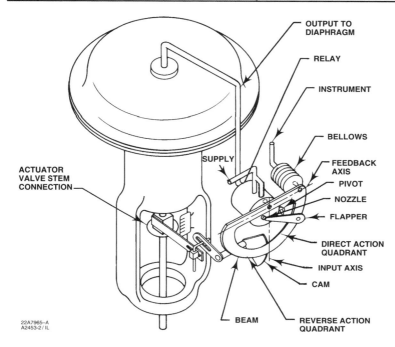

OUTPUT TO
DIAPHRAGM

RELAY

INSTRUMENT

BELLOWS

FEEDBACK
AXIS

PIVOT

NOZZLE

FLAPPER

DIRECT ACTION
QUADRANT

INPUT AXIS

CAM

REVERSE ACTION
QUADRANT

BEAM

SUPPLY

ACTUATOR
VALVE STEM
CONNECTION

22A7965–A
A2453-2 / IL

Figure 4-2. Positioner Schematic for Diaphragm Actuator

In the past, an in-plant person, with the aid of the FlowScanner™ system, could diagnose the health of a valve through a series of off-line tests. Customers used to replacing valves on a routine basis, now are better able to detect, before removing the valve, the physical condition of the valve.

Digital instruments allow an extension of this service with added enhancements:

● It is now possible to diagnose the health of a valve remotely.

● On-line diagnostics enable predictive maintenance.

These two additional elements are extremely important to the user. The remote capability allows monitoring valves and reporting to the user on the condition of their asset. Those who make, supply, and service valves for a living now assist the customer in the diagnosis of valve condition to a level never before possible. Predictive maintenance offers additional savings for the customer. It is now possible to see the performance of the valve as it operates. Watching performance decline over time enables the user to predict when replacement is necessary. It can even indicate the need for a different product, such as a sliding stem valve in the place of a butterfly valve.

Other Control Valve Accessories

Figure 4-5 illustrates a top-mounted handwheel for a direct-acting diaphragm actuator. This unit can be used as an adjustable travel stop to limit travel in the upward direction or to manually close push-down-to-close valves.

Figure 4-6 illustrates a top-mounted handwheel for a reverse-acting dia-

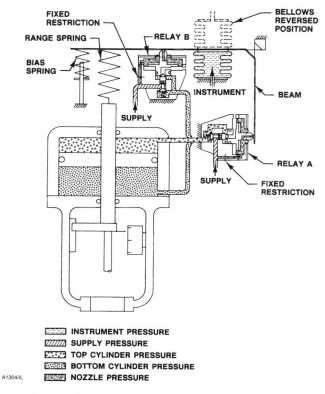

FIXED RESTRICTION
RANGE SPRING
RELAY B
BELLOWS REVERSED POSITION
BIAS SPRING
INSTRUMENT
BEAM
SUPPLY
RELAY A
SUPPLY
FIXED RESTRICTION

INSTRUMENT PRESSURE
SUPPLY PRESSURE
TOP CYLINDER PRESSURE
BOTTOM CYLINDER PRESSURE
A1304/IL
NOZZLE PRESSURE

Figure 4-3. Positioner Schematic for Piston Actuator

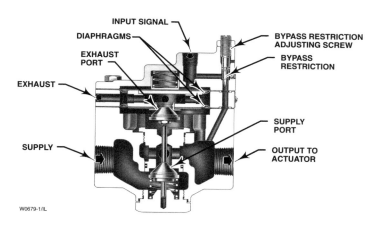

INPUT SIGNAL
DIAPHRAGMS
EXHAUST PORT
EXHAUST
SUPPLY
BYPASS RESTRICTION ADJUSTING SCREW
BYPASS RESTRICTION
SUPPLY PORT
OUTPUT TO ACTUATOR
W0679-1/IL

Figure 4-4. Volume Booster

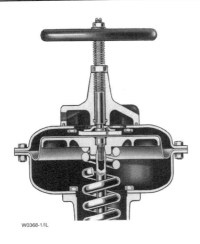

W0368-1/IL

Figure 4-5. Top-Mounted Hand-wheel for Direct-Acting Diaphragm Actuator

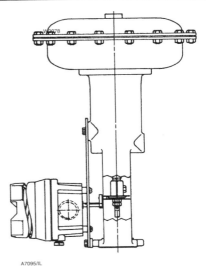

A7095/IL

W2078/IL

Figure 4-7. Cam-Operated Limit Switches

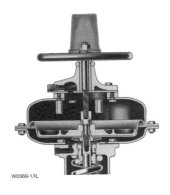

W0369-1/IL

Figure 4-6. Top-Mounted Hand-wheel for Reverse-Acting Dia-phragm Actuator

phragm actuator. This unit can be used as an adjustable travel stop to limit travel in the downward direction or to manually close push-down-to-open valves.

Limit Switches

Limit switches operate discrete inputs to a distributed control system, signal lights, small solenoid valves, electric relays, or alarms. The cam-operated type (figure 4-7) is typically used with two to four individual switches oper-ated by movement of the valve stem. An assembly that mounts on the side of the actuator houses the switches. Each switch adjusts individually and can be supplied for either alternating current or direct current systems. Oth-er styles of valve-mounted limit switches are also available.

Solenoid Valve Manifold

The actuator type and the desired fail-safe operation determine the selection of the proper solenoid valve (figure 4-8). The solenoids can be used on double-acting pistons or single-acting diaphragm actuators.

69

W7007/IL

Figure 4-8. Solenoid Valve

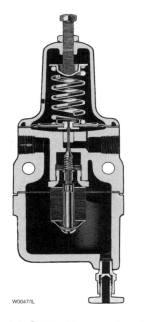

W0047/IL

Figure 4-9. Supply Pressure Regulator with Filter and Moisture Trap

Supply Pressure Regulator

Supply pressure regulators (figure 4-9), commonly called airsets, reduce plant air supply to valve positioners and other control equipment. Com-

mon reduced-air-supply pressures are 20, 35 and 60 psig. The regulator mounts integrally to the positioner, or nipple-mounts or bolts to the actuator.

Pneumatic Lock-Up Systems

Pneumatic lock-up systems (figure 4-10) are used with control valves to lock in existing actuator loading pressure in the event of supply pressure failure. These devices can be used with volume tanks to move the valve to the fully open or closed position on loss of pneumatic air supply. Normal operation resumes automatically with restored supply pressure. Functionally similar arrangements are available for control valves using diaphragm actuators.

Fail-Safe Systems for Piston Actuators

In these fail-safe systems (figure 4-11), the actuator piston moves to the top or bottom of the cylinder when supply pressure falls below a pre-determined value. The volume tank, charged with supply pressure, provides loading pressure for the actuator piston when supply pressure fails, thus moving the piston to the desired position. Automatic operation resumes, and the volume tank is recharged when supply pressure is restored to normal.

Electro-Pneumatic Transducers

Figure 4-12 illustrates an electro-pneumatic transducer. The transducer receives a direct current input signal and uses a torque motor, nozzle-flapper, and pneumatic relay to convert the electric signal to a proportional pneumatic output signal. Nozzle pressure operates the relay and is piped to the torque motor feedback bellows to provide a comparison between input signal and nozzle pressure. As shown, the transducer can be mounted directly on a control valve and operate the valve without need for additional boosters or positioners.

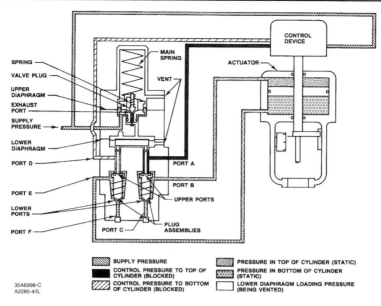

Figure 4-10. Lock-Up System Schematic for Piston Actuator

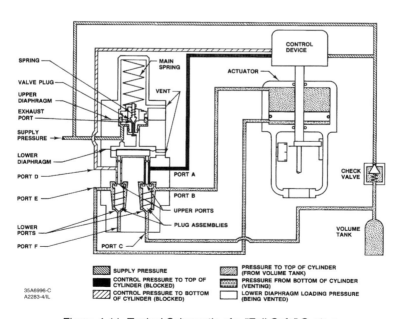

Figure 4-11. Typical Schematic of a "Fail-Safe" System

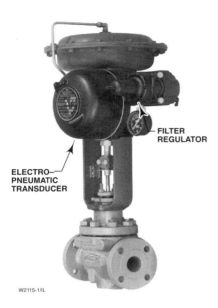

W2115-1/IL

ELECTRO—
PNEUMATIC
TRANSDUCER

FILTER
REGULATOR

Figure 4-12. Electro-Pneumatic Transducer with Supply Regulator for Operation of Diaphragm-Actuated Control Valve

W4930/IL

Figure 4-13. Electro-Pneumatic Positioner on Diaphragm Actuator

Electro-Pneumatic Valve Positioners

Electro-pneumatic positioners (figure 4-13) are used in electronic control loops to operate pneumatic diaphragm control valve actuators. The positioner receives a 4 to 20 mA DC input signal, and uses an I/P converter, nozzle-flapper, and pneumatic relay to convert the input signal to a pneumatic output signal. The output signal is applied directly to the actuator diaphragm, producing valve plug position that is proportional to the input signal. Valve plug position is mechanically fed back to the torque comparison of plug position and input signal. Split-range operation capability can provide full travel of the actuator with only a portion of the input signal range.

PC Diagnostic Software

PC diagnostic software provides a consistent, easy to use interface to every field instrument within a plant. For the first time, a single resource can be used to communicate and analyze field electronic "smart" devices such as pressure xmtrs, flow xmtrs, etc., not pneumatic positioners, boosters.

Users can benefit from reduced training requirements and reduced software expense. A single purchase provides the configuration environment for all products. Products and services are available that were not possible with stand-alone applications. The integrated product suite makes higher level applications and services possible.

Chapter 5

Control Valve Selection

Control valves handle all kinds of fluids at temperatures from the cryogenic range to well over 1000°F (538°C). Selection of a control valve body assembly requires particular consideration to provide the best available combination of valve body style, material, and trim construction design for the intended service. Capacity requirements and system operating pressure ranges also must be considered in selecting a control valve to ensure satisfactory operation without undue initial expense.

Reputable control valve manufacturers and their representatives are dedicated to helping select the control valve most appropriate for the existing service conditions. Because there are frequently several possible correct choices for an application, it is important that all the following information be provided:

- Type of fluid to be controlled

- Temperature of fluid

- Viscosity of fluid

- Specific gravity of fluid

- Flow capacity required (maximum and minimum)

- Inlet pressure at valve (maximum and minimum)

- Outlet pressure (maximum and minimum)

- Pressure drop during normal flowing conditions

- Pressure drop at shutoff

- Maximum permissible noise level, if pertinent, and the measurement reference point

- Degrees of superheat or existence of flashing, if known

• Inlet and outlet pipeline size and schedule

• Special tagging information required

• Body Material (ASTM A216 grade WCC, ASTM A217 grade WC9, ASTM A351 CF8M, etc.)

• End connections and valve rating (screwed, Class 600 RF flanged, Class 1500 RTJ flanges, etc.)

• Action desired on air failure (valve to open, close, or retain last controlled position)

• Instrument air supply available

• Instrument signal (3 to 15 psig, 4 to 20 mA, Hart, etc.)

In addition the following information will require the agreement of the user and the manufacturer depending on the purchasing and engineering practices being followed.

• Valve type number

• Valve size

• Valve body construction (angle, double-port, butterfly, etc.)

• Valve plug guiding (cage-style, port-guided, etc.)

• Valve plug action (push down to close or push down to open)

• Port size (full or restricted)

• Valve trim materials required

• Flow action (flow tends to open valve or flow tends to close valve)

• Actuator size required

• Bonnet style (plain, extension, etc.)

74

• Packing material (PTFE V-ring, laminated graphite, environmental sealing systems, etc.)

• Accessories required (positioner, handwheel, etc.)

Some of these options have been discussed in previous chapters of this book, and others will be explored in this and following chapters.

VALVE SELECTION PROCESS

```
DETERMINE SERVICE CONDITIONS
• (P₁, ΔP, Q, T₁, Fluid Properties, Allow-
able Noise, etc).
• Select appropriate ANSI Pressure Class
required for valve body and trim.
```

⬇

```
CALCULATE PRELIMINARY Cᵥ REQUIRED
• Check noise and cavitation levels
```

⬇

```
SELECT TRIM TYPE
• If no noise or cavitation indication, choose
standard trim.
• If aerodynamic noise is high, choose Whis-
per Trim®.
• If liquid noise is high and/or cavitation is in-
dicated, choose Cavitrol® III trim.
```

⬇

```
SELECT VALVE BODY AND TRIM SIZE
• Select valve body and trim size with re-
quired Cᵥ.
• Note travel, trim group, and shutoff options.
```

⬇

```
SELECT TRIM MATERIALS
Select trim materials for your application;
make sure trim selected is available in the
trim group for the valve size selected.
```

⬇

```
OPTIONS
Consider options on shutoff, stem packing,
etc.
```

Valve Body Materials

Body material selection is usually based on the pressure, temperature, corrosive properties, and erosive properties of the flow media. Sometimes a compromise must be reached in selecting a material. For instance, a material with good erosion resistance may not be satisfactory because of poor corrosion resistance when handling a particular fluid.

Some service conditions require use of exotic alloys and metals to withstand particular corrosive properties of the flowing fluid. These materials are much more expensive than common metals, so economy may also be a factor in material selection. Fortunately, the majority of control valve applications handle relatively non-corrosive fluids at reasonable pressures and temperatures. Therefore, cast carbon steel is the most commonly used valve body material and can provide satisfactory service at much lower cost than the exotic alloy materials.

Specifications have been developed for ordering highly corrosion resistant, high nickel alloy castings. These specifications represent solutions to problems encountered with those alloys. These problems included unacceptable corrosion resistance compared to the wrought materials, poor weldability, poor casting integrity

Designations for the High Nickel Alloys

Casting Designations	Equivalent Wrought Tradenames	Generic Designations	UNS Numbers for Wrought Equivalents
CF3		304L	S30403
CF8		304	S30400
CF3M		316L	S31603
CF8M		316	S31600
CG8M		317	S31700
CK3MCuN	Avesta 254 SMO[1]	Alloy 254	S31254
CN7M	Carpenter 20Cb3[2]	Alloy 20	N08020
CU5MCuC	Incoloy 825[3]	Alloy 825	N08825
CW12MW	Obsolete Hastelloy C[4]	Alloy C	N10002
CW2M	New Hastelloy C[4]	Alloy C276	N10276
CX2MW	Hastelloy C22[4]	Alloy C22	N06022
CW6MC	Inconel 625[3]	Alloy 625	N06625
CY40	Inconel 600[3]	Alloy 600	N06600
CZ100	Nickel 200	Alloy 200	N02200
LCB		LCB	J03003
LCC		LCC	J02505
M25S	S–Monel[3]	Alloy S	
M35–1	Monel 400[3]	Alloy 400	N04400
N12MV	Obsolete Hastelloy B[4]	Alloy B	N10001
N7M	Hastelloy B2[4]	Alloy B2	N10665
WCB		WCB	J03002
WCC		WCC	J02503

1. Trademark of Avesta AB
2. Tradenames of Carpenter Technology
3. Tradenames of Inco Alloys International
4. Tradename of Haynes International

and unacceptable lead times. The specifications include foundry qualification, dedicated pattern equipment, pattern alloy qualification, heat qualification, and detailed controls on raw material, visual inspection, weld repairs, heat treatment, and non–destructive testing. A listing of these exotic alloys appears in the Designations for the High Nickel Alloys Table.

The following descriptions and tables provide basic information on various popular castable materials used for control valve bodies. ASTM material designations are included. Use of proper ASTM designations is consid-

ered good practice and is encouraged in specifying materials, particularly for pressure-containing parts. Additional engineering data on these and other materials is included in Chapter 10.

Cast Carbon Steel (ASTM A216 Grade WCC)—WCC is the most popular steel material used for valve bodies in moderate services such as air, saturated or superheated steam, non-corrosive liquids and gases. WCC is not used above 800°F (427°C) as the carbon rich phase might be converted to graphite. It can be welded without heat treatment unless nominal thickness exceeds 1-1/4 inches (32 mm).

Pressure-Temperature Ratings for Standard Class ASTM A216 Grade WCC Valves (in accordance with ASME B16.34-1996)

TEMPERATURE, °F	WORKING PRESSURES BY CLASS, PSIG				
	150	300	600	900	1500
	Psig				
−20 to 100	290	750	1,500	2,250	3,750
200	260	750	1,500	2,250	3,750
300	230	730	1,455	2,185	3,640
400	200	705	1,410	2,115	3,530
500	170	665	1,330	1,995	3,325
600	140	605	1,210	1,815	3,025
650	125	590	1,175	1,765	2,940
700	110	570	1,135	1,705	2,840
750	95	505	1,010	1,510	2,520
800	80	410	825	1,235	2,060
°C	Bar				
−29 to 38	20	52	103	155	259
93	18	52	103	155	259
149	16	50	100	151	251
204	14	49	97	146	243
260	12	46	92	138	229
316	10	42	83	125	209
343	9	41	81	122	203
371	8	39	78	118	196
399	7	35	70	104	174
427	6	28	57	85	142

Cast Chromium-Molybdenum Steel (ASTM A217 Grade WC9)—This is the standard Cr-Mo grade. WC9 has replaced C5 as the standard because of superior casting and welding properties. WC9 has successfully replaced C5 in all applications for several years. The chromium and molybdenum provide erosion-corrosion and creep resistance, making it useful to 1100°F (593°C). WC9 requires preheating before welding and heat treatment after welding.

Pressure-Temperature Ratings for Standard Class ASTM A217 Grade WC9 Valves (in accordance with ASME B16.34–1996)

TEMPERATURE, °F	WORKING PRESSURES BY CLASS, PSIG				
	150	300	600	900	1500
−20 to 100	290	750	1,500	2,250	3,750
200	260	750	1,500	2,250	3,750
300	230	730	1,455	2,185	3,640
400	200	705	1,410	2,115	3,530
500	170	665	1,330	1,995	3,325
600	140	605	1,210	1,815	3,025
650	125	590	1,175	1,765	2,940
700	110	570	1,135	1,705	2,840
750	95	530	1,065	1,595	2,660
800	80	510	1,015	1,525	2,540
850	65	485	975	1,460	2,435
900	50	450	900	1,350	2,245
950	35	375	755	1,130	1,885
1000	20	260	520	780	1,305
1050	20[1]	175	350	525	875
1100	20[1]	110	220	330	550
°C	Bar				
−29 to 38	20	52	103	155	259
93	18	52	103	155	259
149	16	50	100	151	251
204	14	49	97	146	243
260	12	46	92	138	229
316	10	42	83	125	209
343	9	41	81	122	203
371	8	39	78	118	196
399	7	37	73	110	183
427	6	35	70	105	175
454	4	33	67	101	168
482	3	31	62	93	155
510	2	26	52	78	130
538	1	18	36	54	90
565	1[1]	12	24	36	60
593	1[1]	8	15	23	38

1. For welding end valves only. Flanged end ratings terminate at 1000°F.

Cast Chromium-Molybdenum Steel (ASTM A217 Grade C5)—In the past C5 was commonly specified for applications requiring chromium-molybdenum steels. However, this material is difficult to cast and tends to form cracks when welded. WC9 has successfully replaced C5 in all applications for several years.

Pressure-Temperature Ratings for Standard Class ASTM A217 Grade C5 Valves (in accordance with ASME B16.34–1996)

TEMPERATURE, °F	WORKING PRESSURE BY CLASS, PSIG				
	150	300	600	900	1500
−20 to 100	290	750	1,500	2,250	3,750
200	260	745	1,490	2,235	3,725
300	230	715	1,430	2,150	3,580
400	200	705	1,410	2,115	3,530
500	170	665	1,330	1,995	3,325
600	140	605	1,210	1,815	3,025
650	125	590	1,175	1,765	2,940
700	110	570	1,135	1,705	2,840
750	95	530	1,055	1,585	2,640
800	80	510	1,015	1,525	2,540
850	65	485	965	1,450	2,415
900	50	370	740	1,110	1,850
950	35	275	550	825	1,370
1000	20	200	400	595	995
1050	20[1]	145	290	430	720
1100	20[1]	100	200	300	495
°C	Bar				
−29 to 38	20	52	103	155	259
93	18	51	103	154	257
149	16	49	99	148	247
204	14	49	97	146	243
260	12	46	92	138	229
316	10	42	83	125	209
343	9	41	81	122	203
371	8	39	78	118	196
399	7	37	73	109	182
427	6	35	70	105	175
454	4	31	67	100	167
482	3	26	51	77	128
510	2	19	38	57	94
538	1	14	28	41	89
565	1[1]	10	20	30	50
593	1[1]	7	14	21	34

1. For welding end valves only. Flanged end ratings terminate at 1000°F.

Cast Type 304L Stainless Steel (ASTM A351 Grade CF3)—This is a good material offering for chemical service valves. 304L is the best mate- rial for nitric acid and certain other chemical service applications. Optimum corrosion resistance is retained even in the as-welded condition.

**Pressure-Temperature Ratings for Standard Class
ASTM A351 Grade CF3 Valves
(in accordance with ASME B16.34–1996)**

TEMPERATURE	WORKING PRESSURES BY CLASS				
	150	300	600	900	1500
°F	Psig				
−20 to 100	275	720	1,440	2,160	3,600
200	230	600	1,200	1,800	3,000
300	205	540	1,080	1,620	2,700
400	190	495	995	1,490	2,485
500	170	465	930	1,395	2,330
600	140	435	875	1,310	2,185
650	125	430	860	1,290	2,150
700	110	425	850	1,275	2,125
750	95	415	830	1,245	2,075
800	80	405	805	1,210	2,015
850	65	395	790	1,190	1,980
900	50	390	780	1,165	1,945
950	35	380	765	1,145	1,910
1000	20	320	640	965	1,605
1050	20[1]	310	615	925	1,545
1100	20[1]	255	515	770	1,285
1150	20[1]	200	400	595	995
1200	20[1]	155	310	465	770
1250	20[1]	115	225	340	565
1300	20[1]	85	170	255	430
1350	20[1]	60	125	185	310
1400	20[1]	50	95	145	240
1450	15[1]	35	70	105	170
1500	10[1]	25	55	80	135
°C	Bar				
−29 to 38	19	50	99	149	248
93	16	41	83	124	207
149	14	37	74	112	186
204	13	34	69	103	171
260	12	32	64	96	161
316	10	30	60	90	151
343	9	30	59	89	148
371	8	29	59	88	147
399	7	29	57	86	143
427	6	28	56	83	139

(continued)

**Pressure-Temperature Ratings for Standard Class
ASTM A351 Grade CF3 Valves
(in accordance with ASME B16.34–1996) (continued)**

TEMPERATURE	WORKING PRESSURES BY CLASS				
	150	300	600	900	1500
°C	Bar				
454	4	27	54	82	137
482	3	27	54	80	134
510	2	26	53	79	132
538	1	22	44	67	111
565	1[1]	21	42	64	107
593	1[1]	18	36	53	89
621	1[1]	14	28	41	69
649	1[1]	11	21	32	53
676	1[1]	8	16	23	39
704	1[1]	6	12	18	30
732	1[1]	4	9	13	21
760	1[1]	3	7	10	17
788	1[1]	2	5	70	12
815	1[1]	2	4	6	9

1. For welding end valves only. Flanged end ratings terminate at 1000°F.

**Cast Type 316 Stainless Steel
(ASTM A351 Grade CF8M)**—This is
the industry standard stainless steel
body material. The addition of molyb-
denum gives Type 316 greater resistance to corrosion, pitting, creep and
oxidizing fluids compared to 304. It
has the widest temperature range of
any standard material: –325°F
(–198°C) to 1500°F (816°C). The
rough castings are heat treated to provide maximum corrosion resistance.

**Cast Type 317 Stainless Steel
(ASTM A479 Grade UNS
S31700)**—S31700 is essentially
S31600 with the nickel and molybde-
num contents increased 1% each.

This affords greater resistance to pitting than is obtained with S31600.
Like S31600, S31700 is completely
austenitic and non-magnetic. Because
its strength is similar to that of
S31600, it has the same pressure-
temperature allowances. CG8M is the
casting version of S31700. It contains
considerable amounts of ferrite (15 to
35%), and therefore is partially to
strongly magnetic. In general, Type
S31700 has better corrosion resistance than S31600 in certain environments because of its higher molybde-
num content. It has excellent
resistance to digester liquor, dry chlo-
rine dioxide and many other pulp and
paper environments.

**Pressure-Temperature Ratings for Standard Class
ASTM A351 Grade CF8M and ASTM A479 Grade UNS S31700 Valves
(in accordance with ASME B16.34–1996)**

TEMPERATURE	WORKING PRESSURES BY CLASS				
	150	300	600	900	1500
°F	Psig				
–20 to 100	275	720	1,440	2,160	3,600

(continued)

**Pressure-Temperature Ratings for Standard Class
ASTM A351 Grade CF8M and ASTM A479 Grade UNS S31700 Valves
(in accordance with ASME B16.34–1996) (continued)**

TEMPERATURE	WORKING PRESSURES BY CLASS				
	150	300	600	900	1500
°F	Psig				
200	235	620	1,240	1,860	3,095
300	215	560	1,120	1,680	2,795
400	195	515	1,025	1,540	2,570
500	170	480	955	1,435	2,390
600	140	450	900	1,355	2,255
650	125	445	890	1,330	2,220
700	110	430	870	1,305	2,170
750	95	425	855	1,280	2,135
800	80	420	845	1,265	2,110
850	65	420	835	1,255	2,090
900	50	415	830	1,245	2,075
950	35	385	775	1,160	1,930
1000	20	350	700	1,050	1,750
1050	20[1]	345	685	1,030	1,720
1100	20[1]	305	610	915	1,525
1150	20[1]	235	475	710	1,185
1200	20[1]	185	370	555	925
1250	20[1]	145	295	440	735
1300	20[1]	115	235	350	585
1350	20[1]	95	190	290	480
1400	20[1]	75	150	225	380
1450	20[1]	60	115	175	290
1500	20[1]	40	85	125	205
°C	Bar				
−29 to 38	19	50	99	149	248
93	16	43	85	128	213
149	15	39	77	116	193
204	13	36	71	106	177
260	12	33	66	99	165
316	10	31	62	93	155
343	9	31	61	92	153
371	8	29	60	90	150
399	7	29	59	88	147
427	6	29	58	87	145
454	4	29	58	87	144
482	3	27	57	86	143
510	2	24	53	80	133
538	1	24	48	72	121
565	1[1]	21	47	71	119

(continued)

Pressure-Temperature Ratings for Standard Class
ASTM A351 Grade CF8M and ASTM A479 Grade UNS S31700 Valves
(in accordance with ASME B16.34–1996) (continued)

TEMPERATURE	WORKING PRESSURES BY CLASS				
	150	300	600	900	1500
°C	Bar				
593	1(1)	16	42	63	105
621	1(1)	13	33	49	82
649	1(1)	10	26	38	64
676	1(1)	8	20	30	51
704	1(1)	6	16	24	40
732	1(1)	4	13	20	33
760	1(1)	3	10	16	26
788	1(1)	2	8	12	20
815	1(1)	2	6	9	14

1. For welding end valves only. Flanged end ratings terminate at 1000°F.

Cast Iron (ASTM A126)—Cast iron is an inexpensive, non-ductile material used for valve bodies controlling steam, water, gas and non-corrosive fluids.

Pressure-Temperature Ratings for ASTM A216 Cast Iron Valves
(in accordance with ASME/ANSI B16.1–1989)

TEMPERATURE	CLASS 125			CLASS 250		
	ASTM A 126			ASTM A 126		
	Class A	Class B		Class A	Class B	
	NPS 1-12	NPS 1-12	NPS 14-24	NPS 1-12	NPS 1-12	NPS 14-24
°F	Psig					
−20 to 150	175	200	150	400	500	300
200	165	190	135	370	460	280
225	155	180	130	355	440	270
250	150	175	125	340	415	260
275	145	170	120	325	395	250
300	140	165	110	310	375	240
325	130	155	105	295	355	230
353	125	150	100	280	335	220
375	- - -	145	- - -	265	315	210
406	- - -	140	- - -	250	290	200
425	- - -	130	- - -	- - -	270	- - -
450	- - -	125	- - -	- - -	250	- - -
°C	Bar					
−29 to 66	12	14	10	28	34	21
93	11	13	9	26	32	19
107	11	12	9	24	30	19
121	10	12	9	23	29	18

(continued)

**Pressure-Temperature Ratings for ASTM A216 Cast Iron Valves
(in accordance with ASME/ANSI B16.1–1989) (continued)**

TEMPERATURE	CLASS 125			CLASS 250		
	ASTM A 126			ASTM A 126		
	Class A	Class B		Class A	Class B	
	NPS 1-12	NPS 1-12	NPS 14-24	NPS 1-12	NPS 1-12	NPS 14-24
°C	Bar					
135	10	12	8	22	27	17
149	10	11	8	21	26	17
163	9	11	7	20	24	16
178	9	10	7	19	23	15
191	- - -	10	- - -	18	22	14
207	- - -	10	- - -	17	20	14
218	- - -	9	- - -	- - -	19	- - -
232	- - -	9	- - -	- - -	17	- - -

**Pressure-Temperature Ratings for ASTM B61 and B62 Cast Bronze Valves
(in accordance with ASME B16.24–1991)**

SERVICE TEMPERATURE		WORKING PRESSURE							
		Class 150				Class 300			
		ASTM B 62 C83600		ASTM B 61 C92200		ASTM B 62 C83600		ASTM B 61 C92200	
°F	°C	psig	bar	psig	bar	psig	bar	psig	bar
−20 to 150	-29 to 66	225	16	225	16	500	34	500	34
175	79	220	15	220	15	480	33	490	34
200	93	210	14	215	15	465	32	475	33
225	107	205	14	210	14	445	31	465	32
250	121	195	13	205	14	425	29	450	31
275	135	190	13	200	14	410	28	440	30
300	149	180	12	195	13	390	27	425	29
350	177	165	11	180	12	350	24	400	28
400	204	- - -	- - -	170	12	- - -	- - -	375	26
406	207	150	10	- - -	- - -	- - -	- - -	- - -	- - -
450	232	135 (1)	9	160	11	280 (1)	19	350	24
500	260	- - -	- - -	150	10	- - -	- - -	325	22
550	288	- - -	- - -	140	10	- - -	- - -	300	21

1. Some codes (e.g., ASME Boiler and Pressure Vessel Code, Section 1; ASME B31.1; ASME B31.5) limit the rating temperature of the indicated material to 406F.

Class Designation and PN Numbers

There are two systems for designating the pressure-temperature ratings of valves. The United States and some other parts of the world use the class designation system. (See Chapter 9) The nominal pressure (PN) designa-tion system is used in Europe and most other parts of the world. In both cases the numerical designation of-fers a convenient round number for reference purposes; however, for the PN designation it is nominally the cold working pressure in bar. In the International Standards Organization (ISO)

Standard 7005-1: 1992 (Metallic flanges—Part 1: Steel flanges), the class designations have been converted to nominal pressure designations. The equivalent PN designations follow:

Class 150: PN 20

Class 300: PN 50

Class 600: PN 110

Class 900: PN 150

Class 1500: PN 260

Class 2500: PN 420

Some standards (for example, ISA S75.15–1993) show PN 100 as equivalent to Class 600 and PN 250 as equivalent to Class 1500; however, future revisions of these standards will use PN 110 and PN 260, respectively.

Face–to Face Dimensions for Flanged Globe–Style Control Valves
Classes 125, 150, 250, 300 and 600 (PN 20, 150, 250, 300 and 100)
(Dimensions in accordance with ISA S75.03-1992)

PRESSURE RATINGS AND END CONNECTIONS

VALVE SIZE		CL 125 FF (CI) CL 150 RF (STL) (PN 20)		CL 150 RTJ (STL) (PN 20)		CL 250 RF (CI) CL 300 RF (STL) (PN 50)		CL 300 RTJ (STL) (PN 50)		CL 600 RF (STL) (PN 100)		CL 600 RTJ (STL) (PN 100)	
DN	NPS	mm	in	mm	in	mm	in	mm	in	mm	in	mm	in
15	1/2	184	7.25	197	7.75	190	7.50	202	7.94	203	8.00	203	8.00
20	3/4	184	7.25	197	7.75	194	7.62	206	8.12	206	8.12	206	8.12
25	1	184	7.25	197	7.75	197	7.75	210	8.25	210	8.25	210	8.25
40	1–1/2	222	8.75	235	9.25	235	9.25	248	9.75	251	9.88	251	9.88
50	2	254	10.00	267	10.50	267	10.50	282	11.12	286	11.25	284	11.37
65	2–1/2	276	10.88	289	11.38	292	11.50	308	12.12	311	12.25	314	12.37
80	3	298	11.75	311	12.25	318	12.50	333	13.12	337	13.25	340	13.37
100	4	352	13.88	365	14.38	368	14.50	384	15.12	394	15.50	397	15.62
150	6	451	17.75	464	18.25	473	18.62	489	19.24	508	20.00	511	20.12
200	8	543	21.38	556	21.88	568	22.38	584	23.00	610	24.00	613	24.12
250	10	673	26.50	686	27.00	708	27.88	724	28.50	752	29.62	755	29.74
300	12	737	29.00	749	29.50	775	30.50	790	31.12	819	32.25	822	32.37
350	14	889	35.00	902	35.50	927	36.50	943	37.12	972	38.25	475	38.37
400	16	1016	40.00	1029	40.50	1057	41.62	1073	42.24	1108	43.62	1111	43.74

Abbreviations used above: FF – Flat Face; RF – Raised Face; RTJ – Ring Type Joint; CI – Cast Iron; STL – Steel

Face-to-Face Dimensions for Flanged Globe–Style Control Valves
Classes 900, 1500 and 2500 (PN 150, 1500, 250 and 420)
(Dimensions in accordance with ISA S75.16-1993)

VALVE SIZE		CL 900 (PN 150)				CL 1500 (PN 250)				CL 2500 (PN 420)			
		mm		in		mm		in		mm		in	
DN	NPS	Short	Long	Short	Long	Short	Long	Short	Long	Short	Long	Short	Long
15	1/2	273	292	10.75	11.50	273	292	10.75	11.50	308	318	12.12	12.50
20	3/4	273	292	10.75	11.50	273	292	10.75	11.50	308	318	12.12	12.50
25	1	273	292	10.75	11.50	273	292	10.75	11.50	308	318	12.12	12.50
40	1–1/2	311	333	12.25	13.12	311	333	12.25	13.12	359	381	14.12	15.00
50	2	340	375	13.38	14.75	340	375	13.38	14.75	– – –	400	– – –	16.25
65	2–1/2	– – –	410	– – –	16.12	– – –	410	– – –	16.12	– – –	441	– – –	17.38
80	3	387	441	15.25	17.38	406	460	16.00	18.12	498	660	19.62	26.00
100	4	464	511	18.25	20.12	483	530	19.00	20.87	575	737	22.62	29.00
150	6	600	714	21.87	28.12	692	768	24.00	30.25	819	864	32.25	34.00
200	8	781	914	30.75	36.00	838	972	33.00	38.25	– – –	1022	– – –	40.25
250	10	864	991	34.00	39.00	991	1067	39.00	42.00	1270	1372	50.00	54.00
300	12	1016	1130	40.00	44.50	1130	1219	44.50	48.00	1321	1575	52.00	62.00
350	14	– – –	1257	– – –	49.50	– – –	1257	– – –	49.50	– – –	– – –	– – –	– – –
400	16	– – –	1422	– – –	56.00	– – –	1422	– – –	56.00	– – –	– – –	– – –	– – –
450	18	– – –	1727	– – –	68.00	– – –	1727	– – –	68.00	– – –	– – –	– – –	– – –

Face-to-Face Dimensions for Buttweld-End Globe-Style Control Valves
Classes 150, 300, 600, 900, 1500 and 2500 (PN 20, 50 100, 150, 250 and 420)
(Dimensions in accordance with ISA S75.15-1993)

| VALVE SIZE | | CL 150, 300 and 600 (PN 20, 50 and 100) | | | | CL 900 and 1500 (PN 150 and 250) | | | | CL 2500 (PN 420) | | | |
| | | mm | | in | | mm | | in | | mm | | in | |
DN	NPS	Short	Long	Short	Long	Short	Long	Short	Long	Short	Long	Short	Long
15	1/2	187	203	7.38	8.00	194	279	7.62	11.00	216	318	8.50	12.50
20	3/4	187	206	7.38	8.25	194	279	7.62	11.00	216	318	8.50	12.50
25	1	187	210	7.38	8.25	197	279	7.75	11.00	216	318	8.50	12.50
40	1–1/2	222	251	8.75	9.88	235	330	9.25	13.00	260	359	10.25	14.12
50	2	254	286	10.00	11.25	292	375	11.50	14.75	318	400	12.50	15.75
65	2–1/2	292	311	11.50	12.25	292	375	11.50	14.75	318	400	12.50	15.75
80	3	318	337	12.50	13.25	318	460	12.50	18.12	381	498	15.00	19.62
100	4	368	394	14.50	15.50	368	530	14.50	20.88	406	575	16.00	22.62
150	6	451	508	17.75	20.00	508	768	24.00	30.25	610	819	24.00	32.25
200	8	543	610	21.38	24.00	610	832	24.00	32.75	762	1029	30.00	40.25
250	10	673	752	26.50	29.62	762	991	30.00	39.00	1016	1270	40.00	50.00
300	12	737	819	29.00	32.35	914	1130	36.00	44.50	1118	1422	44.00	56.00
350	14	851	1029	33.50	40.50	---	1257	---	49.50	---	1803	---	71.00
400	16	1016	1108	40.00	43.62	---	1422	---	56.00	---	---	---	---
450	18	1143	---	45.00	---	---	1727	---	68.00	---	---	---	---

Face-to-Face Dimensions for Socket Weld–End Globe–Style Control Valves
Classes 150, 300, 600, 900, 1500 and 2500 (PN 20, 50, 100, 150, 250 and 420)
(Dimensions in accordance with ISA S75.12-1993)

VALVE SIZE		CL 150, 300 and 600 (PN 20, 50 and 100)				CL 900 and 1500 (PN 150 and 250)				CL 2500 (PN 420)			
		mm		in		mm		in		mm		in	
DN	NPS	Short	Long	Short	Long	Short	Long	Short	Long	Short	long	Short	Long
15	1/2	170	206	6.69	8.12	178	279	7.00	11.00	216	318	8.50	12.50
20	3/4	170	210	6.69	8.25	178	279	7.00	11.00	216	318	8.50	12.50
25	1	197	210	7.75	8.25	178	279	7.00	11.00	216	318	8.50	12.50
40	1–1/2	235	251	9.25	9.88	235	330	9.25	13.00	260	381	10.25	15.00
50	2	267	286	10.50	11.25	292	375	11.50	14.75	324	400	12.75	15.75
65	2–1/2	292	311	11.50	12.25	292	– – –	11.50	– – –	324	– – –	12.75	– – –
80	3	318	337	12.50	13.25	318	533	12.50	21.00	381	660	15.00	26.00
100	4	368	394	14.50	15.50	368	530	14.50	20.88	406	737	16.00	29.00

Face-to-Face Dimensions for Screwed-End Globe-Style Control Valves
Classes 150, 300 and 600 (PN 20, 50 and 100)
(Dimensions in accordance with ISA S75.12–1993)

VALVE SIZE		CLASSES 150, 300 AND 600 (PN 20, 50 AND 100)			
		mm		in	
DN	NPS	Short	Long	Short	Long
15	1/2	165	206	6.50	8.12
20	3/4	165	210	6.50	8.25
25	1	197	210	7.75	8.25
40	1-1/2	235	251	9.25	9.88
50	2	267	286	10.50	11.25
65	2-1/2	292	311	11.50	12.26

Face-to-Centerline Dimensions for Raised Face
Globe-Style Angle Control Valves
Classes 150, 300 and 600 (PN 20, 50 and 100)
(Dimensions in accordance with ISA S75.22–1992)

VALVE SIZE		CLASS 150 (PN 20)		CLASS 300 (PN 50)		CLASS 600 (PN 100)	
DN	NPS	mm	in	mm	in	mm	in
25	1	92	3.62	99	3.88	105	4.12
40	1-1/2	111	4.37	117	4.62	125	4.94
50	2	127	5.00	133	5.25	143	5.62
80	3	149	5.88	159	6.25	168	6.62
100	4	176	6.94	184	7.25	197	7.75
150	6	226	8.88	236	9.31	254	10.00
200	8	272	10.69	284	11.19	305	12.00

Face-to-Face Dimensions for Separable Flanged Globe-Style Control Valves
Classes 150, 300 and 600 (PN 20, 50 and 100)
(Dimensions in accordance with ISA S75.20–1991)

VALVE SIZE		CLASSES 150, 300 AND 600 (PN 20, 50 AND 100)	
DN	NPS	mm	in
25	1	216	8.50
40	1-1/2	241	9.50
50	2	292	11.50
80	3	356	14.00
100	4	432	17.00

Face-to-Face Dimensions for Flangeless, Partial-Ball Control Valves
Classes 150, 300 and 600 (PN 20, 50 and 100)
(Dimensions in accordance with ISA S75.04–1995)

VALVE SIZE		CLASSES 150, 300 AND 600 (PN 20, 50 AND 100)	
DN	NPS	mm	in
20	3/4	76	3.00
25	1	102	4.00
40	1-1/2	114	4.50
50	2	124	4.88
80	3	165	6.50
100	4	194	7.62
150	6	229	9.00
200	8	243	9.56
250	10	297	11.69
300	12	338	13.31
350	14	400	15.75
400	16	400	15.75
450	18	457	18.00
500	20	508	20.00
600	24	610	24.00

Face-to-Face Dimensions for Single Flange (Lug-Type) and
Flangeless (Wafer-Type) Butterfly Control Valves
(Dimensions in accordance with MSS–SP–67–1995)

VALVE SIZE		DIMENSIONS FOR NARROW VALVE BODY INSTALLED [1][2]	
NPS	DN	in	mm
1-1/2	40	1.31	33.3
2	50	1.69	42.9
2-1/2	65	1.81	46.0
3	80	1.81	46.0
4	100	2.06	52.3
6	150	2.19	55.6
8	200	2.38	60.5
10	250	2.69	68.3
12	300	3.06	77.7
14	350	3.06	77.7
16	400	3.12	79.2
18	450	4.00	101.6
20	500	4.38	111.2

1. Bodies compatible with Class 125 cast iron flanges or Class 150 steel flanges.
2. This is the dimension of the valve face-to-face after it is installed in the pipeline. It does not include the thickness of gaskets if separate gaskets are used. It does include the thickness of gaskets or seals that are an integral part of the valve; however, this dimension is established with the gaskets or seals compressed.

**Face-to-Face Dimensions for High Pressure Butterfly Valves with Offset Design
Classes 150, 300 and 600 (PN 20, 50 and 100)
(Dimensions in accordance with MSS SP–68–1997)**

VALVE SIZE		CLASS 150 (PN 20)		CLASS 300 (PN 50)		CLASS 600 (PN 100)	
NPS	DN	in	mm	in	mm	in	mm
3	80	1.88	48	1.88	48	2.12	54
4	100	2.12	54	2.12	54	2.50	64
6	150	2.25	57	2.31	59	3.06	78
8	200	2.50	63	2.88	73	4.00	102
10	250	2.81	71	3.25	83	4.62	117
12	300	3.19	81	3.62	92	5.50	140
14	350	3.62	92	4.62	117	6.12	155
16	400	4.00	101	5.25	133	7.00	178
18	450	4.50	114	5.88	149	7.88	200
20	500	5.00	127	6.25	159	8.50	216
24	600	6.06	154	7.12	181	9.13	232

Wear & Galling Resistance Chart Of Material Combinations

	304	316	Bronze	Inconel 600, 625	Monel 400	Hastelloy B2	Hastelloy C276	Titanium	Nickel	Alloy 20	Type 416 Hard	Type 440 Hard	17-4PH	Alloy 6 (CoCr–A)	ENC*	Cr plate	Al Bronze
304 SST	P	P	F	P	P	P	P	P	P	P	F	F	F	F	F	F	F
316 SST	P	P	F	P	P	P	P	P	P	P	F	F	F	F	F	F	F
Bronze	F	F	S	F	F	F	F	F	F	F	S	S	S	S	S	S	F
Inconel 600, 625	P	P	F	P	P	P	P	P	P	P	F	F	F	F	F	F	F
Monel 400	P	P	F	P	P	P	P	P	P	P	F	F	F	F	F	S	F
Hastelloy B2	P	P	F	P	P	P	P	P	P	P	F	F	F	S	S	S	F
Hastelloy C276	P	P	F	P	P	P	P	P	P	P	F	F	F	S	S	S	F
Titanium	P	P	F	P	P	P	P	P	P	P	F	F	F	S	F	F	F
Nickel	P	P	F	P	P	P	P	P	P	P	F	F	F	F	F	F	F
Alloy 20	P	P	F	P	P	P	P	P	P	P	F	F	F	S	F	F	F
Type 416 Hard	F	F	S	F	F	F	F	F	F	F	S	S	S	S	S	S	S
Type 440 Hard	F	F	S	F	F	F	F	F	F	F	S	S	S	S	S	S	S
17-4 PH	F	F	S	F	F	F	F	F	F	F	S	S	S	S	S	S	S
Alloy 6(CoCr–A)	F	F	S	F	F	S	S	S	F	S	S	S	S	S	S	S	S
ENC	F	F	S	F	S	S	S	F	F	S	S	S	S	S	F	S	S
Cr Plate	F	F	S	F	S	S	S	F	F	S	S	S	S	S	F	F	S
Al Bronze	F	F	F	F	F	F	F	F	F	F	S	S	S	S	S	S	F

Monel and Inconel are Trademarks of Inco Alloys International
Hastelloy is a Trademark of Haynes International
S—Satisfactory
F—Fair
P—Poor

Control Valve Seat Leakage Classifications
(In accordance with ANSI/FCI 70-2-1991)

Leakage Class Designation	Maximum Leakage Allowable	Test Medium	Test Pressures	Testing Procedures Required for Establishing Rating
I	- - -	- - -	- - -	No test required provided user and supplier so agree.
II	0.5% of rated capacity	Air or water at 10–52°C (50–125°F)	3-4 bar (45–60 psig) or max. operating differential, whichever is lower.	Pressure applied to valve inlet, with outlet open to atmosphere or connected to a low head loss measuring device, full normal closing thrust provided by actuator.
III	0.1% of rated capacity	As above	As above	As above.
IV	0.01% of rated capacity	As above	As above	As above.
V	0.0005ml per minute of water per inch of orifice diameter per psi differential ($5 \times 10^{-12}m^3$ per second of water per mm of orifice diameter per bar differential).	Water at 10–52°C (50–125°F)	Max. service pressure drop across valve plug, not to exceed ANSI body rating, or lesser pressure by agreement.	Pressure applied to valve inlet after filling entire body cavity and connected piping with water and stroking valve plug closed. Use net specified max. actuator thrust, but no more, even if available during test. Allow time for leakage flow to stabilize.
VI	Not to exceed amounts shown in following table based on port diameter.	Air or nitrogen at 10–52°C (50–125°F)	3.5 bar (50 psig) or max. rated differential pressure across valve plug, whichever is lower.	Pressure applied to valve inlet. Actuator should be adjusted to operating conditions specified with full normal closing thrust applied to valve plug seat. Allow time for leakage flow to stabilize and use suitable measuring device.

Class VI Maximum Seat Leakage Allowable
(In accordance with ANSI/FCI 70-2-1991)

NOMINAL PORT DIAMETER		BUBBLES PER MINUTE[1]	
in	mm	ml per minute	Bubbles per minute
1	25	0.15	1
1-1/2	38	0.30	2
2	51	0.45	3
2-1/2	64	0.60	4
3	76	0.90	6
4	102	1.70	11
6	152	4.00	27
8	203	6.75	45

1. Bubbles per minute as tabulated are a suggested alternative based on a suitably calibrated measuring device, in this case a 1/4 inch (6.3 mm) O.D. x 0.032 inch (0.8 mm) wall tube submerged in water to a depth of from 1/8 to 1/4 inch (3 to 6 mm). The tube end shall be cut square and smooth with no chamfers or burrs, and the tube axis shall be perpendicular to the surface of the water. Other apparatus may be constructed and the number of bubbles per minute may differ from those shown as long as they correctly indicate the flow in ml per minute.

Typical Valve Trim Material Temperature Limits

MATERIAL	APPLICATION	LOWER		UPPER	
		°F	°C	°F	°C
304 SST, S30400, CF8	uncoated plugs and seats	−450	−268	600	316
316 SST, S31600, CF8M	uncoated plugs and seats	−450	−268	600	316
317 SST, S31700, CG8M	uncoated plugs and seats	−450	−268	600	316
416 SST, S41600, 38 HRC min	cages, plugs and seats	−20	−29	800	427
CA6NM, 32 HRC min	cages, plugs and seats	−20	−29	900	482
Nitronic 50[1], S20910 high strength condition	shafts, stems and pins	−325	−198	1100	593
440 SST, S44004	bushings, plugs and seats	−20	−29	800	427
17−4 PH, S17400, CB7Cu−1, H1075 condition	cages, plugs and seats	−80	−62	800	427
Alloy 6, R30006, CoCr−A	plugs and seats	−325	−198	1500	816
Electroless Nickel Coating	trim coating	−325	−198	750	400
Hard Chromium Plating	trim coating	−325	−198	600	316
Hard Chromium Plating on V−balls	trim coating	−325	−198	800	427
Hard Chromium Coating	trim coating	−325	−198	1100	593
Monel [2] K500, N05500	uncoated plugs and seats	−325	−198	800	427
Monel [2] 400, N04400	uncoated plugs and seats	−325	−198	800	427
Hastelloy [3] B2, N10665, N7M	uncoated plugs and seats	−325	−198	800	427
Hastelloy [3] C276, N10276, CW2M	uncoated plugs and seats	−325	−198	800	427
Titanium Grades 2, 3, 4, C2, C3, C4	uncoated plugs and seats	−75	−59	600	316
Nickel, N02200, CZ100	uncoated plugs and seats	−325	−198	600	316
Alloy 20, N08020, CN7M	uncoated plugs and seats	−325	−198	600	316
NBR, nitrile rubber	seats	−20	−29	200	93
FKM Fluoroelastomer (Viton[4])	seats	0	−18	400	204
PTFE, polytetrafluoroethylene	seats	−450	−268	450	232
PA (nylon)	seats	−60	−51	200	93
HDPE, high density polyethylene	seats	−65	−54	185	85
CR, chloroprene (Neoprene[2])	seats	−40	−40	180	82

1. Trademark of Armco Steel Corp.
2. Monel and Inconel are tradenames of Inco Alloys International
3. Hastelloy is a tradename of Haynes International
4. Trademark of E. I. DuPont Co.

Service Temperature Limitations for Elastomers

Temperature ranges indicated in the Service Temperature Limitations table suggest limits within which the materials will function adequately. Tempera-tures shown are not necessarily inher-ent temperature limits. Dynamic forces imposed on the materials are also considered. Frequently, tear strength and other physical properties decrease rapidly as service tempera-ture increases.

Ambient Temperature Corrosion Information

This corrosion table is intended to give only a general indication of how various metals will react when in contact with certain fluids. The recommendations cannot be absolute because concentration, temperature, pressure and other conditions may alter the suitability of a particular metal. There are also economic considerations that may influence metal selection. Use this table as a guide only. A = normally suitable; B = minor to moderate effect, proceed with caution; C = unsatisfactory.

Fluid	Alum	Brass	Cast Iron & Steel	416 & 440C	17–4 SST	304 SST	316 SST	Duplex SST	254 SMO	Alloy 20	Alloy 400	Alloy C276	Alloy B2	Alloy 6	Tita–nium	Zirco–nium
Acetaldehyde	A	A	C	A	A	A	A	A	A	A	A	A	A	A	A	A
Acetic Acid, Air Free	C	C	C	C	C	C	A	A	A	A	A	A	A	A	A	A
Acetic Acid, Aerated	C	C	C	C	B	B	A	A	A	A	C	A	A	A	A	A
Acetone	B	A	A	A	A	A	A	A	A	A	A	A	A	A	A	B
Acetylene	A	A	A	A	A	A	A	A	A	A	A	A	A	A	A	A
Alcohols	A	A	A	A	A	A	A	A	A	A	A	A	A	A	A	A
Aluminum Sulfate	C	C	C	C	B	A	A	A	A	A	B	A	A	A	A	A
Ammonia	A	C	A	A	A	C	B	A	A	A	A	A	A	B	A	A
Ammonium Chloride	C	C	C	C	C	C	B	A	A	A	B	A	A	A	A	B
Ammonium Hydroxide	A	C	A	A	A	A	A	A	A	A	C	A	A	A	A	A
Ammonium Nitrate	B	C	B	B	A	A	A	A	A	A	C	A	A	A	C	A
Ammonium Phosphate (Mono–Basic)	B	B	C	B	B	A	A	A	A	A	B	A	A	A	A	A
Ammonium Sulfate	C	C	C	C	B	B	A	A	A	A	A	A	A	A	A	A
Ammonium Sulfite	C	C	C	C	B	A	A	A	A	A	C	A	A	A	A	A
Aniline	C	C	C	C	A	A	A	A	A	A	B	A	A	A	A	A
Asphalt	A	A	A	A	A	A	A	A	A	A	A	A	A	A	A	A
Beer	A	A	B	B	A	A	A	A	A	A	A	A	A	A	A	A
Benzene (Benzol)	A	A	A	A	A	A	A	A	A	A	A	A	A	A	A	A
Benzoic Acid	A	B	C	C	A	A	A	A	A	A	B	A	A	A	A	A
Boric Acid	C	B	C	C	A	A	A	A	A	A	A	A	A	A	A	A
Bromine, Dry	C	C	C	C	B	B	B	A	A	A	A	A	A	A	C	C
Bromine, Wet	C	C	C	C	C	C	C	C	C	C	A	A	A	C	C	C
Butane	A	A	B	A	A	A	A	A	A	A	A	A	A	A	A	A
Calcium Chloride	C	C	B	C	C	B	B	A	A	A	A	A	B	B	C	C
Calcium Hypochlorite	C	C	C	C	C	C	C	A	A	A	C	A	B	B	A	A

(continued)

Ambient Temperature Corrosion Information (continued)

This corrosion table is intended to give only a general indication of how various metals will react when in contact with certain fluids. The recommendations cannot be absolute because concentration, temperature, pressure and other conditions may alter the suitability of a particular metal. There are also economic considerations that may influence metal selection. Use this table as a guide only. A = normally suitable; B = minor to moderate effect, proceed with caution; C = unsatisfactory.

Fluid	Alum	Brass	Cast Iron & Steel	416 & 440C	17–4 SST	304 SST	316 SST	Duplex SST	254 SMO	Alloy 20	Alloy 400	Alloy C276	Alloy B2	Alloy 6	Tita-nium	Zirco-nium
Carbon Dioxide, Dry	A	A	A	A	A	A	A	A	A	A	A	A	A	A	A	A
Carbon Dioxide, Wet	A	B	C	C	A	A	A	A	A	A	A	A	A	A	A	A
Carbon Disulfide	C	C	A	B	B	A	A	A	A	A	B	A	A	A	A	A
Carbonic Acid	A	B	C	C	A	A	A	A	A	A	A	A	A	A	A	A
Carbon Tetrachloride	A	A	B	B	A	A	A	A	A	A	A	A	A	A	A	A
Caustic Potash (see Potassium Hydroxide)																
Caustic Soda (see Sodium Hydroxide)																
Chlorine, Dry	C	C	A	C	B	B	B	A	A	A	A	A	A	A	C	A
Chlorine, Wet	C	C	C	C	C	C	C	C	C	C	B	B	B	C	A	A
Chromic Acid	C	C	C	C	C	C	C	B	A	C	C	A	B	C	A	A
Citric Acid	B	C	C	C	B	B	A	A	A	A	A	A	A	A	A	A
Coke Oven Acid	C	B	A	A	A	A	B	A	A	A	B	A	A	C	A	A
Copper Sulfate	C	C	C	C	C	C	B	A	A	A	C	A	A	C	A	A
Cottonseed Oil	A	A	A	A	A	A	A	A	A	A	A	A	A	A	A	A
Creosote	C	C	A	A	A	A	A	A	A	A	A	A	A	A	A	A
Dowtherm	A	A	A	A	A	A	A	A	A	A	A	A	A	A	A	A
Ethane	A	A	A	A	A	A	A	A	A	A	A	A	A	A	A	A
Ether	A	A	B	A	A	A	A	A	A	A	A	A	A	A	A	A
Ethyl Chloride	C	B	C	C	B	B	B	A	A	A	A	A	A	A	A	A
Ethylene	A	A	A	A	A	A	A	A	A	A	A	A	A	A	A	A

(continued)

Ambient Temperature Corrosion Information (continued)

This corrosion table is intended to give only a general indication of how various metals will react when in contact with certain fluids. The recommendations cannot be absolute because concentration, temperature, pressure and other conditions may alter the suitability of a particular metal. There are also economic considerations that may influence metal selection. Use this table as a guide only. A = normally suitable; B = minor to moderate effect, proceed with caution; C = unsatisfactory.

Fluid	Alum	Brass	Cast Iron & Steel	416 & 440C	17–4 SST	304 SST	316 SST	Duplex SST	254 SMO	Alloy 20	Alloy 400	Alloy C276	Alloy B2	Alloy 6	Tita– nium	Zirco– nium
Ethylene Glycol	A	A	A	A	A	A	A	A	A	A	A	A	A	A	A	A
Ferric Chloride	C	C	C	C	C	C	C	C	B	C	C	A	C	C	A	A
Fluorine, Dry	B	B	A	C	B	B	B	A	A	A	A	A	A	A	C	C
Fluorine, Wet	C	C	C	C	C	C	C	C	C	C	B	B	B	C	C	C
Formaldehyde	A	A	B	A	A	A	A	A	A	A	A	A	A	A	A	A
Formic Acid	B	C	C	C	C	C	B	A	A	A	C	A	B	B	C	A
Freon, Wet	C	C	B	C	B	B	A	A	A	A	A	A	A	A	A	A
Freon, Dry	A	A	B	A	A	A	A	A	A	A	A	A	A	A	A	A
Furfural	A	A	A	B	A	A	A	A	A	A	B	A	A	A	A	A
Gasoline, Refined	A	A	A	A	A	A	A	A	A	A	A	A	A	A	A	A
Glucose	A	A	A	A	C	A	A	C	A	A	C	A	A	A	C	A
Hydrochloric Acid (Aerated)	C	C	C	C	C	C	C	C	C	A	C	B	A	C	C	A
Hydrochloric Acid (Air Free)	C	C	C	C	C	C	C	C	C	A	C	B	A	A	C	A
Hydrofluoric Acid(Aerated)	C	C	C	C	C	C	C	C	C	C	B	B	B	C	C	C
Hydrofluoric Acid (Air Free)	C	C	C	C	C	C	C	C	C	C	A	B	B	A	C	C
Hydrogen	A	A	A	C	B	A	A	A	A	A	A	A	A	A	C	A
Hydrogen Peroxide	A	C	C	C	B	A	A	A	A	A	C	A	C	A	A	A
Hydrogen Sulfide	C	C	C	C	C	A	A	A	A	A	C	A	A	A	A	A
Iodine	C	C	C	C	A	A	A	A	A	A	C	A	A	A	C	B
Magnesium Hydroxide	B	B	A	A	A	A	A	A	A	A	A	A	A	A	A	A
Mercury	C	C	A	A	A	A	A	A	A	A	B	A	A	A	C	A
Methanol	A	A	A	A	A	A	A	A	A	A	A	A	A	A	A	A
Methyl Ethyl Ketone	A	A	A	A	A	A	A	A	A	A	A	A	A	A	A	A
Milk	A	A	C	A	A	A	A	A	A	A	A	A	A	A	A	A
Natural Gas	A	A	A	A	A	A	A	A	A	A	A	A	A	A	A	A

(continued)

97

Ambient Temperature Corrosion Information (continued)

This corrosion table is intended to give only a general indication of how various metals will react when in contact with certain fluids. The recommendations cannot be absolute because concentration, temperature, pressure and other conditions may alter the suitability of a particular metal. There are also economic considerations that may influence metal selection. Use this table as a guide only. A = normally suitable; B = minor to moderate effect, proceed with caution; C = unsatisfactory.

Fluid	Alum	Brass	Cast Iron & Steel	416 & 440C	17-4 SST	304 SST	316 SST	Duplex SST	254 SMO	Alloy 20	Alloy 400	Alloy C276	Alloy B2	Alloy 6	Titanium	Zirconium
Nitric Acid	C	C	C	C	A	A	A	A	A	A	C	B	C	C	A	A
Oleic Acid	C	C	C	B	B	B	A	A	A	A	C	A	A	A	A	A
Oxalic Acid	C	C	C	C	B	B	B	A	A	A	B	A	A	B	C	C
Oxygen	C	A	C	C	B	B	B	B	B	B	A	B	B	B	C	C
Petroleum Oils, Refined	A	A	A	A	A	A	A	A	A	A	A	A	A	A	A	A
Phosphoric Acid (Aerated)	C	C	C	C	B	A	A	A	A	A	C	A	A	A	C	A
Phosphoric Acid (Air Free)	C	C	C	C	B	B	B	A	A	A	B	A	A	B	C	A
Picric Acid	C	C	C	C	B	B	A	A	A	A	C	A	A	A	A	A
Potash/Potassium Carbonate	C	C	B	B	A	A	A	A	A	A	A	A	A	A	A	A
Potassium Chloride	C	C	B	C	C	B	B	A	A	A	A	A	A	A	A	A
Potassium Hydroxide	C	C	B	B	A	A	A	A	A	A	A	A	A	A	A	A
Propane	A	A	A	A	A	A	A	A	A	A	A	A	A	A	A	A
Rosin	A	A	B	A	A	A	A	A	A	A	A	A	A	A	A	A
Silver Nitrate	C	C	C	C	B	A	A	A	A	A	C	A	A	A	A	A
Soda Ash (see Sodium Carbonate)																
Sodium Acetate	A	A	A	A	A	A	A	A	A	A	A	A	A	A	A	A
Sodium Carbonate	C	C	A	B	A	B	B	A	A	A	A	A	A	A	A	A
Sodium Chloride	C	A	C	C	B	B	B	A	A	A	A	A	A	A	A	A
Sodium Chromate	A	A	A	A	A	A	A	A	A	A	A	A	A	A	A	A
Sodium Hydroxide	C	C	A	B	B	B	A	A	A	A	A	A	A	A	A	A
Sodium Hypochlorite	C	C	C	C	C	C	C	C	C	C	C	A	B	C	A	A
Sodium Thiosulfate	C	C	C	C	B	B	A	A	A	A	A	A	A	A	A	A
Stannous Chloride	C	A	C	C	C	C	B	A	A	A	C	A	A	B	A	A
Steam	A	A	A	A	A	A	A	A	A	A	A	A	A	A	A	A

(continued)

Ambient Temperature Corrosion Information (continued)

This corrosion table is intended to give only a general indication of how various metals will react when in contact with certain fluids. The recommendations cannot be absolute because concentration, temperature, pressure and other conditions may alter the suitability of a particular metal. There are also economic considerations that may influence metal selection. Use this table as a guide only. A = normally suitable; B = minor to moderate effect, proceed with caution; C = unsatisfactory.

Fluid	Alum	Brass	Cast Iron & Steel	416 & 440C	17-4 SST	304 SST	316 SST	Duplex SST	254 SMO	Alloy 20	Alloy 400	Alloy C276	Alloy B2	Alloy 6	Tita-nium	Zirco-nium
Stearic Acid	C	B	B	B	B	A	A	A	A	A	A	A	A	B	A	A
Sulfate Liquor (Black)	C	C	A	C	C	B	A	A	A	A	A	A	A	A	A	A
Sulfur	A	B	A	A	A	A	A	A	A	A	C	A	A	A	A	A
Sulfur Dioxide, Dry	C	C	C	C	C	C	B	A	A	A	C	A	A	B	A	A
Sulfur Trioxide, Dry	C	C	C	C	C	C	B	A	A	A	B	A	A	B	A	A
Sulfuric Acid (Aerated)	C	C	C	C	C	C	C	A	A	A	C	A	C	B	C	A
Sulfuric Acid (Air Free)	C	C	C	C	C	C	C	A	A	A	B	A	A	B	C	A
Sulfurous Acid	C	C	C	C	C	B	B	A	A	A	C	A	A	B	A	A
Tar	A	A	A	A	A	A	A	A	A	A	A	A	A	A	A	A
Trichloroethylene	B	B	B	B	B	B	A	A	A	A	A	A	A	A	A	A
Turpentine	A	A	B	A	A	A	A	A	A	A	A	A	A	A	A	A
Vinegar	B	B	C	C	A	A	A	A	A	A	A	A	A	A	A	A
Water, Boiler feed, Amine Treated	A	A	A	A	A	A	A	A	A	A	A	A	A	C	A	A
Water, Distilled	A	A	C	C	C	A	B	A	A	A	A	A	A	A	A	A
Water, Sea	C	A	C	C	C	C	A	A	A	A	A	A	A	A	A	A
Whiskey and Wines	A	A	C	C	A	A	A	A	A	A	A	A	A	A	A	A
Zinc Chloride	C	C	C	C	C	C	C	B	B	B	A	A	A	B	A	A
Zinc Sulfate	C	C	C	C	A	A	A	A	A	A	A	A	A	A	A	A

Elastomer Information

Selection of a suitable elastomer material for use in control valve applications requires knowledge of the service conditions in which the material will be used, as well as knowledge of the general properties of the material itself. Service temperature, pressure, rate of flow, type of valve action (throttling or on–off), and chemical composition of the fluid should all be known. Usage ratings listed below (Excellent, VG=Very Good, Good, Fair, Poor, VP=Very Poor,) should be used as a guide only. Specific compounds within any one material may vary, which could change the usage ratings.

Property	ACM, ANIM[1] Polyacrylic	AU, EU[2] Polyurethane	CO, ECO Epichlorohydrin	CR Chloroprene Neoprene	EPM, EPDM[3] Ethylene Propylene	FKM,[1,2] Fluoroelastomer Viton[4]	FFKM Perfluoroelastomer	IIR Butyl	VMQ Silicone	NBR Nitrile Buna N	NR Natural Rubber	SBR Buna-S GRS	TFE/P Tetrafluoroethylene propylene copolymer
Tensile, psi (MPa) Pure Gum	100(0.7)	– – –	2000(14)	3500(24)	– – –	– – –	– – –	3000(21)	200–450 (1.4–3)	600(4)	3000(21)	400(3)	– – –
Reinforced	1800(12)	6500(45)	2500(17)	3500(24)	2500(17)	2300(16)	3200(22)	3000(21)	1100(8)	4000(28)	4500(31)	3000(21)	2800(19)
Tear Resistance	Fair	Excellent	Good	Good	Poor	Good	– – –	Good	Poor–Fair	Fair	Excellent	Poor–Fair	Good
Abrasion Resistance	Good	Excellent	Fair	Excellent	Good	VG	– – –	Fair	Poor	Good	Excellent	Good	Good
Aging: Sunlight	Excellent	Excellent	Good	Excellent	Excellent	Excellent	Excellent	Excellent	Good	Poor	Poor	Poor	– – –
Oxidation	Excellent	Excellent	Good	Good	Good	Excellent	Excellent	Good	VG	Fair	Good	Fair	Excellent
Heat: (Max. Temp.)	350°F (117°C)	200°F (93°C)	275°F (135°C)	200°F (93°C)	350°F (117°C)	400°F (204°C)	550°F (288°C)	200°F (93°C)	450°F (232°C)	250°F (121°C)	200°F (93°C)	200°F (93°C)	400°F (204°C)
Flex Cracking Resistance	Good	Excellent	– – –	Excellent	– – –	– – –	– – –	Excellent	Fair	Good	Excellent	Good	– – –
Compression Set Resistance	Good	Good	Fair	Excellent	Fair	Poor	– – –	Fair	Good	VG	Good	Good	Good
Solvent Resistance: Aliphatic Hydrocarbon	Good	VG	Excellent	Fair	Poor	Excellent	Excellent	Poor	Poor	Good	VP	VP	Good
Aromatic Hydrocarbon	Poor	Fair	Good	Poor	Fair	VG	Excellent	VP	VP	Fair	VP	VP	Fair
Oxygenated Solvent	Poor	Poor	– – –	Fair	– – –	Good	Excellent	Good	Poor	Poor	Good	Good	Poor
Halogenated Solvent	Poor	– – –	– – –	VP	Poor	– – –	Excellent	Poor	VP	VP	VP	VP	Poor/Good

(continued)

Elastomer Information (continued)

Selection of a suitable elastomer material for use in control valve applications requires knowledge of the service conditions in which the material will be used, as well as knowledge of the general properties of the material itself. Service temperature, pressure, rate of flow, type of valve action (throttling or on–off), and chemical composition of the fluid should all be known. Usage ratings listed below (Excellent, VG=Very Good, Good, Fair, Poor, VP=Very Poor,) should be used as a guide only. Specific compounds within any one material may vary, which could change the usage ratings.

Property	ACM, ANIM[1] Polyacrylic	AU, EU[2] Polyurethane	CO, ECO Epichlorohydrin	CR Chloroprene Neoprene	EPM, EPDM[3] Ethylene Propylene	FKM,[1,2] Fluoroelastomer Viton[4]	FFKM Perfluoroelastomer	IIR Butyl	VMQ Silicone	NBR Nitrile Buna N	NR Natural Rubber	SBR Buna-S GRS	TFE/P Tetrafluoroethylene propylene copolymer
Oil Resistance:													
Low Aniline Mineral Oil	Excellent	– – –	– – –	Fair	Poor	Excellent	Excellent	VP	Poor	Excellent	VP	VP	Excellent
High Aniline Mineral Oil	Excellent	– – –	– – –	Good	Poor	Excellent	Excellent	VP	Good	Excellent	VP	VP	Fair
Synthetic Lubricants	Fair	– – –	Excellent	VP	Poor	– – –	Excellent	Poor	Fair	Fair	VP	VP	Excellent
Organic Phosphates	Poor	Poor	Excellent	VP	VG	Poor	Excellent	Good	Poor	VP	VP	VP	Good
Gasoline Resistance:													
Aromatic	Fair	Fair	Excellent	Poor	Fair	Good	Excellent	VP	Poor	Good	VP	VP	Poor
Non-Aromatic	Poor	Good	Excellent	Good	Poor	VG	Excellent	VP	Good	Excellent	VP	VP	Fair
Acid Resistance:													
Dilute (Under 10%)	Poor	Fair	Good	Fair	VG	Excellent	Excellent	Good	Fair	Good	Good	Good	Excellent
^Concentrated[5]	Poor	Poor	Good	Fair	Good	VG	Excellent	Fair	Poor	Poor	Fair	Poor	Good
Low Temperature Flexibility (Max)	−10°F (−23°C)	−40°F (−40°C)	−40°F (−40°C)	−40°F (−40°C)	−50°F (−45°C)	−30°F (−34°C)	0°F (−18°C)	−40°F (−40°C)	−100°F (−73°C)	−40°F (−40°C)	−65°F (−54°C)	−50°F (−46°C)	0°F (−18°C)
Permeability to Gases	Good	Good	Excellent	VG	Good	Good	Fair	VG	Fair	Fair	Fair	Fair	– – –
Water Resistance	Fair	Fair	Fair	Fair	VG	Excellent	Excellent	VG	Fair	VG	Good	VG	Excellent
Alkali Resistance:													
Dilute (Under 10 %)	Poor	Fair	Excellent	Good	Excellent	Excellent	Excellent	VG	Fair	Good	Good	Good	Excellent
Concentrated	Poor	Poor	Excellent	Good	Good	VG	Excellent	VG	Poor	Fair	Fair	Fair	Good

(continued)

Elastomer Information (continued)

Selection of a suitable elastomer material for use in control valve applications requires knowledge of the service conditions in which the material will be used, as well as knowledge of the general properties of the material itself. Service temperature, pressure, rate of flow, type of valve action (throttling or on–off), and chemical composition of the fluid should all be known. Usage ratings listed below (Excellent, VG=Very Good, Good, Fair, Poor, VP=Very Poor,) should be used as a guide only. Specific compounds within any one material may vary, which could change the usage ratings.

Property	ACM, ANIM[1] Poly–acrylic	AU, EU[2] Poly–ure–thane	CO, ECO Epi–chloro–hydrin	CR Chloro–prene Neo–prene	EPM, EPDM[3] Ethylene Pro–pylene	FKM,[1,2] Fluro–elast–omer Viton[4]	FFKM Per–fluoro–elast–omer	IIR Butyl	VMQ Silicone	NBR Nitrile Buna N	NR Natural Rubber	SBR Buna-S GRS	TFE/P Tetra–fluoro–ethylene pro–pylene copoly–mer
Resilience	VP	Fair	Fair	VG	VG	Good	– –	VG	Good	Fair	VG	Fair	– –
Elongation (Max)	200%	625%	400%	500%	500%	425%	142%	700%	300%	500%	700%	500%	400%

1. Do not use with steam.
2. Do not use with ammonia.
3. Do not use with petroleum base fluids. Use with ester Base (non–flammable) hydraulic oils and low pressure steam applications to 300°F (149°C).
4. Trademark of E.I. DuPont Co.
5. Except Nitric and Sulfuric.

Fluid Compatibility

This table rates and compares the compatibility of elastomer material with specific fluids. Note that this information should be used as a guide only. An elastomer which is compatible with a fluid may not be suitable over the entire range of its temperature capability. In general, chemical compatibility decreases with an increase in service temperature.

KEY: A+=Best Possible Selection A=Generally Compatible B=Marginally Compatible C=Not Recommended —=no data

NOTE: These recommendations are to be used as a general guide only. Full details regarding pressure, temperature, chemical considerations, and the mode of operation must be considered when selecting an elastomer.

FLUID	ACM, ANM Poly-acrylic	AU, EU Poly-urethane	CO, ECO Epichloro-hydrin	CR Chloro-prene Neoprene[1]	EPM, EPDM Ethylene Propylene	FKM Fluoro-elastomer Viton[1]	FFKM Perfluoro-elastomer	IIR Butyl	VMQ Silicone	NBR Nitrile Buna N	NR Natural Rubber	TFE/P Tetra-fluoro ethylene-propylene copolymer
Acetic Acid (30%)	C	C	C	C	A+	C	A+	A	A	B	B	C
Acetone	C	C	C	C	A	C	A	A	C	C	C	C
Air, Ambient	A	A	—	A	A	A	A	A	A	A	B	A
Air, Hot (200°F, 93°C)	B	B	—	C	A	A	A	A	A	A	B	A
Air, Hot (400°F, 204°C)	C	C	—	C	C	A	A	C	A	C	C	A
Alcohol, Ethyl	C	C	—	A	A	C	A	A	A	A	A	A
Alcohol, Methyl	C	C	B	A+	A	C	A	A	A	A	A	A
Ammonia, Anhydrous, Liquid	C	C	—	A+	A	C	A	A	B	B	C	A
Ammonia, Gas (Hot)	C	C	—	B	B	C	A	B	A	C	C	A+
Beer (Beverage)	C	C	A	A	A	A	A	C	A	A	A	A
Benzene	C	C	C	C	C	A	A	C	C	C	C	C
Black Liquor	C	C	—	B	B	A+	A	C	C	B	B	A
Blast Furnace Gas	C	C	—	C	C	A+	A	C	A	C	C	A
Brine (Calcium Chloride)	A	A	A	A	A	A	A	A	A	A	A	A
Butadiene Gas	C	C	C	C	C	A+	A	C	C	C	C	—
Butane Gas	A	C	A	A	C	A	A	C	C	A+	C	B
Butane, Liquid	A	C	A	B	C	A	A	C	C	A	C	C
Carbon Tetrachloride	C	C	B	C	C	A+	A	C	C	C	C	C

ELASTOMER RATINGS FOR COMPATIBILITY WITH FLUID

(continued)

103

Fluid Compatibility (continued)

This table rates and compares the compatibility of elastomer material with specific fluids. Note that this information should be used as a guide only. An elastomer which is compatibile with a fluid may not be suitable over the entire range of its temperature capability. In general, chemical compatibility decreases with an increase in service temperature.

KEY: A+=Best Possible Selection   A=Generally Compatible   B=Marginally Compatible   C=Not Recommended   –=no data

NOTE: These recommendations are to be used as a general guide only. Full details regarding pressure, temperature, chemical considerations, and the mode of operation must be considered when selecting an elastomer.

ELASTOMER RATINGS FOR COMPATIBILITY WITH FLUID

FLUID	ACM, ANM Poly-acrylic	AU, EU Poly-urethane	CO, ECO Epichloro-hydrin	CR Chloro-prene Neoprene[1]	EPM, EPDM Ethylene Propylene	FKM Fluoro-elastomer Viton[1]	FFKM Perfluoro-elastomer	IIR Butyl	VMQ Silicone	NBR Nitrile Buna N	NR Natural Rubber	TFE/P Tetra-fluoro ethylene-propylene copolymer
Chlorine, Dry	C	C	B	C	C	A+	A	C	C	C	C	C
Chlorine, Wet	C	C	B	C	C	A+	A	C	C	C	C	B
Coke Oven Gas	C	C	–	C	C	A+	A	C	B	C	C	A
Dowtherm A[2]	C	C	C	C	C	A+	A	C	C	C	C	B
Ethyl Acetate	C	C	C	C	B	C	A	B	B	C	C	C
Ethylene Glycol	C	B	A	A	A+	A	A	A	A	A	A	A
Freon 11[1]	A	C	–	C	C	B+	B	C	C	B	C	C
Freon 12[1]	B	A	A	A+	B	B	B	B	C	A	B	C
Freon 22[1]	B	C	A	A+	A	C	A	A	C	C	A	C
Freon 114[1]	–	A	A	A	A	A	B	A	C	A	A	C
Freon Replacements[1] (See Suva)[1]												
Gasoline	C	B	A	C	C	A	A	C	C	A+	C	C
Hydrogen Gas	B	A	–	A	A	A	A	A	C	A	B	A
Hydrogen Sulfide (Dry)	C	B	B	A	A+	C	A	A	C	A	A	A
Hydrogen Sulfide (Wet)	C	C	B	A	A+	C	A	A	C	C	C	A
Jet Fuel (JP–4)	B	B	A	C	C	A	A	C	C	A	C	B

(continued)

Fluid Compatibility (continued)

This table rates and compares the compatibility of elastomer material with specific fluids. Note that this information should be used as a guide only. An elastomer which is compatible with a fluid may not be suitable over the entire range of its temperature capability. In general, chemical compatibility decreases with an increase in service temperature.

KEY: A+=Best Possible Selection A=Generally Compatible B=Marginally Compatible C=Not Recommended −=no data

NOTE: These recommendations are to be used as a general guide only. Full details regarding pressure, temperature, chemical considerations, and the mode of operation must be considered when selecting an elastomer.

ELASTOMER RATINGS FOR COMPATIBILITY WITH FLUID

FLUID	ACM, ANM Poly–acrylic	AU, EU Poly–urethane	CO, ECO Epichloro–hydrin	CR Chloro–prene Neoprene[1]	EPM, EPDM Ethylene Propylene	FKM Fluoro–elastomer Viton[1]	FFKM Perfluoro–elastomer	IIR Butyl	VMQ Silicone	NBR Nitrile Buna N	NR Natural Rubber	TFE/P Tetra–fluoro ethylene–propylene copolymer
Methylene Chloride	C	C	−	C	C	B+	A+	C	C	C	C	B
Milk	C	C	−	A	A	A	A	A	A	A+	A	A
Naphthalene	−	B	−	C	C	A+	A	C	C	C	C	B
Natural Gas	B	B	A	A	C	A	A	C	C	A+	B	A
Natural Gas +H₂S (Sour Gas)	C	B	A	A+	C	C	A	C	C	B	C	A
Natural Gas, Sour + Ammonia	C	C	−	B+	C	C	A	C	C	B	C	A+
Nitric Acid (10%)	C	C	C	C	B	A+	A	A	C	C	C	A
Nitric Acid (50–100%)	C	C	C	C	C	A+	A	A	C	C	C	B
Nitric Acid Vapor	C	C	C	B	B	A	A	B	C	C	C	A
Nitrogen	A	A	A	A	A	A	A	A	A	A	A	A
Oil (Fuel)	B	C	A	B	C	A	A	C	C	A+	C	A
Ozone	B	A	A	B	A	A	A	B	A	C	C	A
Paper Stock	−	C	−	B	B	A	A	B	C	B	C	−
Propane	A	B	A	A	C	A	A	C	C	A+	C	A
Sea Water	C	B	−	B	A	A	A	A	A	A	B	A
Sea Water + Sulfuric Acid	C	B	−	B	B	A	A	B	C	C	C	A
Soap Solutions	C	C	A	A	A	A	A	A	A	A	B	A

(continued)

Fluid Compatibility (continued)

This table rates and compares the compatibility of elastomer material with specific fluids. Note that this information should be used as a guide only. An elastomer which is compatibile with a fluid may not be suitable over the entire range of its temperature capability. In general, chemical compatibility decreases with an increase in service temperature.

KEY: A+=Best Possible Selection   A=Generally Compatible   B=Marginally Compatible   C=Not Recommended   —=no data

NOTE: These recommendations are to be used as a general guide only. Full details regarding pressure, temperature, chemical considerations, and the mode of operation must be considered when selecting an elastomer.

ELASTOMER RATINGS FOR COMPATIBILITY WITH FLUID

FLUID	ACM, ANM Poly-acrylic	AU, EU Poly-urethane	CO, ECO Epichloro-hydrin	CR Chloroprene Neoprene[1]	EPM, EPDM Ethylene Propylene	FKM Fluoro-elastomer Viton[1]	FFKM Perfluoro-elastomer	IIR Butyl	VMQ Silicone	NBR Nitrile Buna N	NR Natural Rubber	TFE/P Tetrafluoroethylene-propylene copolymer
Steam	C	C	C	C	B+	C	A	B	C	C	C	A+
Sulfer Dioxide (Dry)	C	–	–	C	A+	–	–	B	B	C	B	–
Sulfur Dioxide (Wet)	C	B	–	B	A+	C	A	A	B	C	C	B
Sulfuric Acid (to 50%)	B	C	B	C	B	A+	A	C	C	C	C	A
Sulfuric Acid (50–100%)	C	C	C	C	C	A+	A	C	C	C	C	A
Suva HCFC–123[1]	–	C	–	A+	A+	B	–	A+	B	C	C	A
Suva HFC134a[1]	–	–	–	B	A	C	–	B	B	A+	B	–
Water (Ambient)	C	C	B	A	A	A	A	A	A	A	A	A
Water (200°F, 93°C)	C	C	B	C	A+	B	A	B	A	C	A	–
Water (300°F, 149°C)	C	C	–	C	B+	C	A	B	C	C	C	–
Water (De-ionized)	C	A	–	A	A	A	A	A	A	A	A	A
Water, White	C	B	–	B	A	A	A	A	B	B	B	–

1. Trademark of E.I. DuPont Co.
2. Trademark of Dow Chemical Co.

Service Temperature Limits for Non–Metallic Materials

ASTM Designations and Tradenames	Generic Description	Temperature Range
CR	Chloroprene	−40 to 180°F, −40 to 82°C
EPDM	Ethylene propylene terpolymer	−40 to 275°F, −40 to 135°C
FFKM, Kalrez[1], Chemraz[2]	Perfluoroelastomer	0 to 500°F, −18 to 260°C
FKM, Viton[1]	Fluoroelastomer	0 to 400°F, −18 to 204°C
FVMQ	Fluorosilicone	−100 to 300°F, −73 to 149°C
NBR	Nitrile	−65 to 180°F, −54 to 82°C
NR	Natural rubber	−20 to 200°F, −29 to 93°C
PUR	Polyurethane	−20 to 200°F, −29 to 93°C
VMQ	Silicone	−80 to 450°F, −62 to 232°C
PEEK	Polyetheretherketone	−100 to 480°F, −73 to 250°C
PTFE	Polytetrafluoroethylene	−100 to 400°F, −73 to 204°C
PTFE, Carbon Filled	Polytetrafluoroethylene, Carbon Filled	−100 to 450°F, −73 to 232°C
PTFE, Glass Filled	Polytetrafluoroethylene, Carbon Filled	−100 to 450°F, −73 to 232°C
TCM Plus[3]	Mineral and MoS2 filled PTFE	−100 to 450°F, −73 to 232°C
TCM Ultra[3]	PEEK and MoS2 filled PTFE	−100 to 500°F, −73 to 260°C
Composition Gasket		−60 to 300°F, −51 to 150°C
Flexible Graphite, Grafoil[4]		−300 to 1000°F, −185 to 540°C

1. Trademark of E.I. DuPont Co.
2. Trademark of Greene, Tweed & Co.
3. Trademark of Fisher Controls
4. Trademark of Union Carbide

Control Valve Flow Characteristics

The flow characteristic of a control valve is the relationship between the flow rate through the valve and the valve travel as the travel is varied from 0 to 100%. Inherent flow characteristic refers to the characteristic observed with a constant pressure drop across the valve. Installed flow characteristic means the one obtained in service where the pressure drop varies with flow and other changes in the system.

Characterizing control valves provides for a relatively uniform control loop stability over the expected range of system operating conditions. To establish the flow characteristic needed to match a given system requires a dynamic analysis of the control loop. Analyses of the more common processes have been performed, howev-er, so some useful guidelines for the selection of the proper flow characteristic can be established. Those guidelines will be discussed after a brief look at the flow characteristics in use today.

Flow Characteristics

Figure 5-1 illustrates typical flow characteristic curves. The quick–opening flow characteristic provides for maximum change in flow rate at low valve travels with a nearly linear relationship. Additional increases in valve travel give sharply reduced changes in flow rate, and when the valve plug nears the wide open position, the change in flow rate approaches zero. In a control valve, the quick opening valve plug is used primarily for on-off service; but it is also suitable for many applications where a linear valve plug would normally be specified.

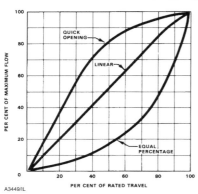

*Figure 5-1. Inherent Valve
Characteristics*

The linear flow characteristic curve shows that the flow rate is directly proportional to the valve travel. This proportional relationship produces a characteristic with a constant slope so that with constant pressure drop, the valve gain will be the same at all flows. (Valve gain is the ratio of an incremental change in valve plug position. Gain is a function of valve size and configuration, system operating conditions and valve plug characteristic.) The linear valve plug is commonly specified for liquid level control and for certain flow control applications requiring constant gain.

In the equal–percentage flow characteristic, equal increments of valve travel produce equal percentage changes in the existing flow. The

change in flow rate is always proportional to the flow rate just before the change in valve plug, disk, or ball position is made. When the valve plug, disk, or ball is near its seat, the flow is small; with a large flow, the change in flow rate will be large. Valves with an equal percentage flow characteristic are generally used on pressure control applications and on other applications where a large percentage of the pressure drop is normally absorbed by the system itself, with only a relatively small percentage available at the control valve. Valves with an equal percentage characteristic should also be considered where highly varying pressure drop conditions can be expected.

Selection of Flow Characteristic

Some guidelines will help in the selection of the proper flow characteristic. Remember, however, that there will be occasional exceptions to most of these guidelines, and that a positive recommendation is possible only by means of a complete dynamic analysis. Where a linear characteristic is recommended, a quick opening valve plug could be used, and while the controller will have to operate on a wider proportional band setting, the same degree of control accuracy may be expected. The tables below give useful guidelines for selecting valve characteristics.

Liquid Level Systems

Control Valve Pressure Drop	Best Inherent Characteristic
Constant ΔP	Linear
Decreasing ΔP with Increasing Load, ΔP at Maximum Load > 20% of Minimum Load ΔP	Linear
Decreasing ΔP with Increasing Load, ΔP at Maximum Load < 20% of Minimum Load ΔP	Equal Percentage
Increasing ΔP with Increasing Load, ΔP at Maximum Load < 200% of Minimum Load ΔP	Linear
Increasing ΔP with Increasing Load, ΔP at Maximum Load > 200% of Minimum Load ΔP	Quick Opening

Flow Control Processes

FLOW MEASURE–MENT SIGNAL TO CONTROLLER	LOCATION OF CONTROL VALVE IN RELATION TO MEASURING ELEMENT	BEST INHERENT CHARACTERISTIC	
		Wide Range of Flow Set Point	Small Range of Flow but Large ΔP Change at Valve with Increasing Load
Proportional To Flow	In Series	Linear	Equal Percentage
	In Bypass[1]	Linear	Equal Percentage
Proportional To Flow Squared	In Series	Linear	Equal Percentage
	In Bypass[1]	Equal Percentage	Equal Percentage
1. When control valve closes, flow rate increases in measuring element.			

Valve Sizing

Standardization activities for control valve sizing can be traced back to the early 1960's when a trade association, the Fluids Control Institute, published sizing equations for use with both compressible and incompressible fluids. The range of service conditions that could be accommodated accurately by these equations was quite narrow, and the standard did not achieve a high degree of acceptance. In 1967, the ISA established a committee to develop and publish standard equations. The efforts of this committee culminated in a valve sizing procedure that has achieved the status of American National Standard. Later, a committee of the International Electrotechnical Commission (IEC) used the ISA works as a basis to formulate international standards for sizing control valves. (Some information in this introductory material has been extracted from ANSI/ISA S75.01 standard with the permission of the publisher, the ISA.) Except for some slight differences in nomenclature and procedures, the ISA and IEC standards have been harmonized. ANSI/ISA Standard S75.01 is harmonized with IEC Standards 534-2-1 and 534-2-2. (IEC Publications 534-2, Sections One and Two for incompressible and compressible fluids, respectively.)

In the following sections, the nomenclature and procedures are explained, and sample problems are solved to illustrate their use.

Sizing Valves for Liquids

Following is a step-by-step procedure for the sizing of control valves for liquid flow using the IEC procedure. Each of these steps is important and must be considered during any valve sizing procedure. Steps 3 and 4 concern the determination of certain sizing factors that may or may not be required in the sizing equation depending on the service conditions of the sizing problem. If one, two, or all three of these sizing factors are to be included in the equation for a particular sizing problem, refer to the appropriate factor determination section(s) located in the text after the sixth step.

1. Specify the variables required to size the valve as follows:

   ● Desired design: refer to the appropriate valve flow coefficient table in this chapter.

   ● Process fluid (water, oil, etc.), and

   ● Appropriate service conditions

   q or w, P_1, P_2 or ΔP, T_1, G_f, P_v, P_c, and υ

The ability to recognize which terms are appropriate for a specific sizing procedure can only be acquired through experience with different valve sizing problems. If any of the above terms appears to be new or unfamiliar, refer to the Abbreviations and Terminology table for a complete definition.

2. Determine the equation constant, N. N is a numerical constant contained in each of the flow equations to provide a means for using different systems of units. Values for these various constants and their applicable units are given in the Equation Constants table.

Use N_1, if sizing the valve for a flow rate in volumetric units (gpm or m^3/h).

Use N_6 if sizing the valve for a flow rate in mass units (lb/h or kg/h).

3. Determine F_p, the piping geometry factor.

F_p is a correction factor that accounts for pressure losses due to piping fittings such as reducers, elbows, or tees that might be attached directly to the inlet and outlet connections of the control valve to be sized. If such fittings are attached to the valve, the F_p factor must be considered in the sizing procedure. If, however, no fittings are attached to the valve, F_p has a value of 1.0 and simply drops out of the sizing equation.

Abbreviations and Terminology

Symbol		Symbol	
C_v	Valve sizing coefficient	P_1	Upstream absolute static pressure
d	Nominal valve size	P_2	Downstream absolute static pressure
D	Internal diameter of the piping	P_c	Absolute thermodynamic critical pressure
F_d	Valve style modifier, dimensionless	P_v	Vapor pressure absolute of liquid at inlet temperature
F_F	Liquid critical pressure ratio factor, dimensionless	ΔP	Pressure drop (P_1-P_2) across the valve
F_k	Ratio of specific heats factor, dimensionless	$\Delta P_{max(L)}$	Maximum allowable liquid sizing pressure drop
F_L	Rated liquid pressure recovery factor, dimensionless	$\Delta P_{max(LP)}$	Maximum allowable sizing pressure drop with attached fittings
F_{LP}	Combined liquid pressure recovery factor and piping geometry factor of valve with attached fittings (when there are no attached fittings, F_{LP} equals F_L), dimensionless	q	Volume rate of flow
F_P	Piping geometry factor, dimensionless	q_{max}	Maximum flow rate (choked flow conditions) at given upstream conditions
G_f	Liquid specific gravity (ratio of density of liquid at flowing temperature to density of water at 60°F), dimensionless	T_1	Absolute upstream temperature (degree K or degree R)
G_g	Gas specific gravity (ratio of density of flowing gas to density of air with both at standard conditions[1], i.e., ratio of molecular weight of gas to molecular weight of air), dimensionless	w	Mass rate of flow
k	Ratio of specific heats, dimensionless	x	Ratio of pressure drop to upstream absolute static pressure ($\Delta P/P_1$), dimensionless
K	Head loss coefficient of a device, dimensionless	x_T	Rated pressure drop ratio factor, dimensionless
M	Molecular weight, dimensionless	Y	Expansion factor (ratio of flow coefficient for a gas to that for a liquid at the same Reynolds number), dimensionless
N	Numerical constant	Z	Compressibility factor, dimensionless
		γ_1	Specific weight at inlet conditions
		υ	Kinematic viscosity, centistokes

1. Standard conditions are defined as 60°F (15.5°C) and 14.7 psia (101.3kPa).

For rotary valves with reducers (swaged installations), F_p factors are included in the appropriate flow coefficient table. For other valve designs and fitting styles, determine the F_p factors by using the procedure for Determining F_p, the Piping Geometry Factor.

Equation Constants[1]

		N	w	q	p[2]	γ	T	d, D
N_1		0.0865	- - -	m³/h	kPa	- - -	- - -	- - -
		0.865	- - -	m³/h	bar	- - -	- - -	- - -
		1.00	- - -	gpm	psia	- - -	- - -	- - -
N_2		0.00214	- - -	- - -	- - -	- - -	- - -	mm
		890	- - -	- - -	- - -	- - -	- - -	inch
N_5		0.00241	- - -	- - -	- - -	- - -	- - -	mm
		1000	- - -	- - -	- - -	- - -	- - -	inch
N_6		2.73	kg/h	- - -	kPa	kg/m³	- - -	- - -
		27.3	kg/h	- - -	bar	kg/m³	- - -	- - -
		63.3	lb/h	- - -	psia	lb/ft³	- - -	- - -
N_7[3]	Normal Conditions $T_N = 0°C$	3.94	- - -	m³/h	kPa	- - -	deg K	- - -
		394	- - -	m³/h	bar	- - -	deg K	- - -
	Standard Conditions $T_s = 15.5°C$	4.17	- - -	m³/h	kPa	- - -	deg K	- - -
		417	- - -	m³/h	bar	- - -	deg K	- - -
	Standard Conditions $T_s = 60°F$	1360	- - -	scfh	psia	- - -	deg R	- - -
N_8		0.948	kg/h	- - -	kPa	- - -	deg K	- - -
		94.8	kg/h	- - -	bar	- - -	deg K	- - -
		19.3	lb/h	- - -	psia	- - -	deg R	- - -
N_9[3]	Normal Conditions $T_N = 0°C$	21.2	- - -	m³/h	kPa	- - -	deg K	- - -
		2120	- - -	m³/h	bar	- - -	deg K	- - -
	Standard Conditions $Ts = 15.5°C$	22.4	- - -	m³/h	kPa	- - -	deg K	- - -
		2240	- - -	m³/h	bar	- - -	deg K	- - -
	Standard Conditions $T_S = 60°F$	7320	- - -	scfh	psia	- - -	deg R	- - -

1. Many of the equations used in these sizing procedures contain a numerical constant, N, along with a numerical subscript. These numerical constants provide a means for using different units in the equations. Values for the various constants and the applicable units are given in the above table. For example, if the flow rate is given in U.S. gpm and the pressures are psia, N_1 has a value of 1.00. If the flow rate is m³/hr and the pressures are kPa, the N_1 constant becomes 0.0865.
2. All pressures are absolute.
3. Pressure base is 101.3 kPa (1.013 bar)(14.7 psia).

4. Determine q_{max} (the maximum flow rate at given upstream conditions) or ΔP_{max} (the allowable sizing pressure drop).

The maximum or limiting flow rate (q_{max}), commonly called choked flow, is manifested by no additional increase in flow rate with increasing pressure differential with fixed upstream conditions. In liquids, choking occurs as a result of vaporization of the liquid when the static pressure within the valve drops below the vapor pressure of the liquid.

The IEC standard requires the calculation of an allowable sizing pressure drop (ΔP_{max}), to account for the possibility of choked flow conditions within the valve. The calculated ΔP_{max} value is compared with the actual pressure drop specified in the service conditions, and the lesser of these two values is used in the sizing equation. If it is desired to use ΔP_{max} to account for the possibility of choked flow conditions, it can be calculated using the procedure for determining q_{max}, the Maximum Flow Rate, or ΔP_{max}, the Allowable Sizing Pressure Drop. If it can be recognized that choked flow conditions will not develop within the valve, ΔP_{max} need not be calculated.

5. Solve for required C_v, using the appropriate equation:

- For volumetric flow rate units—

$$C_v = \frac{q}{N_1 F_p \sqrt{\frac{P_1 - P_2}{G_f}}}$$

- For mass flow rate units—

$$C_v = \frac{w}{N_6 F_p \sqrt{(P_1 - P_2)\gamma}}$$

In addition to C_v, two other flow coefficients, K_v and A_v, are used, particularly outside of North America. The following relationships exist:

$$K_v = (0.865)(C_v)$$

$$A_v = (2.40 \times 10^{-5})(C_v)$$

6. Select the valve size using the appropriate flow coefficient table and the calculated C_v value.

Determining F_p, the Piping Geometry Factor

Determine an F_p factor if any fittings such as reducers, elbows, or tees will be directly attached to the inlet and outlet connections of the control valve that is to be sized. When possible, it is recommended that F_p factors be determined experimentally by using the specified valve in actual tests. The F_p factors for rotary valves used with reducers have all been determined in this manner, and their values are listed in the flow coefficient tables.

For F_p values not listed in the flow coefficient tables, calculate the F_p factor using the following equation.

$$F_p = \left[1 + \frac{\Sigma K}{N_2} \left(\frac{C_v}{d^2} \right)^2 \right]^{-1/2}$$

where,

N_2 = Numerical constant found in the Equation Constants table

d = Assumed nominal valve size

C_v = Valve sizing coefficient at 100-percent travel for the assumed valve size

In the above equation, the ΣK term is the algebraic sum of the velocity head loss coefficients of all of the fittings that are attached to the control valve.

$$\Sigma K = K_1 + K_2 + K_{B1} - K_{B2}$$

where,

K_1 = Resistance coefficient of upstream fittings

K_2 = Resistance coefficient of downstream fittings

K_{B1} = Inlet Bernoulli coefficient

K_{B2} = Outlet Bernoulli coefficient

The Bernoulli coefficients, K_{B1} and K_{B2}, are used only when the diameter of the piping approaching the valve is different from the diameter of the piping leaving the valve, whereby:

$$K_{B1} \text{ or } K_{B2} = 1 - \left(\frac{d}{D} \right)^4$$

where,

d = Nominal valve size

D = Internal diameter of piping

If the inlet and outlet piping are of equal size, then the Bernoulli coefficients are also equal, $K_{B1} = K_{B2}$, and therefore they are dropped from the equation.

The most commonly used fitting in control valve installations is the short-length concentric reducer. The equations for this fitting are as follows:

- For an inlet reducer—

$$K_1 = 0.5 \left(1 - \frac{d^2}{D^2} \right)^2$$

- For an outlet reducer—

$$K_2 = 1.0\left(1 - \frac{d^2}{D^2}\right)^2$$

- For a valve installed between identical reducers—

$$K_1 + K_2 = 1.5\left(1 - \frac{d^2}{D^2}\right)^2$$

Determining q_{max} (the Maximum Flow Rate) or ΔP_{max} (the Allowable Sizing Pressure Drop)

Determine either q_{max} or ΔP_{max} if it is possible for choked flow to develop within the control valve that is to be sized. The values can be determined by using the following procedures.

Determining q_{max} (the Maximum Flow Rate)

$$q_{max} = N_1 F_L C_v \sqrt{\frac{P_1 - F_F P_v}{G_f}}$$

Values for F_F, the liquid critical pressure ratio factor, can be obtained from figure 5-2, or from the following equation:

$$F_F = 0.96 - 0.28 \sqrt{\frac{P_v}{P_c}}$$

Values of F_L, the recovery factor for valves installed without fittings attached, can be found in the flow coefficient tables. If the given valve is to be installed with fittings such as reducer attached to it, F_L in the equation must be replaced by the quotient F_{LP}/F_p, where:

$$F_{LP} = \left[\frac{K_1}{N_2}\left(\frac{C_v}{d^2}\right)^2 + \frac{1}{F_L^2}\right]^{-1/2}$$

and

$$K_1 = K_1 + K_{B1}$$

where,

K_1 = Resistance coefficient of upstream fittings

K_{B1} = Inlet Bernoulli coefficient

(See the procedure for Determining F_p, the Piping Geometry Factor, for definitions of the other constants and coefficients used in the above equations.)

Determining ΔP_{max} (the Allowable Sizing Pressure Drop)

ΔP_{max} (the allowable sizing pressure drop) can be determined from the following relationships:

For valves installed without fittings—

$$\Delta P_{max(L)} = F_L^2(P_1 - F_F P_v)$$

For valves installed with fittings attached—

$$\Delta P_{max(LP)} = \left(\frac{F_{LP}}{F_p}\right)^2 (P_1 - F_F P_V)$$

where,

P_1 = Upstream absolute static pressure

P_2 = Downstream absolute static pressure

P_v = Absolute vapor pressure at inlet temperature

Values of F_F, the liquid critical pressure ratio factor, can be obtained from figure 5-2 or from the following equation:

$$F_F = 0.96 - 0.28 \sqrt{\frac{P_v}{P_c}}$$

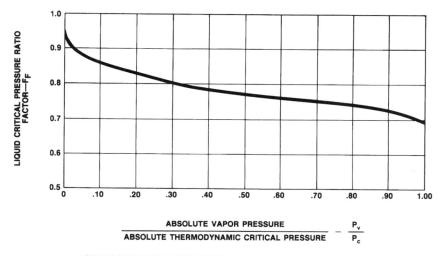

$$\frac{\text{ABSOLUTE VAPOR PRESSURE}}{\text{ABSOLUTE THERMODYNAMIC CRITICAL PRESSURE}} = \frac{P_v}{P_c}$$

USE THIS CURVE FOR LIQUIDS OTHER THAN WATER. DETERMINE THE
VAPOR PRESSURE/CRITICAL PRESSURE RATIO BY DIVIDING THE LIQUID
VAPOR PRESSURE AT THE VALVE INLET BY THE CRITICAL PRESSURE OF
THE LIQUID. ENTER ON THE ABSCISSA AT THE RATIO JUST CALCULATED
AND PROCEED VERTICALLY TO INTERSECT THE CURVE. MOVE
HORIZONTALLY TO THE LEFT AND READ THE CRITICAL PRESSURE RATIO,
F_F, ON THE ORDINATE.

Figure 5-2. Liquid Critical Pressure Ratio Factor for All Fluids

Values of F_L, the recovery factor for valves installed without fittings attached, can be found in the flow coefficient tables. An explanation of how to calculate values of F_{LP}, the recovery factor for valves installed with fittings attached, is presented in the procedure for determining q_{max} (the Maximum Flow Rate).

Once the ΔP_{max} value has been obtained from the appropriate equation, it should be compared with the actual service pressure differential ($\Delta P = P_1 - P_2$). If ΔP_{max} is less than ΔP, this is an indication that choked flow conditions will exist under the service conditions specified. If choked flow conditions do exist ($\Delta P_{max} < P_1 - P_2$), then step 5 of the procedure for Sizing Valves for Liquids must be modified by replacing the actual service pressure differential ($P_1 - P_2$) in the appropriate valve sizing equation with the calculated ΔP_{max} value.

Note

Once it is known that choked flow conditions will develop within the specified valve design (ΔP_{max} is calculated to be less than ΔP), a further distinction can be made to determine whether the choked flow is caused by cavitation or flashing. The choked flow conditions are caused by flashing if the outlet pressure of the given valve is less than the vapor pressure of the flowing liquid. The choked flow conditions are caused by cavitation if the outlet pressure of the valve is greater than the vapor pressure of the flowing liquid.

Liquid Sizing Sample Problem

Assume an installation that, at initial plant start-up, will not be operating at maximum design capability. The lines are sized for the ultimate system capacity, but there is a desire to install a control valve now which is sized only for currently anticipated requirements. The line size is 8 inches, and a Class 300 globe valve with an equal percentage cage has been specified. Standard concentric reducers will be used to install the valve into the line. Determine the appropriate valve size.

1. Specify the necessary variables required to size the valve:

• Desired valve design—Class 300 globe valve with equal percentage cage and an assumed valve size of 3 inches.

• Process fluid—liquid propane

• Service conditions—

$q = 800$ gpm

$P_1 = 300$ psig = 314.7 psia

$P_2 = 275$ psig = 289.7 psia

$\Delta P = 25$ psi

$T_1 = 70°F$

$G_f = 0.50$

$P_v = 124.3$ psia

$P_c = 616.3$ psia

2. Determine an N_1 value of 1.0 from the Equation Constants table.

3. Determine F_p, the piping geometry factor.

Because it is proposed to install a 3-inch valve in an 8-inch line, it will be necessary to determine the piping geometry factor, F_p, which corrects for losses caused by fittings attached to the valve.

$$F_p = \left[1 + \frac{\Sigma K}{N_2}\left(\frac{C_v}{d^2}\right)^2 \right]^{-1/2}$$

where,

$N_2 = 890$, from the Equation Constants table

$d = 3$ in., from step 1

$C_v = 121$, from the flow coefficient table for a Class 300, 3 in. Globe valve with equal percentage cage

To compute ΣK for a valve installed between identical concentric reducers:

$$\Sigma K = K_1 + K_2$$

$$= 1.5\left(1 - \frac{d^2}{D^2}\right)^2$$

$$= 1.5\left(1 - \frac{(3)^2}{(8)^2}\right)^2$$

$$= 1.11$$

where,

$D = 8$ in., the internal diameter of the piping so,

$$F_p = \left[1 + \frac{1.11}{890}\left(\frac{121}{3^2}\right)^2 \right]^{-1/2}$$

$$= 0.90$$

4. Determine ΔP_{max} (the Allowable Sizing Pressure Drop.)

Based on the small required pressure drop, the flow will not be choked ($\Delta P_{max} > \Delta P$).

5. Solve for C_v, using the appropriate equation.

$$C_v = \frac{q}{N_1 F_P \frac{\sqrt{P_1 - P_2}}{G_f}}$$

$$= \frac{800}{(1.0)(0.90)\sqrt{\frac{25}{0.5}}}$$

$$= 125.7$$

6. Select the valve size using the flow coefficient table and the calculated C_v value.

The required C_v of 125.7 exceeds the capacity of the assumed valve, which has a C_v of 121. Although for this example it may be obvious that the next larger size (4 inches) would be the correct valve size, this may not always be true, and a repeat of the above procedure should be carried out.

Assuming a 4-inch valve, $C_v = 203$. This value was determined from the flow coefficient table for a Class 300, 4-inch globe valve with an equal percentage cage.

Recalculate the required C_v using an assumed C_v value of 203 in the F_p calculation.

where,

$$\Sigma K = K_1 + K_2$$

$$= 1.5\left(1 - \frac{d^2}{D^2}\right)^2$$

$$= 1.5\left(1 - \frac{16}{64}\right)^2$$

$$= 0.84$$

and

$$F_p = \left[1.0 + \frac{\Sigma K}{N_2}\left(\frac{C_v}{d^2}\right)^2\right]^{-1/2}$$

$$= \left[1.0 + \frac{0.84}{890}\left(\frac{203}{4^2}\right)^2\right]^{-1/2}$$

$$= 0.93$$

and

$$C_v = \frac{q}{N_1 F_p \sqrt{\frac{P_1 - P_2}{G_f}}}$$

$$= \frac{800}{(1.0)(0.93)\sqrt{\frac{25}{0.5}}}$$

$$= 121.7$$

This solution indicates only that the 4-inch valve is large enough to satisfy the service conditions given. There may be cases, however, where a more accurate prediction of the C_v is required. In such cases, the required C_v should be redetermined using a new F_p value based on the C_v value obtained above. In this example, C_v is 121.7, which leads to the following result:

$$F_p = \left[1.0 + \frac{\Sigma K}{N_2}\left(\frac{C_v}{d^2}\right)^2\right]^{-1/2}$$

$$= \left[1.0 + \frac{0.84}{890}\left(\frac{121.7}{4^2}\right)^2\right]^{-1/2}$$

$$= 0.97$$

The required C_v then becomes:

$$C_v = \frac{q}{N_1 F_p \sqrt{\frac{P_1 - P_2}{G_f}}}$$

$$= \frac{800}{(1.0)(0.97)\sqrt{\frac{25}{0.5}}}$$

$$= 116.2$$

Because this newly determined C_v is very close to the C_v used initially for this recalculation (116.2 versus 121.7), the valve sizing procedure is complete, and the conclusion is that a 4-inch valve opened to about 75-percent of total travel should be adequate for the required specifications.

Sizing Valves for Compressible Fluids

Following is a six-step procedure for the sizing of control valves for compressible flow using the ISA standardized procedure. Each of these steps is important and must be considered during any valve sizing procedure. Steps 3 and 4 concern the determination of certain sizing factors that may or may not be required in the sizing equation depending on the service conditions of the sizing problem. If it is necessary for one or both of these sizing factors to be included in the sizing equation for a particular sizing problem, refer to the appropriate factor determination section(s), which is referenced and located in the following text.

1. Specify the necessary variables required to size the valve as follows:

   • Desired valve design (e.g. balanced globe with linear cage); refer to the appropriate valve flow coefficient table

   • Process fluid (air, natural gas, steam, etc.) and

   • Appropriate service conditions—

   q, or w, P_1, P_2 or ΔP, T_1, G_g, M, k, Z, and γ_1

The ability to recognize which terms are appropriate for a specific sizing procedure can only be acquired through experience with different valve sizing problems. If any of the above terms appear to be new or unfamiliar, refer to the Abbreviations and Terminology table for a complete definition.

2. Determine the equation constant, N. N is a numerical constant contained in each of the flow equations to provide a means for using different systems of units. Values for these various constants and their applicable units are given in the Equation Constants table.

Use either N_7 or N_9 if sizing the valve for a flow rate in volumetric units (scfh or m³/h). Which of the two constants to use depends upon the specified service conditions. N_7 can be used only if the specific gravity, G_g, of the following gas has been specified along with the other required service conditions. N_9 can be used only if the molecular weight, M, of the gas has been specified.

Use either N_6 or N_8 if sizing the valve for a flow rate in mass units (lb/h or kg/h). Which of the two constants to use depends upon the specified service conditions. N_6 can be used only if the specific weight, γ_1, of the flowing gas has been specified along with the other required service conditions. N_8 can be used only if the molecular weight, M, of the gas has been specified.

3. Determine F_p, the piping geometry factor. F_p is a correction factor that accounts for any pressure losses due to piping fittings such as reducers, elbows, or tees that might be attached directly to the inlet and outlet connections of the control valves to be sized. If such fittings are attached to the valve, the F_p factor must be considered in the sizing procedure. If, however, no fittings are attached to the valve, F_p has a value of 1.0 and simply drops out of the sizing equation.

Also, for rotary valves valves with reducers, F_p factors are included in the appropriate flow coefficient table. For other valve designs and fitting styles, determine the F_p factors by using the procedure for Determining F_p the Piping Geometry Factor, which is located in the section for Sizing Valves for Liquids.

4. Determine Y, the expansion factor, as follows:

$$Y = 1 - \frac{x}{3F_k \, x_T}$$

where,

F_k = k/1.4, the ratio of specific heats factor

k = Ratio of specific heats

x = $\Delta P/P_1$, the pressure drop ratio

x_T = The pressure drop ratio factor for valves installed without attached fittings. More definitively, x_T is the pressure drop ratio required to produce critical, or maximum, flow through the valve when F_k = 1.0

If the control valve to be installed has fittings such as reducers or elbows attached to it, then their effect is accounted for in the expansion factor equation by replacing the x_T term with a new factor x_{TP}. A procedure for determining the x_{TP} factor is described in the section for Determining x_{TP}, the Pressure Drop Ratio Factor.

Note

Conditions of critical pressure drop are realized when the value of x become equal to or exceed the appropriate value of the product of either Fk x_T or F_k x_{TP} at which point:

$$y = 1 - \frac{x}{3F_k \ x_T} = 1 - 1/3 = 0.667$$

Although in actual service, pressure drop ratios can, and often will, exceed the indicated critical values, this is the point where critical flow conditions develop. Thus, for a constant P_1, decreasing P_2 (i.e., increasing ΔP) will not result in an increase in the flow rate through the valve. Values of x, therefore, greater than the product of either $F_k x_T$ or $F_k x_{TP}$ must never be substituted in the expression for Y. This means that Y can never be less than 0.667. This same limit on values of x also applies to the flow equations that are introduced in the next section.

5. Solve for the required C_v using the appropriate equation:

For volumetric flow rate units—

- If the specific gravity, G_g, of the gas has been specified:

$$C_v = \frac{q}{N_7 \ F_p \ P_1 \ Y \sqrt{\frac{x}{G_g \ T_1 \ Z}}}$$

- If the molecular weight, M, of the gas has been specified:

$$C_v = \frac{q}{N_7 \ F_p \ P_1 \ Y \sqrt{\frac{x}{M \ T_1 \ Z}}}$$

For mass flow rate units—

- If the specific weight, γ_1, of the gas has been specified:

$$C_v = \frac{w}{N_6 F_p Y \sqrt{x \ P_1 \ \gamma_1}}$$

- If the molecular weight, M, of the gas has been specified:

$$C_v = \frac{w}{N_8 \ F_p \ P_1 \ Y \sqrt{\frac{x \ M}{T_1 \ Z}}}$$

In addition to C_v, two other flow coefficients, K_v and A_v, are used, particularly outside of North America. The following relationships exist:

$$K_v = (0.865)(C_v)$$

$$A_v = \left(2.40 \ X \ 10^{-5}\right)(C_v)$$

6. Select the valve size using the appropriate flow coefficient table and the calculated C_v value.

Note

Once the valve sizing procedure is completed, consideration can be made for aerodynamic noise prediction. To determine the gas flow sizing coefficient (C_g) for use in the aerodynamic noise prediction tech-

nique, use the following equation:

$$C_g = 40 \ C_v \ \sqrt{x_T}$$

Determining x_{TP}, the Pressure Drop Ratio Factor

If the control valve is to be installed with attached fittings such as reducers or elbows, then their effect is accounted for in the expansion factor equation by replacing the x_T term with a new factor, x_{TP}.

$$x_{TP} = \frac{x_T}{F_p^2}\left[1 + \frac{x_T \ K_i}{N_5}\left(\frac{C_v}{d^2}\right)^2 \right]^{-1}$$

where,

N_5 = Numerical constant found in the Equation Constants table

d = Assumed nominal valve size

C_v = Valve sizing coefficient from flow coefficient table at 100 percent travel for the assumed valve size

F_p = Piping geometry factor

x_T = Pressure drop ratio for valves installed without fittings attached. x_T values are included in the flow coefficient tables

In the above equation, K_i, is the inlet head loss coefficient, which is defined as:

$$K_i = K_1 + K_{B1}$$

where,

K_1 = Resistance coefficient of upstream fittings (see the procedure for Determining F_p, the Piping Geometry Factor, which is contained in the section for Sizing Valves for Liquids).

K_{B1} = Inlet Bernoulli coefficient (see the procedure for Deter-

mining F_p, the piping Geometry factor, which is contained in the section for Sizing Valves for Liquids.)

Compressible Fluid Sizing Sample Problem No. 1

Determine the size and percent opening for a Fisher Design V250 ball valve operating with the following service conditions. Assume that the valve and line size are equal.

1. Specify the necessary variables required to size the valve:

• Desired valve design—Design V250 valve

• Process fluid—Natural gas

• Service conditions—

P_1 = 200 psig = 214.7 psia

P_2 = 50 psig = 64.7 psia

ΔP = 150 psi

$x = \Delta P/P_1 = 150/214.7 = 0.70$

$T_1 = 60°F = 520°R$

$M = 17.38$

$G_g = 0.60$

$k = 1.31$

$q = 6.0 \times 10^6$ scfh

2. Determine the appropriate equation constant, N, from the Equation Constants table.

Because both G_g and M have been given in the service conditions, it is possible to use an equation containing either N_7 or N_9. In either case, the end result will be the same. Assume that the equation containing G_g has been arbitrarily selected for this problem. Therefore $N_7 = 1360$.

3. Determine F_p, the piping geometry factor. Since valve and line size are assumed equal, $F_p = 1.0$.

4. Determine Y, the expansion factor.

$$F_k = \frac{k}{1.40}$$

$$= \frac{1.31}{1.40}$$

$$= 0.94$$

It is assumed that an 8-inch Design V250 valve will be adequate for the specified service conditions. From the flow coefficient table, x_T for an 8-inch Design V250 valve at 100-percent travel is 0.137.

$x = 0.70$ (This was calculated in step 1.)

Since conditions of critical pressure drop are realized when the calculated value of x becomes equal to or exceeds the appropriate value of $F_k x_T$, these values should be compared.

$$F_k x_T = (0.94) \ (0.137)$$

$$= 0.129$$

Because the pressure drop ratio, $x = 0.70$ exceeds the calculated critical value, $F_k x_T = 0.129$, choked flow conditions are indicated. Therefore, $Y = 0.667$, and $x = F_K X_T = 0.129$.

5. Solve for required C_v using the appropriate equation.

$$C_v = \frac{q}{N_7 \ F_p \ P_1 \ Y \sqrt{\frac{x}{G_g \ T_1 \ Z}}}$$

The compressibility factor, Z, can be assumed to be 1.0 for the gas pressure and temperature given and $F_p = 1$ because valve size and line size are equal.

So,

$$C_v = \frac{6.0 \ \times \ 10^6}{(1360)(1.0)(214.7)(0.667) \sqrt{\frac{0.129}{(0.6)(520)(1.0)}}}$$

$$= 1515$$

6. Select the valve size using the appropriate flow coefficient table and the calculated C_v value.

The above result indicates that the valve is adequately sized (rated $C_v = 2190$). To determine the percent valve opening, note that the required C_v occurs at approximately 83 degrees for the 8-inch Design V250 valve. Note also that, at 83 degrees opening, the x_T value is 0.252, which is substantially different from the rated value of 0.137 used initially in the problem. The next step is to rework the problem using the x_T value for 83 degrees travel.

The $F_k \ x_T$ product must now be recalculated.

$$x = F_k \ x_T$$

$$= (0.94) \ (0.252)$$

$$= 0.237$$

The required C_v now becomes:

$$C_v = \frac{q}{N_7 \ F_p \ P_1 \ Y \sqrt{\frac{x}{G_g \ T_1 \ Z}}}$$

$$= \frac{6.0 \ \times \ 10^6}{(1360)(1.0)(214.7)(0.667) \sqrt{\frac{0.237}{(0.6)(520)(1.0)}}}$$

$$= 1118$$

The reason that the required C_v has dropped so dramatically is attributable solely to the difference in the x_T values at rated and 83 degrees travel. A C_v of 1118 occurs between 75 and 80 degrees travel.

The appropriate flow coefficient table indicates that x_T is higher at 75 degrees travel than at 80 degrees travel. Therefore, if the problem were to be reworked using a higher x_T value, this should result in a further decline in the calculated required C_v.

Reworking the problem using the x_T value corresponding to 78 degrees travel (i.e., $x_T = 0.328$) leaves:

$$x = F_k \ x_T$$

$$= (0.94) \ (0.328)$$

$$= 0.308$$

and,

$$C_v = \frac{q}{N_7 \ F_p \ P_1 \ Y \sqrt{\frac{x}{G_g \ T_1 \ z}}}$$

$$= \frac{6.0 \ \times \ 10^6}{(1360)(1.0)(214.7)(0.667) \sqrt{\frac{0.308}{(0.6)(520)(1.0)}}}$$

$$= 980$$

The above C_v of 980 is quite close to the 75 degree travel C_v. The problem could be reworked further to obtain a more precise predicted opening; however, for the service conditions given, an 8-inch Design V250 valve installed in an 8-inch line will be approximately 75 degrees open.

Compressible Fluid Sizing Sample Problem No. 2

Assume steam is to be supplied to a process designed to operate at 250 psig. The supply source is a header maintained at 500 psig and 500°F. A 6-inch line from the steam main to the process is being planned. Also, make the assumption that if the required valve size is less than 6 inches, it will be installed using concentric reducers. Determine the appropriate Design ED valve with a linear cage.

1. Specify the necessary variables required to size the valve:

a. Desired valve design—Class 300 Design ED valve with a linear cage. Assume valve size is 4 inches.

b. Process fluid—superheated steam

c. Service conditions—

$w = 125,000$ lb/h

$P_1 = 500$ psig $= 514.7$ psia

$P_2 = 250$ psig $= 264.7$ psia

$\Delta P = 250$ psi

$x = \Delta P/P_1 = 250/514.7 = 0.49$

$T_1 = 500°F$

$\gamma_1 = 1.0434$ lb/ft^3 (from Properties of Saturated Steam table)

$k = 1.28$ (from Properties of Saturated Steam table)

2. Determine the appropriate equation constant, N, from the Equation Constants table.

Because the specified flow rate is in mass units, (lb/h), and the specific weight of the steam is also specified, the only sizing equation that can be used is that which contains the N_6 constant. Therefore,

$$N_6 = 63.3$$

3. Determine F_p, the piping geometry factor.

$$F_p = \left[1 + \frac{\Sigma K}{N_2} \left(\frac{C_v}{d^2} \right)^2 \right]^{-1/2}$$

where,

$N_2 = 890$, determined from the Equation Constants table

$d = 4$ in.

$C_v = 236$, which is the value listed in the manufacturer's Flow Coefficient table for a 4-inch Design ED valve at 100-percent total travel.

and

$$\Sigma K = K_1 + K_2$$

$$= 1.5 \left(1 - \frac{d^2}{D^2} \right)^2$$

$$= 1.5\left(1 - \frac{4^2}{6^2}\right)^2$$

$$= 0.463$$

Finally:

$$F_p = \left[1 + \frac{0.463}{890}\left(\frac{(1.0)(236)}{(4)^2}\right)^2\right]^{-1/2}$$

$$= 0.95$$

4. Determine Y, the expansion factor.

$$Y = 1 - \frac{x}{3F_k\ x_{TP}}$$

where,

$$F_k = \frac{k}{1.40}$$

$$= \frac{1,28}{1.40}$$

$$= 0.91$$

$x = 0.49$ (As calculated in step 1.)

Because the 4-inch valve is to be installed in a 6-inch line, the x_T term must be replaced by x_{TP}.

$$x_{TP} = \frac{x_T}{F_p{}^2}\left[1 + \frac{x_T\ K_i}{N_5}\left(\frac{C_v}{d^2}\right)^2\right]^{-1}$$

where,

$N_5 = 1000$, from the Equation Constants table

$d = 4$ in.

$F_p = 0.95$, determined in step 3

$x_T = 0.688$, a value determined from the appropriate listing in the manufacturer's Flow Coefficient table

$C_v = 236$, from step 3

and

$$K_i = K_1 + K_{B1}$$

$$= 0.5\left(1 - \frac{d^2}{D^2}\right)^2 + \left[1 - \left(\frac{d}{D}\right)^4\right]$$

$$= 0.5\left(1 - \frac{4^2}{6^2}\right)^2 + \left[1 - \left(\frac{4}{6}\right)^4\right]$$

$$= 0.96$$

where $D = 6$ in.

so:

$$x_{TP} = \frac{0.69}{0.95^2}\left[1\frac{(0.69)(0.96)}{1000}\left(\frac{236}{4^2}\right)^2\right]^{-1}$$

$$= 0.67$$

Finally:

$$Y = 1 - \frac{x}{3\ F_k\ x_{TP}}$$

$$= 1 - \frac{0.49}{(3)\ (0.91)\ (0.67)}$$

$$= 0.73$$

5. Solve for required C_v using the appropriate equation.

$$C_v = \frac{w}{N_6\ F_P\ Y\ \sqrt{x\ P_1\ \gamma_1}}$$

$$C_v = \frac{125,000}{(63.3)(0.95)(0.73)\ \sqrt{(0.49)(514.7)(1.0434)}}$$

$$= 176$$

6. Select the valve size using the appropriate manufacturer's Flow Coefficient table and the calculated C_v value.

Refer to the manufacturer's Flow Coefficient tables for Design ED valves with linear cage. Because the assumed 4-inch valve has a C_V of 236 at 100-percent travel and the next smaller size (3 inches) has a C_V of only 148, it can be surmised that the assumed size is correct. In the event that the calculated required C_V had been small enough to have been handled by the next smaller size or if it had been larger than the rated C_V for the assumed size, it would have been necessary to rework the problem again using values for the new assumed size.

Representative Sizing Coefficients for Single–Ported Globe Style Valve Bodies

Valve Size (inches)	Valve Plug Style	Flow Characteristic	Port Dia. (in.)	Rated Travel (in.)	C_V	F_L	X_T	F_D
1/2	Post Guided	Equal Percentage	0.38	0.50	2.41	0.90	0.54	0.61
3/4	Post Guided	Equal Percentage	0.56	0.50	5.92	0.84	0.61	0.61
1	Micro Form™	Equal Percentage	3/8	3/4	3.07	0.89	0.66	0.72
			1/2	3/4	4.91	0.93	0.80	0.67
			3/4	3/4	8.84	0.97	0.92	0.62
	Cage Guided	Linear	1 5/16	3/4	20.6	0.84	0.64	0.34
		Equal Percentage	1 5/16	3/4	17.2	0.88	0.67	0.38
1 1/2	Micro–Form™	Equal Percentage	3/8	3/4	3.20	0.84	0.65	0.72
			1/2	3/4	5.18	0.91	0.71	0.67
			3/4	3/4	10.2	0.92	0.80	0.62
	Cage Guided	Linear	1 7/8	3/4	39.2	0.82	0.66	0.34
		Equal Percentage	1 7/8	3/4	35.8	0.84	0.68	0.38
2	Cage Guided	Linear	2 5/16	1 1/8	72.9	0.77	0.64	0.33
		Equal Percentage	2 5/16	1 1/8	59.7	0.85	0.69	0.31
3	Cage Guided	Linear	3 7/16	1 1/2	148	0.82	0.62	0.30
		Equal Percentage			136	0.82	0.68	0.32
4	Cage Guided	Linear	4 3/8	2	236	0.82	0.69	0.28
		Equal Percentage			224	0.82	0.72	0.28
6	Cage Guided	Linear	7	2	433	0.84	0.74	0.28
		Equal Percentage			394	0.85	0.78	0.26
8	Cage Guided	Linear	8	3	846	0.87	0.81	0.31
		Equal Percentage			818	0.86	0.81	0.26

Representative Sizing Coefficients for Rotary Shaft Valves

Valve Size (inches)	Valve Style	Degrees of Valve Opening	C_v	F_L	X_T	F_D
1	V–Notch Ball Valve	60	15.6	0.86	0.53	
		90	34.0	0.86	0.42	
1 1/2	V–Notch Ball Valve	60	28.5	0.85	0.50	
		90	77.3	0.74	0.27	
2	V–Notch Ball Valve	60	59.2	0.81	0.53	
		90	132	0.77	0.41	
	High Performance Butterfly Valve	60	58.9	0.76	0.50	0.49
		90	80.2	0.71	0.44	0.70
3	V–Notch Ball Valve	60	120	0.80	0.50	0.92
		90	321	0.74	0.30	0.99
	High Performance Butterfly Valve	60	115	0.81	0.46	0.49
		90	237	0.64	0.28	0.70
4	V–Notch Ball Valve	60	195	0.80	0.52	0.92
		90	596	0.62	0.22	0.99
	High Performance Butterfly Valve	60	270	0.69	0.32	0.49
		90	499	0.53	0.19	0.70
6	V–Notch Ball Valve	60	340	0.80	0.52	0.91
		90	1100	0.58	0.20	0.99
	High Performance Butterfly Valve	60	664	0.66	0.33	0.49
		90	1260	0.55	0.20	0.70
8	V–Notch Ball Valve	60	518	0.82	0.54	0.91
		90	1820	0.54	0.18	0.99
	High Performance Butterfly Valve	60	1160	0.66	0.31	0.49
		90	2180	0.48	0.19	0.70
10	V–Notch Ball Valve	60	1000	0.80	0.47	0.91
		90	3000	0.56	0.19	0.99
	High Performance Butterfly Valve	60	1670	0.66	0.38	0.49
		90	3600	0.48	0.17	0.70

(continued)

Representative Sizing Coefficients for Rotary Shaft Valves (continued)

Valve Size (inches)	Valve Style	Degrees of Valve Opening	C_v	F_L	X_T	F_D
12	V–Notch Ball Valve	60	1530	0.78	0.49	0.92
		90	3980	0.63	0.25	0.99
	High Performance Butterfly Valve	60	2500			0.49
		90	5400			0.70
16	V–Notch Ball Valve	60	2380	0.80	0.45	0.92
		90	8270	0.37	0.13	1.00
	High Performance Butterfly Valve	60	3870	0.69	0.40	
		90	8600	0.52	0.23	

Actuator Sizing

Actuators are selected by matching the force required to stroke the valve with an actuator that can supply that force. For rotary valves a similar process matches the torque required to stroke the valve with an actuator that will supply that torque. The same fundamental process is used for pneumatic, electric, and electrohydraulic actuators.

Globe Valves

The force required to operate a globe valve includes:

- Force to overcome static unbalance of the valve plug

- Force to provide a seat load

- Force to overcome packing friction

- Additional forces required for certain specific applications or constructions

Total force required = A + B + C + D

A. Unbalance Force

The unbalance force is that resulting from fluid pressure at shutoff and in the most general sense can be expressed as:

Unbalance force = net pressure differential X net unbalance area

Frequent practice is to take the maximum upstream gauge pressure as the net pressure differential unless the process design always ensures a back pressure at the maximum inlet pressure. Net unbalance area is the port area on a single seated flow up design. Unbalance area may have to take into account the stem area depending on configuration. For balanced valves there is still a small unbalance area. This data can be obtained from the manufacturer. Typical port areas for balance valves flow up and unbalanced valves in a flow down configuration are listed below;

Typical Unbalance Areas of Control Valves

Port Diameter	Unbalance Area Single seated unbalanced valves	Unbalance Area Balanced Valves
1/4	.028	- - -
3/8	0.110	- - -
1/2	0.196	- - -
3/4	0.441	- - -
1	0.785	- - -
1 5/16	1.35	0.04
1 7/8	2.76	0.062
2 5/16	4.20	0.27
3 7/16	9.28	0.118
4 3/8	15.03	0.154
7	38.48	0.81
8	50.24	0.86

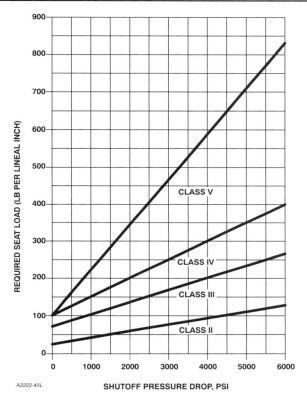

Figure 5-3. Required Seat Load for Metal Seated Class V Valves and Valves in Boiler Feed Water Service; also Suggested Seat Load to Prolong Seat Life and Shutoff Capacity for ANSI/FCI 70-2 and IEC 534-4 Leak Classes II, III, and IV

Leak Class	Recommended Seat Load
Class I	As required by customer specification, no factory leak test required
Class II	20 pounds per lineal inch of port circumference
Class III	40 pounds per lineal inch of port circumference
Class IV	Standard (Lower) Seat only—40 pounds per lineal inch of port circumference (up through a 4-3/8 inch diameter port) Standard (Lower) Seat only—80 pounds per lineal inch of port circumference (larger than 4-3/8 inch diameter port)
Class V	Metal Seat—determine pounds per lineal inch of port circumference from figure 5-3
Class VI	Metal Seat—300 pounds per lineal inch of port circumference

B. Force to Provide Seat Load

Seat load, usually expressed in pounds per lineal inch of port circumference, is determined by shutoff requirements. Use the following guidelines to determine the seat load required to meet the factory acceptance tests for ANSI/FCI 70-2-1991 and IEC 534-4 (1986) leak classes II through VI. See table for recommended seat load.

Because of differences in the severity of service conditions, do not construe these leak classifications and corresponding leakage rates as indicators of field performance. To prolong seat life and shutoff capabilities, use a higher than recommended seat load. See Figure 5-3 for suggested seat loads. If tight shutoff is not a prime consideration, use a lower leak class.

Leakage class numbers are ANSI/FCI 70-2-1991 and IEC 534-4 (1986) leak classes.

C. Packing Friction

Packing friction is determined by stem size, packing type, and the amount of compressive load placed on the packing by the process or the bolting. Packing friction is not 100% repeatable in its friction characteristics. Newer live loaded packing designs can have significant friction forces especially if graphite packing is used. The table below lists typical packing friction values.

Typical Packing Friction Values

STEM SIZE (INCHES)	CLASS	PTFE PACKING		GRAPHITE RIBBON/ FILAMENT
		Single	Double	
5/16	All	20	30	- - -
3/8	125 150 250 300	38	56	- - - 125 - - - 190
	600 900 1500			250 320 380
1/2	125 150 250 300	50	75	- - - 180 - - - 230
	600 900 1500 2500			320 410 500 590
5/8	125 150 250 300 600	63	95	- - - 218 - - - 290 400
3/4	125 150 250 300	75	112.5	- - - 350 - - - 440
	600 900 1500 2500			660 880 1100 1320
1	300 600 900 1500 2500	100	150	610 850 1060 1300 1540
1-1/4	300 600 900 1500 2500	120	180	800 1100 1400 1700 2040
2	300 600 900 1500 2500	200	300	1225 1725 2250 2750 3245

Values shown are frictional forces typically encountered when using standard packing flange bolt torquing procedures.

D. Additional Forces

Additional forces may be required to stroke the valve such as: bellow stiffness; unusual frictional forces resulting from seals; or special seating forces for soft metal seals as an example. The manufacturer should either supply this information or take it into account when sizing an actuator.

Actuator Force Calculations

Pneumatic diaphragm actuators provide a net force with the additional air pressure after compressing the spring in air to close, or with the net precompression of the spring in air to open. This may be calculated in pounds per square inch of pressure differential.

For example: Suppose 275 lbf. is required to close the valve calculated following the process described earlier. An air-to-open actuator with 100 square inches of diaphragm area and a bench set of 6 to 15 psig is one available option. The expected operating range is 3 to 15 psig. The precompression can be calculated as the difference between the lower end of the bench set (6 psig) and the beginning of the operating range (3 psig). This 3 psig is used to overcome the precompression so the net precompression force must be;

3 psig X 100 sq. in. = 300 lbf.

This exceeds the force required and is an adequate selection.

Piston actuators with springs are sized in the same manner. The thrust from piston actuators without springs can simply be calculated as:

Piston Area X Minimum Supply Pressure = Available Thrust

(be careful to maintain compatibility of units)

In some circumstances an actuator could supply too much force and cause the stem to buckle, to bend sufficiently to cause a leak, or to damage valve internals. This could occur because the actuator is too large or the

maximum air supply exceeds the minimum air supply available.

The manufacturer normally takes responsibility for actuator sizing and should have methods documented to check for maximum stem loads. Manufacturers also publish data on actuator thrusts, effective diaphragm areas, and spring data.

Rotary Actuator Sizing

In selecting the most economical actuator for a rotary valve, the determining factors are the torque required to open and close the valve and the torque output of the actuator.

This method assumes the valve has been properly sized for the application and the application does not exceed pressure limitations for the valve.

Torque Equations

Rotary valve torque equals the sum of a number of torque components. To avoid confusion, a number of these have been combined and a number of calculations have been performed in advance. Thus, the torques required for each valve type can be represented with two simple and practical equations.

Breakout Torque

$$T_B = A(\Delta P_{shutoff}) + B$$

Dynamic Torque

$$T_D = C(\Delta P_{eff})$$

The specific A, B, and C factors for each valve design are included in following tables.

Typical Rotary Shaft Valve Torque Factors
V–Notch Ball Valve with Composition Seal

VALVE SIZE, INCHES	VALVE SHAFT DIAMETER, INCHES	A Composition Bearings	B	C 60 Degrees	C 70 Degrees	MAXIMUM T$_D$, LBF•IN.
2	1/2	0.15	80	0.11	0.60	515
3	3/4	0.10	280	0.15	3.80	2120
4	3/4	0.10	380	1.10	18.0	2120
6	1	1.80	500	1.10	36.0	4140
8	1-1/4	1.80	750	3.80	60.0	9820
10	1-1/4	1.80	1250	3.80	125	9820
12	1-1/2	4.00	3000	11.0	143	12,000
14	1-3/4	42	2400	75	413	23,525
16	2	60	2800	105	578	23,525
18	2-1/8	60	2800	105	578	55,762
20	2-1/2	97	5200	190	1044	55,762

High Performance Butterfly Valve with Composition Seal

VALVE SIZE, INCHES	SHAFT DIAMETER INCHES	A	B	C 60°	C 75°	C 90°	MAXIMUM TORQUE, INCH-POUNDS Breakout T$_B$	MAXIMUM TORQUE, INCH-POUNDS Dynamic T$_D$
3	1/2	0.50	136	0.8	1.8	8	280	515
4	5/8	0.91	217	3.1	4.7	25	476	1225
6	3/4	1.97	403	30	24	70	965	2120
8	1	4.2	665	65	47	165	1860	4140
10	1-1/4	7.3	1012	125	90	310	3095	9820
12	1-1/2	11.4	1422	216	140	580	4670	12,000

Maximum Rotation

Maximum rotation is defined as the angle of valve disk or ball in the fully open position.

Normally, maximum rotation is 90 degrees. The ball or disk rotates 90 degrees from the closed position to the wide open position.

Some of the pneumatic spring-return piston and pneumatic spring-and-diaphragm actuators are limited to 60 or 75 degrees rotation.

For pneumatic spring-and-diaphragm actuators, limiting maximum rotation allows for higher initial spring compression, resulting in more actuator breakout torque. Additionally, the effective length of each actuator lever changes with valve rotation. Published torques, particularly for pneumatic pis-

ton actuators, reflect this changing lever length.

Non-Destructive Test Procedures

Successful completion of specific non-destructive examinations is required for valves intended for nuclear service and may be required by codes or customers in non-nuclear applications, particularly in the power industry. Also, successful completion of the examinations may permit uprating of ASME Standard Class buttwelding end valves to a Special Class rating. The Special Class rating permits use of the butt-welding end valves at higher pressures than allowed for Standard Class valves. Procedures required for uprating to the Special Class are detailed in ASME Standard B16.34.

While it is not feasible to present complete details of code requirements for non-destructive examinations, this book will summarize the principles and procedures of four major types of non-destructive examinations defined in ANSI, ASME, and ASTM standards.

Magnetic Particle (Surface) Examination

Magnetic particle examination can be used only on materials which can be magnetized. The principle includes application of a direct current across a piece to induce a magnetic field in the piece. Surface or shallow subsurface defects distort the magnetic field to the extent that a secondary magnetic field develops around the defect. If a magnetic powder, either dry or suspended in liquid, is spread over the magnetized piece, areas of distorted magnetic field will be visible, indicating a defect in the piece in the area of distortion. After de-magnetizing the piece by reversing the electric current, it may be possible to weld repair the defect (normal procedure with castings) or it may be necessary to replace the piece (normal procedure with forgings and bar stock parts). After repair or replacement, the magnetic particle examination must be repeated.

Liquid Penetrant (Surface) Examination

This examination method permits detection of surface defects not visible to the naked eye. The surface to be examined is cleaned thoroughly and dried. The liquid penetrant dye, either water or solvent soluble, is applied by dipping, brushing, or spraying, and allowed time to penetrate. Excess penetrant is washed or wiped off (depending on the penetrant used). The surface is again thoroughly dried and a developer (liquid or powder) is applied. Inspection is performed under the applicable light source. (Some developers require use of an ultraviolet or black light to expose defective areas). If defects are discovered and repaired by welding, the piece must be re-examined after repair.

Radiographic (Volumetric) Examination

Radiography of control valve parts works on the principle that X-rays and gamma rays will pass through metal objects which are impervious to light rays and will expose photographic film just as light rays will. The number and intensity of the rays passing through the metal object depend on the density of the object. Subsurface defects represent changes in density of the material and can therefore be photographed radiographically. The piece to be inspected is placed between the X-ray or gamma ray source and the photographic film. Detail and contrast sensitivity are determined by radiographing one or more small flat plates of specified thickness at the same time the test subject is exposed. The small flat plate, called a penetrameter, has several holes of specified diameters drilled in it. Its image on the exposed film, along with the valve body or other test subject, makes it possible to determine the detail and contrast sensitivity of the radiograph.

Radiography can detect such casting defects as gas and blowholes, sand inclusions, internal shrinkage, cracks, hot tears, and slag inclusions. In castings for nuclear service, some defects such as cracks and hot tears are expressly forbidden and cannot be repaired. The judgment and experience of the radiographer is important because he must compare the radiograph with the acceptance criteria (ASTM reference radiographs) to determine the adequacy of the casting. When weld repairs are required, the casting must be radiographed again after the repair.

Ultrasonic (Volumetric) Examination

This method monitors sound wave reflections from the piece being inspected to determine the depth and size of any defects. Ultrasonic examination can detect foreign materials and discontinuities in fine-grained metal and thus lends itself to volumetric examination of structures such as plate, bar, and forgings. The test is normally conducted either with a special oil called a coupler or under water to ensure efficient transmission of sound waves. The sound waves are generated by a crystal probe and are reflected at each interface in the piece being tested, that is, at each outer face of the piece itself and at each face of the damaged or malformed internal portion. These reflections are received by the crystal probe and displayed on a screen to reveal the location and severity of the defect.

Cavitation and Flashing

Choked Flow Causes Flashing and Cavitation

The IEC liquid sizing standard calculates an allowable sizing pressure drop, ΔPmax. If the actual pressure drop across the valve, as defined by the system conditions of P1 and P2, is greater than ΔPmax then either flashing or cavitation may occur. Structural damage to the valve and adjacent piping may also result. Knowledge of what is actually happening within the valve will permit selection of a valve that can eliminate or reduce the effects of cavitation and flashing.

The physical phenomena label is used to describe flashing and cavitation because these conditions represent actual changes in the form of the fluid media. The change is from the liquid state to the vapor state and results from the increase in fluid velocity at or just downstream of the greatest flow restriction, normally the valve port. As liquid flow passes through the restric-

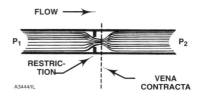

FLOW ⟶

P_1

RESTRIC-
TION

A3444/IL

P_2

VENA
CONTRACTA

Figure 5–4. Vena Contracta Illustration

tion, there is a necking down, or contraction, of the flow stream. The minimum cross–sectional area of the flow stream occurs just downstream of the actual physical restriction at a point called the vena contracta, as shown in figure 5–4.

To maintain a steady flow of liquid through the valve, the velocity must be greatest at the vena contracta, where cross sectional area is the least. The increase in velocity (or kinetic energy) is accompanied by a substantial decrease in pressure (or potential energy) at the vena contracta. Further downstream, as the fluid stream expands into a larger area, velocity decreases and pressure increases. But, of course, downstream pressure never recovers completely to equal the pressure that existed upstream of the valve. The pressure differential (ΔP) that exists across the valve is a measure of the amount of energy that was dissipated in the valve. Figure 5–5 provides a pressure profile explaining the differing performance of a streamlined high recovery valve, such as a ball valve, and a valve with lower recovery capabilities due to greater internal turbulence and dissipation of energy.

Regardless of the recovery characteristics of the valve, the pressure differential of interest pertaining to flashing and cavitation is the differential between the valve inlet and the vena contracta. If pressure at the vena contracta should drop below the vapor pressure of the fluid (due to increased fluid velocity at this point) bubbles will form in the flow stream. Formation of

FLOW ⟶

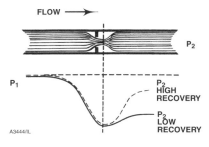

P₁

A3444/IL

P_2

P_2 HIGH RECOVERY

P_2 LOW RECOVERY

Figure 5–5. Comparison of Pressure Profiles for High and low Recovery Valves

W2843/IL

Figure 5–7. Typical Appearance of Cavitation Damage

W2842/IL

Figure 5–6. Typical Appearance of Flashing Damage

bubbles will increase greatly as vena contracta pressure drops further below the vapor pressure of the liquid. At this stage, there is no difference between flashing and cavitation, but the potential for structural damage to the valve definitely exists.

If pressure at the valve outlet remains below the vapor pressure of the liquid, the bubbles will remain in the downstream system and the process is said to have flashed. Flashing can produce serious erosion damage to the valve trim parts and is characterized by a smooth, polished appearance of the eroded surface, as shown in figure 5–6. Flashing damage is normally greatest at the point of highest velocity, which is usually at or near the seat line of the valve plug and seat ring.

On the other hand, if downstream pressure recovery is sufficient to raise the outlet pressure above the vapor pressure of the liquid, the bubbles will collapse, or implode, producing cavitation. Collapsing of the vapor bubbles releases energy and produces a noise similar to what one would expect if gravel were flowing through the valve. If the bubbles collapse in close proximity to solid surfaces in the valve, the energy released will gradually tear away the material leaving a rough, cinderlike surface as shown in figure 5–7. Cavitation damage may extend to the adjacent downstream pipeline, if that is where pressure recovery occurs and the bubbles collapse. Obviously, high recovery valves tend to be more subject to cavitation, since the downstream pressure is more likely to rise above the liquid's vapor pressure.

Valve Selection for Flashing Service

As shown in figure 5–6, flashing damage is characterized by a smooth, polished appearance of the eroded surfaces. To review, flashing occurs because P2 is less than Pv. P2 is the pressure downstream of the valve and is a function of the downstream process and piping. Pv is a function of the fluid and operating temperature. Therefore, the variables that define flashing are not directly controlled by the valve. This further means there is no way for any control valve to prevent flashing. Since flashing cannot be prevented by the valve the best solution is to select a valve with proper geometry and materials to avoid or minimize damage.

In general erosion is minimized by:

 • preventing or reducing the particle (liquid droplets in this case) impact with the valve surfaces

 • making those surfaces as hard as possible

 • lowering the velocity of the erosive flow

Selecting a valve with as few fluid directional changes as possible provides the least number of particle impacts. Sliding stem angle valves are traditional solutions which provide such a flow path. Some rotary valves, such as eccentric rotary plug, and V–ball valves, also offer straight–through flow paths. Valves with expanded flow areas downstream of the throttling point are beneficial because the erosive velocity is reduced. For those areas where the fluid must impact the valve surfaces, at the seating surfaces for example, choose materials that are as hard as possible. Generally the harder the material the longer it will resist erosion.

Fluids that are both flashing and corrosive can be especially troublesome. Flashing water in a steel valve is an example of the synergistic result of both corrosion and erosion. The water causes corrosion of steel and the flashing causes erosion of the resultant, soft, oxide layer; these combine to create damage worse than either individual mechanism would. The solution in this case is to prevent the corrosion by selecting, as a minimum, a low–alloy steel.

Valve Selection for Cavitation Service

Cavitation damage is characterized by a rough, cinder–like appearance of the eroded surface as shown in figure 5–7. It is distinctly different from the smooth, polished appearance caused by the erosion of flashing. The previous section describes how cavitation occurs when the vena contracta pressure is less than Pv, and P2 is greater than Pv. Cavitation can be treated by several means.

The first is to eliminate the cavitation and thus the damage by managing the pressure drop. If the pressure drop across the valve can be controlled such that the local pressure never drops below the vapor pressure, then no vapor bubbles will form. Without vapor bubbles to collapse, there is no cavitation. To eliminate cavitation the total pressure drop across the valve is split, using multiple–stage trims, into smaller portions. Each of these small drops keeps its vena contracta pressure above the vapor pressure so no vapor bubbles are formed.

The second method does not eliminate the cavitation but rather minimizes or isolates the damage much the same as with flashing solutions. This method aims to isolate the cavitation from valve surfaces and to harden those surfaces that the cavitation does impact.

A third method is to change the system in a manner to prevent the causes of cavitation. If the P2 can be raised enough so that the vena contracta pressure does not fall below the vapor pressure, that is the valve is no longer choked, then cavitation will be avoided. P2 can be raised by moving the valve to a location that has more static head on the downstream side. Applying an orifice plate or similar backpressure device can also raise P2 at the valve; the downside is the potential for the cavitation to transfer from the valve to the orifice plate.

Noise Prediction

Aerodynamic

Industry leaders use the International Electrotechnical Commission standard *IEC 534-8-3: Industrial-process control valves—Part 8: Noise Considerations—Section 3: Control valve aerodynamic noise prediction* method. This method consists of a mix of thermodynamic and aerodynamic theory and some empirical information. The design of the method allows a noise prediction for a valve based only on the measurable geometry of the valve and the service conditions applied to the valve. There is no need for specific empirical data for each valve design and size. Because of this pure analytical approach to valve noise prediction the IEC method allows an objective evaluation of alternatives.

The method defines five basic steps to a noise prediction:

1—Calculate the total stream power in the process at the vena contracta. The noise of interest is generated by the valve in and downstream of the vena contracta. If the total power dissipated by throttling at the vena contracta can be calculated, then the fraction that is noise power can be determined. Since power is the time rate of energy, a form of the familiar equation for calculating kinetic energy can be used. The kinetic energy equation is $1/2\ mv^2$ where m is mass and v is velocity. If the mass flow rate is substituted for the mass term, then the equation calculates the power. The velocity is the vena contracta velocity and is calculated with the energy equation of the First Law of Thermodynamics.

2—Determine the fraction of total power that is acoustic power. The method considers the process conditions applied across the valve to determine the particular noise generating mechanism in the valve. There are five defined regimes dependent on the relationship of the vena contracta pressure and the downstream pressure. For each of these regimes an acoustic efficiency is defined and calculated. This acoustic efficiency establishes the fraction of the total stream power, as calculated in Step 1, which is noise power. In designing a quiet valve, lower acoustic efficiency is one of the goals.

3—Convert acoustic power to sound pressure. The final goal of the IEC prediction method is determination of the sound pressure level at a reference point outside the valve where human hearing is a concern. Step 2 delivers acoustic power, which is not directly measurable. Acoustic or sound pressure is measurable and therefore has become the default expression for noise in most situations. Converting from acoustic power to the sound pressure uses basic acoustic theory.

4—Account for the transmission loss of the pipewall and restate the sound pressure at the outside surface of the pipe. Steps 1 through 3 are involved with the noise generation process inside the pipe. There are times when this is the area of interest, but the noise levels on the outside of the pipe are the prime requirement. The method must account for the change in the noise as the reference location moves from inside the pipe to outside the pipe. The pipe wall has physical characteristics, due to its material, size, and shape, that define how well the noise will transmit through the pipe. The fluid-borne noise inside the pipe must interact with the inside pipe wall to cause the pipe wall to vibrate, then the vibration must transmit through the pipe wall to the outside pipe wall, and there the outside pipe wall must interact with the atmosphere to generate sound waves. These three steps of noise transmission are dependent on the noise frequency. The method represents the frequency of the valve noise by determining the peak frequency of the valve noise spectrum. The method also determines the pipe transmission loss as a function of frequency. The method then compares the internal noise spectrum and the transmission-loss spectrum to determine how much the external sound pressure will be attenuated by the pipe wall.

5—Account for distance and calculate the sound pressure level at the observer's location. Step 4 delivers the external sound pressure level at the outside surface of the pipe wall. Again, basic acoustic theory is applied to calculate the sound pressure level at the observer's location. Sound power is constant for any given situation, but the associated sound pressure level varies with the area the power is spread over. As the observer moves farther away from the pipe wall, the total area the sound power is spread over increases. This causes the sound pressure level to decrease.

Hydrodynamic

Noticeable hydrodynamic noise is usually associated with cavitation. The traditional description of the sound is as rocks flowing inside the pipe. This association of hydrodynamic noise with cavitation is reflected in the various prediction methods available today. The methods account for one noise characteristic for liquids in non-choked flow situations and another characteristic in choked, cavitating flow situations.

There are a variety of situations where the fluid is a two-phase mixture. These include liquid-gas two-phase fluids at the inlet of the valve, flashing fluids, and fluids that demonstrate out-gassing due to throttling. Noise prediction methods for these cases are not yet well established. Test results and field surveys of installed multi-phase systems indicate these noise levels do not contribute to overall

plant noise levels or exceed worker exposure levels.

Noise Control

In closed systems (not vented to atmosphere), any noise produced in the process becomes airborne only by transmission through the valves and adjacent piping that contain the flow-stream. The sound field in the flow-stream forces these solid boundaries to vibrate. The vibrations cause disturbances in the ambient atmosphere that are propagated as sound waves.

Noise control employs either source treatment, path treatment, or both. Source treatment, preventing or attenuating noise at its source, is the most desirable approach, if economically and physically feasible.

Recommended cage-style source treatment approaches are depicted in figure 5-8. The upper view shows a cage with many narrow parallel slots designed to minimize turbulence and provide a favorable velocity distribution in the expansion area. This economical approach to quiet valve design can provide 15 to 20 dBA noise reduction with little or no decrease in flow capacity.

The lower view in figure 5-8 shows a two-stage, cage-style trim designed for optimum noise attenuation where pressure drop ratios ($\Delta P/P_1$) are high.

To obtain the desired results, restrictions must be sized and spaced in the primary cage wall so that the noise generated by jet interaction is not greater than the summation of the noise generated by the individual jets.

This trim design can reduce the valve noise by as much as 30 dBA. The final design shown uses a combination of several noise reduction strategies to reduce valve noise up to 40 dBA. Those strategies are:

• Unique passage shape reduces the conversion of total stream power generated by the valve into noise power.

W1257/IL

W6980/IL

*Figure 5-8. Valve Trim Design for
Reducing Aerodynamic Noise*

• Multistage pressure reduction divides the stream power between stages and further reduces the acoustic conversion efficiency.

• Frequency spectrum shifting reduces acoustic energy in the audible range by capitalizing on the transmission loss of the piping.

• Exit jet independence is maintained to avoid noise regeneration due to jet coalescence.

• Velocity management is accomplished with expanding areas to accommodate the expanding gas.

• Complementary body designs prevent flow impingement on the body wall and secondary noise sources.

For control valve applications operating at high pressure ratios ($\Delta P/P_1 >$ 0.8) the series restriction approach,

splitting the total pressure drop between the control valve and a fixed restriction (diffuser) downstream of the valve can be effective in minimizing noise. To optimize the effectiveness of a diffuser, it must be designed (special shape and sizing) for each given installation so that the noise levels generated by the valve and diffuser are equal. Figure 5-9 shows a typical installation.

Control systems venting to atmosphere are generally very noisy because of the high pressure ratios and high exit velocities involved. Dividing the total pressure drop between the actual vent and an upstream control valve, by means of a vent diffuser, quiets both the valve and the vent. A properly sized vent diffuser and valve combination, such as that shown in figure 5-10, can reduce the overall system noise level as much as 40 dBA.

Source treatment for noise problems associated with control valves handling liquid is directed primarily at eliminating or minimizing cavitation. Because flow conditions that will produce cavitation can be accurately predicted, valve noise resulting from cavitation can be eliminated by application of appropriate limits to the service conditions at the valve by use of break-down orifices, valves in series, etc. Another approach to source treatment is using special valve trim that uses the series restriction concept to eliminate cavitation as shown in figure 5-11.

A second approach to noise control is that of path treatment. The fluid stream is an excellent noise transmission path. Path treatment consists of increasing the impedance of the transmission path to reduce the acoustic energy communicated to the receiver.

Dissipation of acoustic energy by use of acoustical absorbent materials is one of the most effective methods of path treatment. Whenever possible the acoustical material should be lo-

140

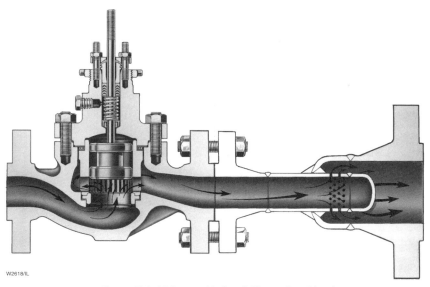

W2618/IL

Figure 5-9. Valve and Inline Diffuser Combination

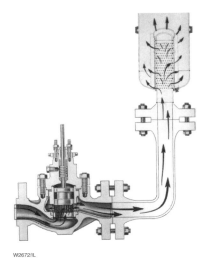

W2672/IL

*Figure 5-10. Valve and Vent
Diffuser Combination*

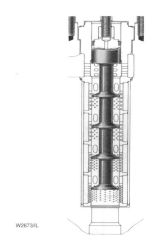

W2673/IL

*Figure 5-11. Special Valve
Design to Eliminate Cavitation*

cated in the flow stream either at or immediately downstream of the noise source. In gas systems, inline silencers effectively dissipate the noise within the fluid stream and attenuate the noise level transmitted to the solid boundaries. Where high mass flow rates and/or high pressure ratios across the valve exist, inline silencers, such as that shown in figure 5-12, are often the most realistic and economical approach to noise control. Use of

141

W1304/IL

Figure 5-12. Typical In-Line Silencer

absorption-type inline silencers can provide almost any degree of attenuation desired. However, economic considerations generally limit the insertion loss to approximately 25 dBA.

Noise that cannot be eliminated within the boundaries of the flow stream must be eliminated by external treatment. This approach to the abatement of control valve noise suggests the use of heavy walled piping, acoustical insulation of the exposed solid boundaries of the fluid stream, use of insulated boxes, buildings, etc., to isolate the noise source.

Path treatment such as heavy wall pipe or external acoustical insulation can be an economical and effective technique for localized noise abatement. However, noise is propagated for long distances via the fluid stream and the effectiveness of the heavy wall pipe or external insulation ends where the treatment ends.

Noise Summary

The amount of noise that will be generated by a proposed control valve installation can be quickly and reasonably predicted by use of industry standard methods. These methods are available in computer software for ease of use. Such sizing and noise prediction tools help in the proper selection of noise reduction equipment such as shown in figures 5-13 and 5-14. Process facility requirements for low environmental impact will continue to drive the need for quieter control valves. The prediction technologies and valve designs that

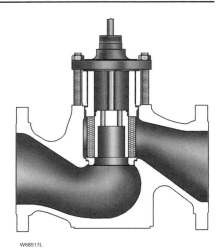

W6851/IL

Figure 5-13. Globe–Style Valve with Noise Abatement Cage for Aerodynamic Flow

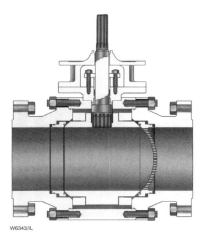

W6343/IL

Figure 5-14. Ball–Style Valve with Attenuator to Reduce Hydrodynamic Noise

deliver this are always being improved. For the latest in either equipment or prediction technology, contact the valve manufacturer's representative.

Packing Selection

The following tables and figures 5-15 and 5-16 offer packing selection

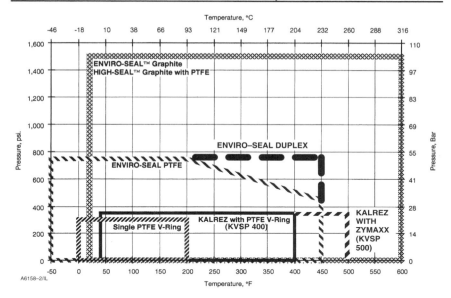

Figure 5–15. Application Guidelines Chart for Environmental Service

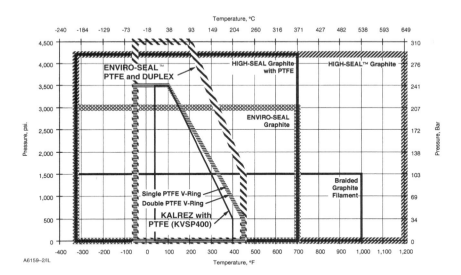

Figure 5–16. Application Guidelines Chart for Non–Environmental Service

guidelines for sliding-stem and rotary
valves.

143

Packing Selection Guidelines for Sliding-Stem Valves

PACKING SYSTEM	MAXIMUM PRESSURE & TEMPERATURE LIMITS FOR 500 PPM SERVICE(1)		APPLICATION GUIDELINE FOR NONENVIRONMENTAL SERVICE(1)		SEAL PERFORMANCE INDEX	SERVICE LIFE INDEX	PACKING FRICTION(2)
	Customary U.S.	Metric	Customary U.S.	Metric			
Single PTFE V-Ring	300 psi 0 to 200°F	20.7 bar -18 to 93°C	-50 to 450°F	-46 to 232°C	Better	Long	Very low
Double PTFE V-Ring	- - -	- - -	-50 to 450°F	-46 to 232°C	Better	Long	Low
ENVIRO-SEAL® PTFE	-50 to 450°F	-46 to 232°C	-50 to 450°F	-46 to 232°C	Superior	Very long	Low
ENVIRO-SEAL® Duplex	750 psi -50 to 450°F	51.7 bar -46 to 232°C	-50 to 450°F	-46 to 232°C	Superior	Very long	Low
KALREZ® with PTFE (KVSP 400)(3)	350 psig 40 to 400°F	24.1 bar 4 to 204	-40 to 400°F	-40 to 204°C	Superior	Long	Low
KALREZ® with ZYMAXX™ (KVSP 500)(3)	350 psig 40 to 500°F	24.1 bar 4 to 260°C	-40 to 500°F	-40 to 260°C	Superior	Long	Low
ENVIRO-SEAL® Graphite	1500 psi 20 to 600°F	103 bar -18 to 315°C	3000 psi -325 to 700°F	207 bar -198 to 371°C	Superior	Very long	High
HIGH-SEAL Graphite with PTFE	1500 psi 20 to 600°F	103 bar -18 to 315°C	4200 psi(4) -325 to 700°F	290 bar(4) -198 to 317°C	Superior	Very long	High
HIGH-SEAL Graphite	- - -	- - -	4200 psi(4) -325 to 1200°F(5)	290 bar(4) -198 to 649°C(5)	Better	Very long	Very high
Braided Graphite Filament			1500 psi -325 to 1000°F(5)	103 bar -198 to 538°C(5)	Acceptable	Acceptable	High

1. The values shown are only guidelines. These guidelines can be exceeded, but shortened packing life or increased leakage might result. The temperature ratings apply to the actual packing temperature, not to the process temperature.
2. See manufacturer for actual friction values.
3. The KALREZ pressure/temperature limits referenced here are for Fisher valve applications only. DuPont may claim higher limits.
4. Except for the 3/8-inch (9.5 mm) stem, 1600 psi (110 bar).
5. Except for oxidizing service, -325 to 700°F (-198 to 371°C).

Packing Selection Guidelines for Rotary Valves

PACKING SYSTEM	MAXIMUM PRESSURE & TEMPERATURE LIMITS FOR 500 PPM SERVICE[1]		APPLICATION GUIDELINE FOR NONENVIRONMENTAL SERVICE[1]		SEAL PERFORMANCE INDEX	SERVICE LIFE INDEX	PACKING FRICTION
	Customary U.S.	Metric	Customary U.S.	Metric			
Single PTFE V–Ring	- - -	- - -	1500 psig −50 to 450°F	103 bar −46 to 232°C	Better	Long	Very low
ENVIRO–SEAL® PTFE	1500 psig −50 to 450°F	103 bar −46 to 232°C	1500 psig −50 to 450°F	103 bar −46 to 232°C	Superior	Very long	Low
KALREZ® with PTFE (KVSP 400)	350 psig 40 to 400°F	24.1 bar 4 to 204	750 psig −40 to 400°F	51 bar −40 to 204°C	Superior	Long	Very low
KALREZ® with ZYMAXX® (KVSP 500)	350 psig 40 to 500°F	24.1 bar 4 to 260	750 psig −40 to 500°F	51 bar −40 to 260°C	Superior	Long	Very low
ENVIRO–SEAL® Graphite	1500 psig 20 to 600°F	103 bar −18 to 315°C	3000 psig −325 to 700°F	207 bar −198 to 371°C	Superior	Very long	Moderate
Graphite Ribbon	- - -	- - -	1500 psig −325 to 1000°F[2]	103 bar −198 to 538°C[2]	Acceptable	Acceptable	High

1. The values shown are only guidelines. These guidelines can be exceeded, but shortened packing life or increased leakage might result. The temperature ratings apply to the actual packing temperature, not to the process temperature.
2. Except for oxidizing service, −325 to 700°F (−198 to 371°C).

Chapter 6

Special Control Valves

As discussed in previous chapters, standard control valves can handle a wide range of control applications. The range of standard applications can be defined as being encompassed by: atmospheric pressure and 6000 psig (414 bar), −150°F (−101°C) and 450°F (232°C), flow coefficient C_v values of 1.0 and 25000, and the limits imposed by common industrial standards. Certainly, corrosiveness and viscosity of the fluid, leakage rates, and many other factors demand consideration even for standard applications. Perhaps the need for careful consideration of valve selection becomes more critical for applications outside the standard limits mentioned above.

This chapter discusses some special applications and control valve modifications useful in controlling them, designs and materials for severe service, and test requirements useful for control valves used in nuclear power plant service.

High Capacity Control Valves

Generally, globe-style valves larger than 12-inch, ball valves over 24-inch, and high performance butterfly valves larger than 48-inch fall in the special valve category. As valve sizes increase arithmetically, static pressure loads at shutoff increase geometrically. Consequently, shaft strength, bearing loads, unbalance forces, and available actuator thrust all become more significant with increasing valve size. Normally maximum allowable pressure drop is reduced on large valves to keep design and actuator requirements within reasonable limits. Even with lowered working pressure ratings, the flow capacity of some

W6119/IL

Figure 6-1. Large Flow Valve Body for Noise Attenuation Service

large-flow valves remains tremendous.

Noise levels must be carefully considered in all large-flow installations because sound pressure levels increase in direct proportion to flow magnitude. To keep valve-originated noise within tolerable limits, large cast or fabricated valve body designs (figure 6-1) have been developed. These bodies, normally cage-style construction, use unusually long valve plug travel, a great number of small flow openings through the wall of the cage and an expanded outlet line connection to minimize noise output and reduce fluid velocity.

Naturally, actuator requirements are severe, and long-stroke, double acting pneumatic pistons are typically specified for large-flow applications. The physical size and weight of the valve and actuator components complicate installation and maintenance procedures. Installation of the valve body
148

assembly into the pipeline and removal and replacement of major trim parts require heavy-duty hoists. Maintenance personnel must follow the manufacturers' instruction manuals closely to minimize risk of injury.

Low Flow Control Valves

Many applications exist in laboratories and pilot plants in addition to the general processing industries where control of extremely low flow rates is required. These applications are commonly handled in one of two ways. First, special trims are often available in standard control valve bodies. The special trim is typically made up of a seat ring and valve plug that have been designed and machined to very close tolerances to allow accurate control of very small flows. These types of constructions can often handle C_v's as low as 0.03. Using these special trims in standard control valves provides economy by reducing the need for spare parts inventory for special valves and actuators. Using this approach also makes future flow expansions easy by simply replacing the trim components in the standard control valve body.

Control valves specifically designed for very low flow rates (figure 6-2) also handle these applications. These valves often handle C_v's as low as 0.000001. In addition to the very low flows, these specialty control valves are compact and light weight because they are often used in laboratory environments where very light schedule piping/tubing is used. These types of control valves are specially designed for the accurate control of very low flowing liquid or gaseous fluid applications.

High-Temperature Control Valves

Control valves for service at temperatures above 450°F (232°C) must be designed and specified with the temperature conditions in mind. At ele-

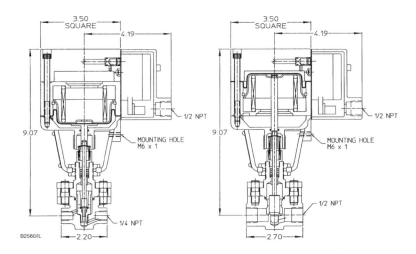

Figure 6-2. Special Control Valve Designed for Very Low Flow Rates

vated temperatures, such as may be encountered in boiler feedwater systems and superheater bypass systems, the standard materials of control valve construction might be inadequate. For instance, plastics, elastomers, and standard gaskets generally prove unsuitable and must be replaced by more durable materials. Metal-to-metal seating materials are always used. Semi-metallic or laminated flexible graphite packing materials are commonly used, and spiral-wound stainless steel and flexible graphite gaskets are necessary.

Cr-Mo steels are often used for the valve body castings for temperatures above 1000°F (538°C). ASTM A217 Grade WC9 is used up to 1100°F (593°C). For temperatures on up to 1500°F (816°C) the material usually selected is ASTM A351 Grade CF8M, Type 316 stainless steel. For temperatures between 1000°F (538°C) and 1500°F (816°C), the carbon content must be controlled to the upper end of the range, 0.04 to 0.08%.

Extension bonnets help protect packing box parts from extremely high temperatures. Typical trim materials include cobalt based Alloy 6, 316 with alloy 6 hardfacing and nitrided 422 SST.

Cryogenic Service Valves

Cryogenics is the science dealing with materials and processes at temperatures below minus 150°F (−101°C). For control valve applications in cryogenic services, many of the same issues need consideration as with high–temperature control valves. Plastic and elastomeric components often cease to function appropriately at temperatures below 0°F (−18°C). In these temperature ranges, components such as packing and plug seals require special consideration. For plug seals, a standard soft seal will become very hard and less pliable thus not providing the shut-off required from a soft seat. Special elastomers have been applied in these temperatures but require special loading to achieve a tight seal.

Packing is a concern in cryogenic applications because of the frost that may form on valves in cryogenic ap-

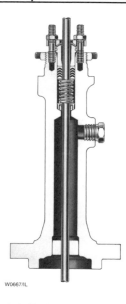

Figure 6-3. Typical Extension Bonnet

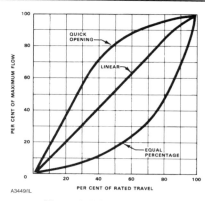

A3449/IL

Figure 6-4. Inherent Valve Characteristics

plications. Moisture from the atmosphere condensates on colder surfaces and where the temperature of the surface is below freezing, the moisture will freeze into a layer of frost. As this frost and ice forms on the bonnet and stem areas of control valves and as the stem is stroked by the actuator, the layer of frost on the stem is drawn through the packing causing tears and thus loss of seal. The solution is to use extension bonnets (figure 6-3) which allow the packing box area of the control valve to be warmed by ambient temperatures, thus preventing frost from forming on the stem and packing box areas. The length of the extension bonnet depends on the application temperature and insulation requirements. The colder the application, the longer the extension bonnet required.

Materials of construction for cryogenic applications are generally CF8M body and bonnet material with 300 series stainless steel trim material. In flashing applications, hard facing might be required to combat erosion.

Customized Characteristics and Noise Abatement Trims

Although control valve characteristics used in standard control valves (figure 6-4) meet the requirements of most applications, often custom characteristics are needed for a given application. In these instances, special trim designs can be manufactured that meet these requirements. For contoured plugs, the design of the plug tip can be modified so that as the plug is moved through its travel range, the unobstructed flow area changes in size to allow for the generation of the specific flow characteristic. Likewise, cages can be redesigned to meet specific characteristics as well. This is especially common in noise abatement type trims where a high level of noise abatement may be required at low flow rates but much lower abatement levels are required for the higher flow rate conditions.

Control Valves for Nuclear Service in the USA

Since 1970, U.S. manufacturers and suppliers of components for nuclear power plants have been subject to the requirements of *Appendix B, Title 10, Part 50* of the *Code of Federal Regu-*

lations entitled *Quality Assurance Criteria for Nuclear Power Plants and Fuel Reprocessing Plants*. The U.S. Nuclear Regulatory Commission enforces this regulation. Ultimate responsibility of proof of compliance to Appendix B rests with the owner of the plant, who must in turn rely on the manufacturers of various plant components to provide documented evidence that the components were manufactured, inspected, and tested by proven techniques performed by qualified personnel according to documented procedures.

In keeping with the requirements of the *Code of Federal Regulations*, most nuclear power plant components are specified in accordance with *Section III* of the *ASME Boiler and Pressure Vessel Code* entitled *Nuclear Power Plant Components*. All aspects of the manufacturing process must be documented in a quality control manual and audited and certified by ASME before actual manufacture of the components. All subsequent manufacturing materials and operations are to be checked by an authorized inspector. All valves manufactured in accordance with Section III requirements receive an ASME code nameplate and an N stamp symbolizing acceptability for service in nuclear power plant applications.

Section III does not apply to parts not associated with the pressure–retaining function, to actuators and accessories unless they are pressure retaining parts, to deterioration of valve components due to radiation, corrosion, erosion, seismic or environmental qualifications, or to cleaning, painting, or packaging requirements. However, customer specifications normally cover these areas. Section III does apply to materials used for pressure retaining parts, to design criteria, to fabrication procedures, to non-destructive test procedures for pressure retaining parts, to hydrostatic testing, and to marking and stamping procedures. ASME Section III is revised by

means of semi-annual addenda, which may be used after date of issue, and which become mandatory six months after date of issue.

Valves Subject to Sulfide Stress Cracking

NACE International is a technical society concerned with corrosion and corrosion-related issues. *NACE MR0175, Sulfide Stress Cracking Resistant Metallic Materials for Oilfield Equipment*, is a standard issued by NACE Task Group T-1F-1 to provide guidelines for the selection of materials that are resistant to failure in hydrogen sulfide-containing oil and gas production environments.

The following statements, although based on the standard mentioned, cannot be presented in the detail furnished in the standard itself and do not guarantee suitability for any given material in hydrogen sulfide-containing sour environments. The reader is urged to refer to the complete standard before selecting control valves for sour gas service. Portions of this standard have been mandated by statute in many states of the U.S.A.

• Most ferrous metals can become susceptible to sulfide stress cracking (SSC) due to hardening by heat treatment and/or cold work. Conversely, many ferrous metals can be heat treated to improve resistance to SSC.

• Carbon and low-alloy steels should be heat treated to a maximum hardness of 22 HRC to improve resistance to SSC.

• Cast iron is not permitted for use as a pressure-containing member in equipment covered by some American Petroleum Institute standards and should not be used in non-pressure containing internal valve parts without the approval of the purchaser.

• Austenitic stainless steels are most resistant to SSC in the annealed condition; some other stainless steels are acceptable up to 35 HRC.

● Copper-base alloys are generally not to be used in critical parts of a valve without the approval of the purchaser.

● Some high-strength alloys are acceptable under specified conditions.

● Chromium, nickel, and cadmium plating offer no protection from SSC.

● Weld repairs or fabrication welds on carbon and low-alloy steels require post-weld heat treatment to assure a maximum hardness of 22 HRC.

● Conventional identification stamping is permissible in low stress areas, such as on the outside diameter of line flanges.

● The standard precludes using ASTM A193 Grade B7 bolting for some applications. Therefore, it might be necessary to derate valves originally designed to use this bolting.

Chapter 7

Steam Conditioning Valves

Steam conditioning valves include those in desuperheating, steam conditioning, and turbine bypass systems, covered in this chapter.

Understanding Desuperheating

Superheated steam provides an excellent source of energy for mechanical power generation. However, in many instances, steam at greatly reduced temperatures, near saturation, proves a more desirable commodity. This is the case for most heat–transfer applications. Precise temperature control is needed to improve heating efficiency; eliminate unintentional superheat in throttling processes; or to protect downstream product and/or equipment from heat related damage. One method to reduce temperature is the installation of a desuperheater.

A desuperheater injects a controlled, predetermined amount of water into a steam flow to lower the temperature of the steam. To achieve this efficiently, the desuperheater must be designed and selected correctly for the application. Although it can appear simplistic in design, the desuperheater must integrate with a wide variety of complex thermal and flow dynamic variables to be effective. The control of the water quantity, and thus the steam temperature, uses a temperature control loop. This loop includes a downstream temperature sensing device, a controller to interpret the measured temperature relative to the desired set point, and the transmission of a proportional signal to a water controlling valve/actuator assembly to meter the required quantity of water.

The success or failure of a particular desuperheater installation rests on a number of physical, thermal, and geo-

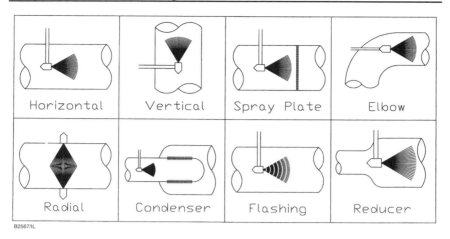

B2567/IL

Figure 7-1. Desuperheater Installations

metric factors. Some of these are obvious and some obscure, but all of them have a varying impact on the performance of the equipment and the system in which it is installed.

The first, and probably the most important factor for efficient desuperheater operation, is to select the correct design for the respective application. Desuperheaters come in all shapes and sizes and use various energy transfer and mechanical techniques to achieve the desired performance within the limits of the system environment. Another section details the differences in the types of desuperheaters available and expected performance.

Technical Aspects of Desuperheating

Some of the physical parameters that affect the performance of a desuperheating system include:

- Installation orientation

- Spraywater temperature

- Spraywater quantity

- Pipeline size

- Steam velocity

- Equipment versus system turndown

Installation orientation is an often overlooked, but critical factor in the performance of the system. Correct placement of the desuperheater can have a greater impact on the operation than the style of the unit itself. For most units, the optimum orientation is in a vertical pipeline with the flow direction up. This is contrary to most installations seen in industry today. Other orientation factors include pipe fittings, elbows, and any other type of pipeline obstruction that exists downstream of the water injection point. Figure 7-1 illustrates variations in the installation of a desuperheater.

Spraywater temperature can have a significant impact on desuperheater performance. Although it goes against logical convention, high–temperature water is better for cooling. As the spraywater temperature increases, flow and thermal characteristics improve and impact the following:

- Surface tension

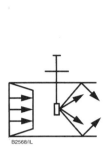
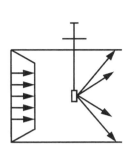
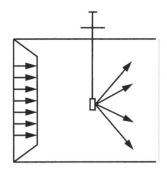

B2568/IL

Figure 7-2. Spray Penetration

- Drop size distribution

- Latent heat of vaporization

- Vaporization rate

Improvements in all these areas, as a result of increased spraywater temperature, improves the overall performance of the system.

The quantity of water to be injected will have a directly proportional effect on the time for vaporization. The heat transfer process is time dependent and, thus, the quantity of spraywater will affect the time for complete vaporization and thermal stability.

To determine the spraywater required (**Qw**) as a function of inlet steam flow (**Q1**), perform a simple heat balance using the following equation:

$$Qw(mass) = Q1 * \left(\frac{H1 - H2}{H2 - Hw} \right)$$

Where **Q** is the mass flow in PPH and **H** is the individual enthalpy values at the inlet, outlet, and spraywater.

When the calculation is performed as a function of outlet steam flow (**Q2**), that is, the combination of inlet steam flow and desuperheating spraywater, use the following equation:

$$Qw(mass) = Q2 * \left(\frac{H1 - H2}{Hw - H1} \right)$$

To perform a basic C_v calculation for initial desuperheater sizing, it is required that the resultant **Qw(mass)** is converted to **Qw(volumetric)**. When using English units the conversion is done as follows:

$$Qw(volumetric) = \frac{Qw(mass) * 0.1247}{pw}$$

Qw(volumetric) is in GPM and ρw is the density of the spraywater in Lbm/Ft^3. Based on this conversion, the sizing can be completed with the following C_v calculation for each set of conditions:

$$C_v = Qw(volumetric) * \sqrt{\frac{SG}{\Delta Pdsh}}$$

Where SG is the specific gravity of the spraywater and $\Delta Pdsh$ is the pressure differential across the proposed desuperheater.

When designing a new desuperheater installation, another concern for proper system performance is the pipeline size. As the line size gets larger, more attention must be paid to the penetration velocity of the spray and the coverage in the flow stream (figure 7-2).

Some single-point, injection type desuperheaters have insufficient nozzle energy to disperse throughout the entire cross sectional flow area of the pipeline. As a result, the spray pattern collapses and thermal stratification occurs, that is, a sub-cooled center core that is shrouded with superheated steam. This condition is normally eliminated after the flow stream has undergone several piping directional changes, but this is not always possible within the limits of the control system or process. Proper placement of high-energy, multi-nozzle units in the larger pipelines normally prevents the formation of thermal stratification.

The maximum and minimum velocity of the steam has a direct relationship on the successful mixing of the water. The velocity directly affects the residence time available for the water to mix with the steam. When the maximum velocity is too high, there potentially is not enough time for the water to mix before it encounters a piping obstruction such as an elbow or tee. Ideal maximum velocity usually ranges from 150-250 feet per second (46–76 meters per second). When the minimum velocity is too low, turbulence is reduced and then the water droplets tend to fall out of suspension in the steam. As a rule, the minimum steam velocity in which water can remain suspended is approximately 30 feet per second (9 meters per second). For applications with lower velocities, proper mixing may be achieved with desuperheaters that offer a venturi or atomizing steam.

One of the most over-used and misunderstood concepts in the area of desuperheating is turndown. When applied to a final control element, such as a valve, turndown is a simple ratio of the maximum to the minimum controllable flow rate. Turndown is sometimes used interchangeably with rangeability. However, the exact meaning differs considerably when it comes to actual performance comparisons.

A desuperheater is not a final control element, and as such, its performance is directly linked to its system environment. The actual system turndown is more a function of the system parameters rather than based on the equipment's empirical flow variations. Once

this is understood, it is obvious that a good desuperheater cannot overcome the failings of a poor system. They must be evaluated on their own merits and weighted accordingly.

Due to improved nozzle design technology, pipe liners are rarely required. Depending on the particulate quality of the water source, in-line strainers may be required.

The previous calculations and recommendations provide the necessary information to select the proper desuperheater design and size. This selection should be based on a variety of application considerations such as:

● Minimum to maximum load requirement rangeability

● Minimum steam velocity

● Straight pipe length and temperature sensor distance after the desuperheater

● Steam pipe line size and

● Pressure differential between water and steam

Typical Desuperheater Designs

Fixed Geometry Nozzle Design

The fixed geometry nozzle design (figure 7-3) is a simple mechanically atomized desuperheater with single or multiple fixed geometry spray nozzles. It is intended for applications with nearly constant load changes (rangeability up to 5:1) and is capable of proper atomization in steam flow velocities as low as 14 feet per second under optimum conditions. Standard installation of this type of unit is through a flanged branch connection tee on a 6-inch or larger steam pipe line. This design is usually not available for large C_v requirements. This unit requires an external water control valve to meter water flow based on a signal from a temperature sensor in the downstream steam line.

W7102/IL

*Figure 7-3. Fixed Geometry
Nozzle Design*

try, back pressure activated spray nozzles. Due to the variable geometry, this unit can handle applications requiring control over moderate load changes (rangeability up to 20:1) and is capable of proper atomization in steam flow velocities as low as 14 feet per second under optimum conditions. Standard installation of this type of unit is through a flanged branch connection tee on an 8-inch or larger steam pipe line. These units are available for large C_v requirements. This design requires an external water control valve to meter water flow based on a signal from a temperature sensor in the downstream steam line.

Self-Contained Design

The self-contained design (figure 7-5) is also mechanically atomized with one or more variable geometry, back pressure activated spray nozzles. As a special feature, this unit incorporates a water flow control element that performs the function normally provided by an external water control valve. This control element has a plug that moves inside a control cage by means of an actuator, which receives a signal from a temperature sensor in the downstream steam line. The water flow then passes to the variable geometry nozzle(s) and is atomized as it enters the steam pipe line. Because of the close coordination of the intrinsic control element and the variable geometry nozzle(s), this unit can handle applications requiring control over moderate to high load changes (rangeability up to 25:1). It offers proper atomization in steam flow velocities as low as 14 feet per second under optimum conditions. Standard installation of this type of unit is through a flanged branch connection tee on an 8-inch or larger steam pipe line. These are available for moderate C_v requirements.

W6310-1/IL

*Figure 7-4. Variable Geometry
Nozzle Design*

Variable Geometry Nozzle Design

The variable geometry nozzle design (figure 7-4) is also a simple mechanically atomized desuperheater, but it employs one or more variable geome-

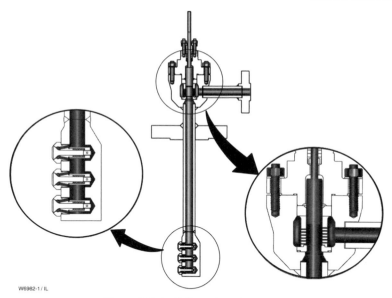

W6982-1 / IL

Figure 7-5. Self-Contained Design

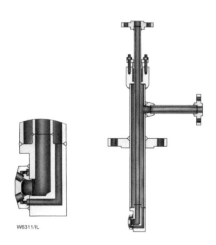

W6311/IL

Figure 7-6. Steam Assisted Design

Steam Atomized Design

The steam atomized design (figure 7-6) incorporates the use of high-pressure steam for rapid and complete atomization of the spraywater. This is especially useful in steam pipe lines that have low steam velocity. The at-

omizing steam, usually twice the main steam line pressure or higher, encounters the water in the spray nozzle chamber where the energy of the expanding atomizing steam is used to atomize the water into very small droplets. These smaller droplets allow for faster conversion to steam and permit the water to remain suspended in a low steam velocity flow, thereby allowing complete vaporization to occur. The steam atomized design, therefore, can properly mix water into steam flow velocities as low as approximately 4 feet per second (1.2 meters per second) under optimum conditions. This design handles applications requiring very high load changes (rangeability up to 50:1). Standard installation of this type of unit is through a flanged branch connection tee on an 8-inch or larger steam pipe line. This design is available for moderate C_v requirements. It requires an external water control valve to meter water flow based on a signal from a temperature sensor in the downstream steam line. This sys-

158

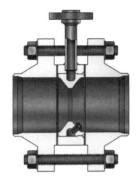

W6313-1/IL

Figure 7-7. Geometry-Assisted Wafer Design

tem also requires a separate on/off valve for the atomizing steam supply.

Geometry-Assisted Wafer Design

The geometry-assisted wafer design (figure 7-7) was originally developed for small steam pipe line sizes of less than 6-inch that were unable to accommodate an insertion style desuperheater. The unit is designed as a wafer that is installed between two flanges in the steam pipe line. A reduced diameter throat venturi allows water to spray completely around the wafer and permits multiple points of spraying either through drilled holes or small nozzles. In addition, the venturi increases the steam velocity at the point of injection, which enhances atomization and mixing in steam flow velocities as low as approximately 10 feet per second (3 meters per second) under optimum conditions. It handles applications requiring control over moderate load change (rangeability up to 20:1). It can be installed in steam pipe line sizes of 1-inch through 24-inch, and is available for moderate C_v requirements. This design requires an external water control valve to meter water flow based on a signal from a temperature sensor in the downstream steam line.

Understanding Steam Conditioning Valves

A steam conditioning valve is used for the simultaneous reduction of steam pressure and temperature to the level required for a given application. Frequently, these applications deal with high inlet pressures and temperatures and require significant reductions of both properties. They are, therefore, best manufactured in a forged and fabricated body that can better withstand steam loads at elevated pressures and temperatures. Forged materials permit higher design stresses, improved grain structure, and an inherent material integrity over cast valve bodies. The forged construction also allows the manufacturer to provide up to Class 4500, as well as intermediate and special class ratings, with greater ease versus cast valve bodies.

Due to frequent extreme changes in steam properties as a result of the temperature and pressure reduction, the forged and fabricated valve body design allows for the addition of an expanded outlet to control outlet steam velocity at the lower pressure. Similarly, with reduced outlet pressure, the forged and fabricated design allows the manufacturer to provide different pressure class ratings for the

159

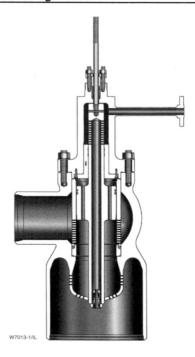

W7013-1/IL

Figure 7-8. Feedforward Design

inlet and outlet connections to more closely match the adjacent piping

Other advantages of combining the pressure reduction and desuperheater function in the same valve versus two separate devices include:

- Improved spraywater mixing due to the optimum utilization of the turbulent expansion zone downstream of the pressure reduction elements

- Improved rangeability

- Increased noise abatement due, in part, to the additional attenuation of noise as a result of the spraywater injection

- In some designs, improved response time due to an integrated feedforward capability

- Ease of installing and servicing only one device

Several available steam conditioning valve designs meet various applications. Typical examples of these follow.

Steam Conditioning Valve Designs

Feedforward Design

The feedforward steam conditioning valve design (figure 7-8) offers all the traditional benefits of the combined valve and features an ability to provide an intrinsic form of feedforward control.

Positioning of the valve plug within the cage controls steam pressure and flow. A signal from the pressure control loop to the valve actuator positions the dynamically balanced valve plug to increase or decrease the amount of flow area. The control cage includes an array of orifices that provide the required flow characteristic. As the plug is lifted from the seat, steam passes through the control cage and down through the seat ring. The valve plug is equipped with a hollow tube both above and below the main plug body. This arrangement connects the valve outlet area (after the seat orifice), with the upper spraywater supply chamber to allow the flow of cooling water.

The upper portion of the water tube is provided with an arrangement of calibrated orifices to allow spraywater to enter and flow down toward the valve outlet. The water tube extends down below the seating surface on the valve plug and is positioned near the flow vena contracta below the main valve seat orifice. The water is injected at a point of high velocity and turbulence, and distributed quickly and evenly throughout the flow stream. Thus, when pressure is recovered downstream of the valve, the water will be almost instantaneously evaporated, providing the required attemperation.

The valve body is provided with a steam seating surface and a water sealing surface. The steam seat provides for positive shut-off (Class IV only) of steam flow. It consists of a replaceable seat ring and a hardened valve plug. Piston rings on the valve plug reduce leakage between the guide surfaces. The water seal provides for sealing of the water and includes a seal bushing to prevent leakage. These two control points are designed so that as the valve plug is lifted to permit flow of steam, a proportional amount of water flow is allowed. This provides an instantaneous increase in water flow as steam demand increases, affording more precise control of pressure and temperature over a wide range of steam flows. This feedforward control is coarse control. An external water control valve is required which, operating on

a signal from a downstream temperature sensor, will provide the required fine tuning control.

Due to the design of the plug used in this style valve, there are certain application restrictions in its use. These restrictions deal primarily with the plug's hollow center and its capacity to pass the required amount of water, as well as the plug's single discharge orifice and its ability to pass enough water and effectively inject the water over the entire steam flow. This style valve is generally supplied as an angle valve, but it can also be supplied as a Y pattern for straight-through installations. In such cases, the application limitations are more restrictive due to spraywater injection into a steam flow that is still changing direction.

Typically this integral feed-forward design is used for process steam reduction stations from the main steam header to the individual process area requirements. It can also be used for other applications where there are small to moderate water addition requirements and small to moderate pressure reduction requirements.

Manifold Design

The manifold steam conditioning valve design (figure 7-9) offers all the benefits of the combined valve but features its ability to provide multi-point water injection with an externally mounted manifold around the valve outlet. With this manifold, large quantities of water can be injected with homogenous distribution throughout the steam outlet flow.

Similarly, positioning of the valve plug within the control cage controls steam pressure and flow. A signal from the pressure control loop to the valve actuator moves the valve plug within the control cage to increase or decrease the amount of free flow area. The control cage has an array of calibrated orifices to provide the control characteristic specified. As the plug is lifted

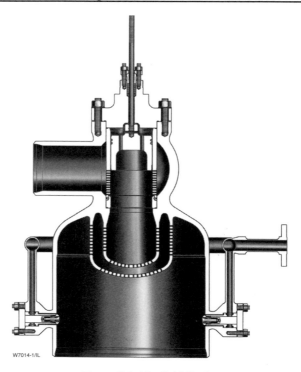

W7014-1/IL

Figure 7-9. Manifold Design

from the seat, steam passes into the center of the control cage and out through the seat ring. The outlet section of the valve is equipped with a combination cooler section/silencer. As the steam leaves the seat ring, it enters a diffuser designed to further decrease steam pressure energy in a controlled-velocity expansion.

Flow is directed radially through the multiple-orifice diffuser, exiting into the enlarged outlet pipe section. This section has been sized to accommodate the large change in specific volume associated with the pressure drop and to keep steam velocities within limits that minimize noise and vibration.

The outlet section is outfitted with a water supply manifold. The manifold (multiple manifolds are also possible) provides cooling water flow to a num-

ber of individual spay nozzles installed in the outlet section. The result is a fine spray mist injected radially into the high turbulence of the steam flow.

The combination of large surface area contact of the water and steam coupled with high turbulence make for efficient mixing and rapid vaporization. Even though there is no intrinsic feedforward in this valve design, it is possible to obtain feedforward with external control devices. In either case, an external water control valve is required which, operating on a signal from a downstream temperature sensor, will provide the required fine tuning for temperature control.

The seat provides for positive shutoff of steam flow. It consists of a replaceable seat ring and a hardened valve plug. Piston rings on the valve plug

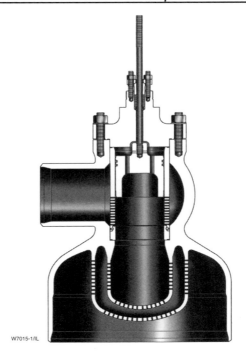

W7015-1/IL

Figure 7-10. Pressure-Reducing-Only Design

reduce leakage between the guide surfaces.

Due to the rugged design of this valve, there are few limitations to its usage. It is available for high pressure applications, high-pressure reductions, very high water addition both in volume and mass percentage of water to steam, multiple noise reducing diffusers for large pressure drops, very large outlets,and for Class V shutoff. This design is standard as an angle valve, but can be supplied in a Y pattern for straight–through installations, and when desired it can be manufactured in a Z pattern for offset installations.

Typically this valve is used in power (utility, cogeneration, and industrial) plant applications around the turbine for startup, bypass, condenser-dump, vent, and export steam. It can also be used for other applications where there are moderate to very large water addition and pressure reduction requirements.

Pressure-Reduction-Only Design

The pressure-reduction-only valve design (figure 7-10), unlike the combined units, is only used for pressure reduction. The special feature for this style valve is that it is a forged and fabricated body, which is a cost-effective solution for high end pressure classes and for incorporating noise attenuation diffusers.

Steam pressure and flow are controlled by the positioning of the valve plug with the control cage. A signal from the pressure control loop to the valve actuator positions the valve plug inside the cage to increase or decrease the amount of flow area. The control cage has an array of orifices that provide the required flow characteristic. As the plug is lifted from the seat, steam passes through the cage and down through the seat ring.

The seat provides for positive shutoff of steam flow. It consists of a replaceable seat ring and a hardened valve plug. Piston rings on the valve plug reduce leakage between the guide surfaces.

Due to the rugged forged design, there are few limitations to its usage. As previously mentioned, its greatest cost effectiveness is when it is in the Class 900 pressure range or greater and when the steam temperature requires a chrome moly, stainless steel or other special material body. It is also cost effective when very large outlets are required to match pipe sizes. This style valve also allows for multiple noise reduction diffusers for large noise reductions and is also available with Class V shutoff. It is standard as an angle valve, but can be supplied as a Y pattern for straight-through installations, and when desired it can be manufactured in a Z pattern for off-set installations.

Typically this valve is used in power (utility, cogeneration, and industrial) plant applications where high pressures and temperatures require pressure reduction only.

Understanding Turbine Bypass Systems

The turbine bypass system has evolved over the last few decades as the mode of power plant operations has changed. It is employed routinely in utility power plants where operations require quick response to wide swings in energy demands. A typical day of power plant operation might start at minimum load, increase to full capacity for most of the day, rapidly reduce back to minimum output, then up again to full load—all within a

twenty-four hour period. Boilers, turbines, condensers and other associated equipment cannot respond properly to such rapid changes without some form of turbine bypass system.

The turbine bypass system allows operation of the boiler independent of the turbine. In the start-up mode, or rapid reduction of generation requirement, the turbine bypass not only supplies an alternate flow path for steam, but conditions the steam to the same pressure and temperature normally produced by the turbine expansion process. By providing an alternate flow path for the steam, the turbine bypass system protects the turbine, boiler, and condenser from damage that may occur from thermal and pressure excursions. For this reason, many turbine bypass systems require extremely rapid open/close response times for maximum equipment protection. This is accomplished with an electrohydraulic actuation system that provides both the forces and controls for such operation.

Additionally, when commissioning a new plant, the turbine bypass system allows start-up and check out of the boiler separately from the turbine. This means quicker plant start-ups, which results in attractive economic gains. It also means that this closed loop system can prevent atmospheric loss of treated feedwater and reduction of ambient noise emissions.

Turbine Bypass System Components

The major elements of a turbine bypass system (figure 7-11) are turbine bypass valves, turbine bypass water control valves, and the electro-hydraulic system.

Turbine Bypass Valves

Whether for low-pressure or high-pressure applications, turbine bypass valves are usually the manifold design steam conditioning valves previously

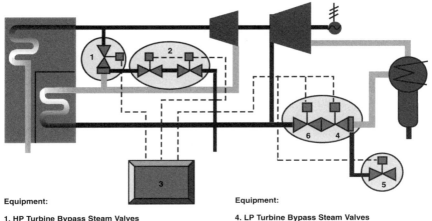

Equipment:

1. HP Turbine Bypass Steam Valves
2. HP Turbine Bypass Control and Water Isolation Valves
3. EHS Electrohydraulic System—
   Electrical Control Logic
   Hydraulic Control Logic
   Accumulators and Accumulator Power System
Hydraulic Power Unit
Control Cabinet
Piston Actuators and Proportional Valves

B2569 / IL

Equipment:

4. LP Turbine Bypass Steam Valves
5. LP Turbine Bypass Water Valves
6. LP Turbine Bypass Steam Stop Valves (optional)
3. EHS Electrohydraulic system

Figure 7-11. Turbine Bypass System

described with tight shutoff (Class V). Because of particular installation requirements these manifold design valves will occasionally be separated into two parts: the pressure-reducing portion of the valve and then the outlet/manifold cooler section located closer to the condenser. Regardless of the configuration, however, a cost effective solution is a fixed-orifice device (usually a sparger) located downstream for final pressure reduction to minimize the size of the outlet pipe to the condenser.

Turbine Bypass Water Control Valves

These valves are required to control

the flow of the water to the turbine bypass valves. Due to equipment protection requirements, it is imperative that these valves provide tight shutoff (Class V).

Electro-Hydraulic System

This system is for actuating the valves. Its primary elements include the actual hydraulic actuators, the hydraulic accumulator and power unit, and the control unit and operating logic.

Chapter 8

Installation and Maintenance

Control valve efficiency directly affects process plant profits. The role a control valve plays in optimizing processes is often overlooked. Many process plant managers focus most resources on distributed control systems and their potential for improving production efficiency. However, it is the final control element (typically a control valve) that actually creates the change in process variable. If the valve is not working properly, no amount of sophisticated electronics at the front end will correct problems at the valve. As many studies have shown, control valves are often neglected to the point that they become the weak link in the process control scheme.

Control valves must operate properly, no matter how sophisticated the automation system or how accurate the instrumentation. Without proper valve operation you cannot achieve high yields, quality products, maximum profits, and energy conservation.

Optimizing control valve efficiency depends on:

1. Correct control valve selection for the application,

2. Proper storage and protection,

3. Proper installation techniques, and

4. An effective predictive maintenance program.

Control valve selection is covered in Chapter 5. The other three topics are included in this chapter.

Proper Storage and Protection

Proper storage and protection should be considered early in the selection process, before the valve is shipped. Typically, manufacturers have packaging standards that are dependent upon the destination and intended length of storage before installation. Because most valves arrive on site some time before installation, many problems can be averted by making sure the details of the installation schedule are known and discussed with the manufacturer at the time of valve selection. In addition, special precautions should be taken upon receipt of the valve at the final destination. For example, the valve must be stored in a clean, dry place away from any traffic or other activity that could damage the valve.

W1916/IL

Figure 8-1. Install the Valve with the Flow Arrow Pointing in the Direction of the Process Flow

Proper Installation Techniques

Always follow the control valve manufacturer's installation instructions and cautions. Typical instructions are summarized here.

Read the Instruction Manual

Before installing the valve, read the instruction manual. Instruction manuals describe the product and review safety issues and precautions to be taken before and during installation. Following the guidelines in the manual helps ensure an easy and successful installation.

Be Sure the Pipeline Is Clean

Foreign material in the pipeline could damage the seating surface of the valve or even obstruct the movement of the valve plug, ball, or disk so that the valve does not shut off properly. To help reduce the possibility of a dangerous situation from occurring, clean all pipelines before installing. Make sure pipe scale, metal chips, welding slag, and other foreign materials are removed. In addition, inspect pipe flanges to ensure a smooth gasket surface. If the valve has screwed end connections, apply a good grade of pipe sealant compound to the male pipeline threads. Do not use sealant

on the female threads because excess compound on the female threads could be forced into the valve body. Excess compound could cause sticking in the valve plug or accumulation of dirt, which could prevent good valve shutoff.

Inspect the Control Valve

Although valve manufacturers take steps to prevent shipment damage, such damage is possible and should be discovered and reported before the valve is installed.

Do not install a control valve known to have been damaged in shipment or while in storage.

Before installing, check for and remove all shipping stops and protective plugs or gasket surface covers. Check inside the valve body to make sure no foreign objects are present.

Use Good Piping Practices

Most control valves can be installed in any position. However, the most common method is with the actuator vertical and above the valve body. If horizontal actuator mounting is necessary, consider additional vertical support for the actuator. Be sure the body is installed so that fluid flow will be in the direction indicated by the flow arrow (figure 8-1) or instruction manual.

Be sure to allow ample space above and below the valve to permit easy re-

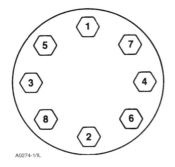

A0274-1/IL

Figure 8-2. Tighten Bolts in a Criss-cross Pattern

moval of the actuator or valve plug for inspection and maintenance. Clearance distances are normally available from the valve manufacturer as certified dimension drawings. For flanged valve bodies, be sure the flanges are properly aligned to provide uniform contact of the gasket surfaces. Snug up the bolts gently after establishing proper flange alignment. Finish tightening them in a criss-cross pattern (figure 8-2). Proper tightening will avoid uneven gasket loading and will help prevent leaks. It also will avoid the possibility of damaging, or even breaking, the flange. This precaution is particularly important when connecting to flanges that are not the same material as the valve flanges.

Pressure taps installed upstream and downstream of the control valve are useful for checking flow capacity or pressure drop. Locate such taps in straight runs of pipe away from elbows, reducers, or expanders. This location minimizes inaccuracies resulting from fluid turbulence.

Use 1/4- or 3/8-inch (6-10 millimeters) tubing or pipe from the pressure connection on the actuator to the controller. Keep this distance relatively short and minimize the number of fittings and elbows to reduce system time lag. If the distance must be long, use a valve positioner or a booster with the control valve.

Control Valve Maintenance

Always follow the control valve manufacturer's maintenance instructions. Typical maintenance topics are summarized here.

Optimization of control valve assets depends on an effective maintenance philosophy and program. Three of the most basic approaches are:

Reactive – Action is taken after an event has occurred. Wait for something to happen to a valve and then repair or replace it.

Preventive – Action is taken on a timetable based on history; that is, try to prevent something bad from happening.

Predictive – Action is taken based on field input using state-of-the-art, non-intrusive diagnostic test and evaluation devices or using smart instrumentation.

Although both reactive and preventive programs work, they do not optimize valve potential. Following are some of the disadvantages of each approach.

Reactive Maintenance

Reactive maintenance allows subtle deficiencies to go unnoticed and untreated, simply because there is no clear indication of a problem. Even critical valves might be neglected until they leak badly or fail to stroke. In some cases, feedback from production helps maintenance react before serious problems develop, but valves might be removed unnecessarily on the suspicion of malfunction. Large valves or those welded in-line can require a day or longer for removal, disassembly, inspection, and reinstallation. Time and resources could be wasted without solving the problem if the symptoms are actually caused by some other part of the system.

Preventive Maintenance

Preventive maintenance generally represents a significant improvement.

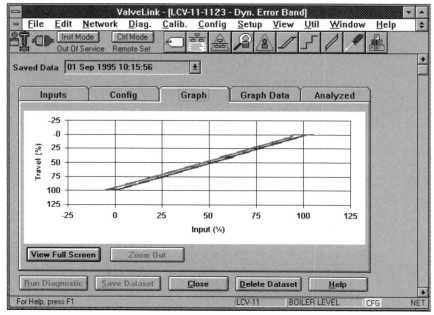

W7046/IL

Figure 8-3. Non-Intrusive Diagnostics Program for Predictive Maintenance

However, because maintenance schedules have been able to obtain little information on valves that are operating, many plants simply overhaul all control valves on a rotating schedule. Such programs result in servicing some valves that need no repair or adjustment and leaving others in the system long after they have stopped operating efficiently.

Predictive Maintenance

Many new techniques are gaining popularity for gathering and monitoring field input for predictive maintenance techniques:

- Non-intrusive diagnostics (figure 8-3),

- Smart positioners,

- Distributive control systems, and

- PLCs (programmable logic controllers).

For even routine maintenance procedures on a control valve, the maintenance person must have thorough understanding of the construction and operation of the valve. Without this knowledge, the equipment could be damaged or the maintenance person or others could be injured. Most valve manufacturers provide safety measures in their instruction manuals. Usually, a sectional drawing of the equipment is furnished to help in understanding the operation of the equipment and in identifying parts.

In all major types of control valves, the actuator provides force to position a movable valve plug, ball, or disk in relation to a stationary seat ring or sealing surface. The movable part should respond freely to changes in actuator force. If operation is not correct, service is needed. Failure to take adequate precautions before maintaining a valve could cause personal injury or equipment damage.

170

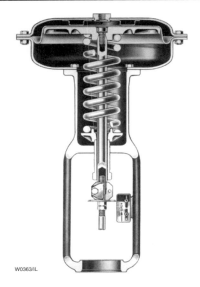

W0363/IL

Figure 8-4. Typical Spring-and-Diaphragm Actuator

W2911/IL

Figure 8-5. Typical Valve Stem Packing Assemblies

Often corporate maintenance policy or existing codes require preventive maintenance on a regular schedule. Usually such programs include inspection for damage of all major valve components and replacement of all gaskets, O-ring seals, diaphragms, and other elastomer parts. Maintenance instructions are normally furnished with the control valve equipment. Follow those instructions carefully. A few items are summarized here.

Actuator Diaphragm

Most pneumatic spring-and-diaphragm actuators (figure 8-4) use a molded diaphragm. The molded diaphragm facilitates installation, provides a relatively uniform effective area throughout valve travel, and permits greater travel than could be possible with a flat-sheet diaphragm. If a flat-sheet diaphragm is used for emergency repair, replace it with a molded diaphragm as soon as possible.

Stem Packing

Packing (figure 8-5), which provides the pressure seal around the stem of a globe-style or angle-style valve body, should be replaced if leakage develops around the stem, or if the valve is completely disassembled for other maintenance or inspection. Before loosening packing nuts, make sure there is no pressure in the valve body.

Removing the packing without removing the actuator is difficult and is not recommended. Also, do not try to blow out the old packing rings by applying pressure to the lubricator hole in the bonnet. This can be dangerous. Also, it frequently does not work very well as many packing arrangements have about half of the rings below the lubricator hole.

A better method is to remove the actuator and valve bonnet and pull out the stem. Push or drive the old packing out the top of the bonnet. Do not

171

use the valve plug stem because the threads could sustain damage.

Clean the packing box. Inspect the stem for scratches or imperfections that could damage new packing. Check the trim and other parts as appropriate. After re-assembling, tighten body/bonnet bolting in a sequence similar to that described for flanges earlier in this chapter.

Slide new packing parts over the stem in proper sequence, being careful that the stem threads do not damage the packing rings. Adjust packing by following the manufacturer's instructions.

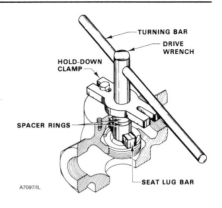

Figure 8-6. Seat Ring Puller

Seat Rings

Severe service conditions can damage the seating surface of the seat ring(s) so that the valve does not shut off satisfactorily. Grinding or lapping the seating surfaces will improve shutoff if damage is not severe. For severe damage, replace the seat ring.

Grinding Metal Seats

The condition of the seating surfaces of the valve plug and seat ring can often be improved by grinding. Many grinding compounds are available commercially. For cage-style constructions, bolt the bonnet or bottom flange to the body with the gaskets in place to position the cage and seat ring properly and to help align the valve plug with the seat ring while grinding . A simple grinding tool can be made from a piece of strap iron locked to the valve plug stem with nuts.

On double-port bodies, the top ring normally grinds faster than the bottom ring. Under these conditions, continue to use grinding compound on the bottom ring, but use only a polishing compound on the top ring. If either of the ports continues to leak, use more grinding compound on the seat ring that is not leaking and polishing compound on the other ring. This procedure grinds down the seat ring that is not leaking until both seats touch at the same time. Never leave one seat ring dry while grinding the other.

After grinding, clean seating surfaces, and test for shutoff. Repeat grinding procedure if leakage is still excessive.

Replacing Seat Rings

Follow the manufacturer's instructions. For threaded seat rings, use a seat ring puller (figure 8-6). Before trying to remove the seat ring(s), check to see if the ring has been tack-welded to the valve body. If so, cut away the weld.

On double-port bodies, one of the seat rings is smaller than the other. On direct-acting valves (push-down-to-close action), install the smaller ring in the body port farther from the bonnet before installing the larger ring. On reverse-acting valves (push-down-to-open action), install the smaller ring in the body port closer to the bonnet before installing larger ring.

Remove all excess pipe compound after tightening the threaded seat ring. Spot weld a threaded seat ring in place to ensure that it does not loosen.

Bench Set

Bench set is initial compression placed on the actuator spring with a spring adjuster. For air-to-open valves, the lower bench set determines the amount of seat load force available and the pressure required to begin valve-opening travel. For air-to-close valves, the lower bench set determines the pressure required to begin valve-closing travel. Seating force is determined by pressure applied minus bench set minus spring compression due to travel (figure 8-7). Because of spring tolerances, there might be some variation in the spring angle. The bench set, when the valve is seated, requires the greatest accu-

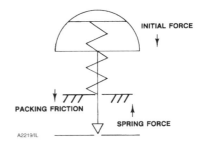

Figure 8-7. Bench Set Seating Force

racy. Refer to manufacturer's instructions for adjusting the spring.

Chapter 9

Standards and Approvals

Control Valve Standards

Numerous standards are applicable to control valves. International and global standards are becoming increasingly important for companies that participate in global markets. Following is a list of codes and standards that have been or will be important in the design and application of control valves.

American Petroleum Institute (API)

Spec 6D (1994), Specification for Pipeline Valves (Gate, Plug, Ball, and Check Valves)

598 (1996), Valve Inspection and Testing

607 (1993), Fire Test for Soft-Seated Quarter-Turn Valves

609 (1997), Lug- and Wafer-Type Butterfly Valves

American Society of Mechanical Engineers (ASME)

B16.1-1989, Cast Iron Pipe Flanges and Flanged Fittings

B16.4-1992, Gray Iron Threaded Fittings

B16.5-1996, Pipe Flanges and Flanged Fittings (for steel, nickel-based alloys, and other alloys)

B16.10-1992, Face-to-Face and End-to-End Dimensions of Valves (see ISA standards for dimensions for most control valves)

B16.24-1991, Cast Copper Alloy Pipe Flanges and Flanged Fittings

B16.25-1997, Buttwelding Ends

B16.34-1996, Valves - Flanged, Threaded, and Welding End

B16.42-1987, Ductile Iron Pipe Flanges and Flanged Fittings

B16.47-1996, Large Diameter Steel Flanges (NPS 26 through NPS 60)

European Committee for Standardization (CEN)

European Industrial Valve Standards

EN 19 (December 1992), Marking

EN 558-1 (October 1995), Face-to-Face and Centre-to-Face Dimensions of Metal Valves for Use in Flanged Pipe Systems - Part 1: PN-Designated Valves

EN 558-2 (March 1995), Face-to-Face and Centre-to-Face Dimensions of Metal Valves for Use in Flanged Pipe Systems - Part 2: Class-Designated Valves

EN 593, Butterfly valves (approved but date not established)

EN 736-1 (June 1995), Terminology - Part 1: Definition of types of valves

EN 736-2 (November 1997), Terminology - Part 2: Definition of components of valves

EN 736-3 Terminology - Part 3: Definition of terms (in preparation)

EN 1349, Industrial Process Control Valves (in preparation)

EN 1503-1, Shell materials - Part 1: Steels (in preparation)

EN 1503-2, Shell materials - Part 2: ISO Steels (in preparation)

EN 1503-3, Shell materials - Part 3: Cast irons (in preparation)

EN 1503-4, Shell materials - Part 4: Copper alloys (in preparation)

EN 12266-1,Testing of valves - Part 1: Tests, test procedures and acceptance criteria (in preparation)

EN 12516-1, Shell design strength - Part 1: Tabulation method for steel valves (in preparation)

EN 12516-2, Shell design strength - Part 2: Calculation method for steel valves (in preparation)

EN 12516-3, Shell design strength - Part 3: Experimental method (in preparation)

EN 12627, Butt weld end design (in preparation)

EN 12760, Socket weld end design (in preparation)

EN 12982, End to end dimensions for butt welding end valves (in preparation)

EN 60534-1 (June 1993), Part 1: Control valve terminology and general considerations

EN 60534-2-1 (June 1993), Part 2: Flow capacity - Section One: Sizing equations for incompressible fluid flow under installed conditions

EN 60534-2-2 (June 1993), Part 2: Flow capacity - Section Two: Sizing equations for compressible fluid flow under installed conditions

EN 60534-2-3 (June 1993), Part 2: Flow capacity - Section Three: Test procedure

EN 60534-8-2 (June 1993), Part 8: Noise considerations - Section Two: Laboratory measurement of noise generated by hydrodynamic flow through control valves

EN 60534-8-3 (February 1996), Part 8: Noise considerations - Section Three: Control valve aerodynamic noise prediction method

EN 60534-8-4 (August 1994), Part 8: Noise considerations - Section Four: Prediction of noise generated by hydrodynamic flow

European Material Standards

EN 10213-1 (February 1996), Technical conditions of delivery of

steel castings for pressure purposes -
Part 1: General

EN 10213-2 (February 1996),
Technical conditions of delivery of
steel castings for pressure purposes -
Part 2: Steel grades for use at room
temperature and elevated
temperatures

EN 10213-3 (February 1996),
Technical conditions of delivery of
steel castings for pressure purposes -
Part 3: Steel grades for use at low
temperatures

EN 10213-4 (February 1996),
Technical conditions of delivery of
steel castings for pressure purposes -
Part 4: Austenitic and austeno-ferritic
steel grades

EN 10222-1, Technical conditions of
delivery of steel forgings for pressure
purposes - Part 1: General (in
preparation)

EN 10222-2, Technical conditions of
delivery of steel forgings for pressure
purposes - Part 2: Ferritic and
martensitic steels for use at elevated
temperatures (in preparation)

EN 10222-3, Technical conditions of
delivery of steel forgings for pressure
purposes - Part 3: Nickel steel for low
temperature (in preparation)

EN 10222-4, Technical conditions of
delivery of steel forgings for pressure
purposes - Part 4: Fine grain steel (in
preparation)

EN 10222-5, Technical conditions of
delivery of steel forgings for pressure
purposes - Part 5: Austenitic
martensitic and austeno-ferritic
stainless steel (in preparation)

European Flange Standards

EN 1092-1, Part 1: Steel flanges PN
designated (in preparation)

EN 1092-2 (September 1997), Part 2:
Cast iron flanges PN designated

EN 1759-1, Part 1: Steel flanges
Class designated (in preparation)

Fluid Controls Institute (FCI)

70-2-1991, Control Valve Seat
Leakage

Instrument Society of America (ISA)

S51.1-1976 (R 1993), Process
Instrumentation Terminology

S75.01-1985 (R 1995), Flow
Equations for Sizing Control Valves

S75.02-1996, Control Valve Capacity
Test Procedures

S75.03-1992, Face-to-Face
Dimensions for Flanged Globe-Style
Control Valve Bodies (Classes 125,
150, 250, 300, and 600)

S75.04-1995, Face-to-Face
Dimensions for Flangeless Control
Valves (Classes 150, 300, and 600)

S75.05-1983, Terminology

S75.07-1987, Laboratory
Measurement of Aerodynamic Noise
Generated by Control Valves

S75.08-1985, Installed Face-to-Face
Dimensions for Flanged Clamp or
Pinch Valves

S75.11-1985 (R 1991), Inherent Flow
Characteristic and Rangeability of
Control Valves

S75.12-1993, Face-to-Face
Dimensions for Socket Weld-End and
Screwed-End Globe-Style Control
Valves (Classes 150, 300, 600, 900,
1500, and 2500)

S75.13-1996, Method of Evaluating
the Performance of Positioners with
Analog Input Signals

S75.14-1993, Face-to-Face
Dimensions for Buttweld-End
Globe-Style Control Valves (Class
4500)

S75.15-1993, Face-to-Face
Dimensions for Buttweld-End
Globe-Style Control Valves (Classes
150, 300, 600, 900, 1500, and 2500)

S75.16-1993, Face-to-Face
Dimensions for Flanged Globe-Style

Control Valve Bodies (Classes 900, 1500, and 2500)

S75.17-1991, Control Valve Aerodynamic Noise Prediction

S75.19-1995, Hydrostatic Testing of Control Valves

S75.20-1991, Face-to-Face Dimensions for Separable Flanged Globe-Style Control Valves (Classes 150, 300, and 600)

S75.22-1992, Face-to-Centerline Dimensions for Flanged Globe-Style Angle Control Valve Bodies (Classes 150, 300, and 600)

RP75.23-1995, Considerations for Evaluating Control Valve Cavitation

International Electrotechnical Commission (IEC)

There are 15 International Electro-technical Commission (IEC) standards for control valves, several of which are based on ISA standards. The IEC encourages national committees to adopt them and to withdraw any corresponding national standards. IEC standards are increasingly being applied by manufacturers and purchasers. Below is a list of IEC industrial-process control valve standards (60534 series).

60534-1 (1987), Part 1: Control valve terminology and general considerations

60534-2 (1978), Part 2: Flow capacity - Section One: Sizing equations for incompressible fluid flow under installed conditions (based on ISA S75.01)

60534-2-2 (1980), Part 2: Flow capacity - Section Two: Sizing equations for compressible fluid flow under installed conditions (based on ISA S75.01)

60534-2-3 (1997), Part 2: Flow capacity - Section Three: Test procedures (based on ISA S75.02)

60534-2-4 (1989), Part 2: Flow capacity - Section Four: Inherent flow characteristics and rangeability (based on ISA S75.11)

60534-3 (1976), Part 3: Dimensions - Section One: Face-to-face dimensions for flanged, two-way, globe-type control valves (based on ISA S75.03)

60534-3-2 (1984), Part 3: Dimensions - Section Two: Face-to-face dimensions for flangeless control valves except wafer butterfly valves (identical to ISA S75.04)

60534-4 (1982), Part 4: Inspection and routine testing (Plus Amendment No. 1, 1986)

60534-5 (1982), Part 5: Marking

60534-6-1 (1997), Part 6: Mounting details for attachment of positioners to control valve actuators - Section One: Positioner mounting on linear actuators

60534-6-2, Part 6: Mounting details for attachment of positioners to control valve actuators - Section Two: Positioner mounting on rotary actuators (in preparation)

60534-7 (1989), Part 7: Control valve data sheet

60534-8-1 (1986), Part 8: Noise considerations - Section One: Laboratory measurement of noise generated by aerodynamic flow through control valves (based on ISA S75.07)

60534-8-2 (1991), Part 8: Noise considerations - Section Two: Laboratory measurement of noise generated by hydrodynamic flow through control valves

60534-8-3 (1995), Part 8: Noise considerations - Section Three: Control valve aerodynamic noise prediction method (based on ISA S75.17)

60534-8-4 (1994), Part 8: Noise considerations - Section Four: Prediction of noise generated by hydrodynamic flow

International Standards Organization (ISO)

5752 (1982), Metal valves for use in flanged pipe systems - Face-to-face and centre-to-face dimensions

7005-1 (1992), Metallic flanges - Part 1: Steel flanges

7005-2 (1988), Metallic flanges - Part 2: Cast iron flanges

7005-3 (1988), Metallic flanges - Part 3: Copper alloy and composite flanges

Manufacturers Standardization Society (MSS)

SP-6-1996, Standard Finishes for Contact Faces of Pipe Flanges and Connecting-End Flanges of Valves and Fittings

SP-25-1993, Standard Marking System for Valves, Fittings, Flanges and Unions

SP-44-1996, Steel Pipe Line Flanges

SP-67-1995, Butterfly Valves

SP-68-1997, High Pressure Butterfly Valves with Offset Design

NACE International

MR0175-97, Standard Material Requirements - Sulfide Stress Cracking Resistant Metallic Materials for Oilfield Equipment

Product Approvals for Hazardous (Classified) Locations

References

Canadian Standards Association (CSA) Standards

C22.1-1994, Canadian Electrical Code (CEC)

C22.2 No. 94-M91, Special Industrial Enclosures

European Committee for Electrotechnical Standardization (CENELEC) Standards

EN 50014-1993, Electrical apparatus for potentially explosive atmospheres—General requirements

Instrument Society of America (ISA) Standards

S12.1-1991, Definitions and Information Pertaining to Electrical Instruments in Hazardous (Classified) Locations

International Electrotechnical Commission (IEC) Standards

60079-4 (1975), Electrical apparatus for explosive gas atmospheres. Part 4: Method of test for ignition temperature

60529 (1989), Degrees of protection provided by enclosures (IP Code)

National Electrical Manufacturer's Association (NEMA) Standards

250-1991, Enclosures for Electrical Equipment (1000 Volts Maximum)

National Fire Protection Association (NFPA) Standards

70-1996, National Electric Code (NEC)

497M-1991, Classification of Gases, Vapors and Dusts for Electrical Equipment in Hazardous (Classified) Locations

North American Approvals

The National Electric Code (NEC) in the United States and the Canadian Electric Code (CEC) require that electrical equipment used in hazardous locations carry the appropriate approval from a recognized approval agency.

Approval Agencies

The three main approval agencies in North America are Factory Mutual

(FM) and Underwriters Laboratories (UL) in the United States and Canadian Standards Association (CSA) in Canada.

Types of Protection

The types of protection commonly used for instruments in North America are:

• **Dust Ignition–proof:** A type of protection that excludes ignitable amounts of dust or amounts that might affect performance or rating and that, when installed and protected in accordance with the original design intent, will not allow arcs, sparks or heat otherwise generated or liberated inside the enclosure to cause ignition of exterior accumulations or atmospheric suspensions of a specified dust.

• **Explosion–proof:** A type of protection that utilizes an enclosure that is capable of withstanding an explosion of a gas or vapor within it and of preventing the ignition of an explosive gas or vapor that may surround it and that operates at such an external temperature that a surrounding explosive gas or vapor will not be ignited thereby.

• **Intrinsically Safe:** A type of protection in which the electrical equipment under normal or abnormal conditions is incapable of releasing sufficient electrical or thermal energy to cause ignition of a specific hazardous atmospheric mixture in its most easily ignitable concentration.

• **Non–Incendive:** A type of protection in which the equipment is incapable, under normal conditions, of causing ignition of a specified flammable gas or vapor-in-air mixture due to arcing or thermal effect.

Nomenclature

Approval agencies within North America classify equipment to be used in

hazardous locations by specifying the location as being Class I or II; Division 1 or 2; Groups A, B, C, D, E, F, or G; and Temperature Code T1 through T6. These designations are defined in the NEC and CEC, as well as the following paragraphs. The approval consists of the type of protection and the class, division, groups, and temperature, e.g. Class I, Division 1, Groups A, B, C, D, T6.

Hazardous Location Classification

Hazardous areas in North America are classified by class, division, and group.

Note

The method of classifying locations as zones instead of divisions was introduced into the 1996 edition of the NEC as an alternate method, but it is not yet in use. The zone method is common in Europe and most other countries.

Class: The Class defines the general nature of the hazardous material in the surrounding atmosphere.

• **Class I**—Locations in which flammable gases or vapors are, or may be, present in the air in quantities sufficient to produce explosive or ignitable mixtures.

• **Class II**—Locations that are hazardous because of the presence of combustible dusts.

• **Class III**—Locations in which easily ignitable fibers or flyings may be present but not likely to be in suspension in sufficient quantities to product ignitable mixtures.

Division: The Division defines the probability of hazardous material being present in an ignitable concentration in the surrounding atmosphere.

See ISA S12.1 for more detailed definitions.

• **Division 1**: Locations in which the probability of the atmosphere being hazardous is high due to flammable material being present continuously, intermittently, or periodically.

• **Division 2**: Locations that are presumed to be hazardous only in an abnormal situation.

Group: The Group defines the hazardous material in the surrounding atmosphere. The specific hazardous materials within each group and their automatic ignition temperatures can be found in Article 500 of the NEC and in NFPA 497M. Groups A, B, C and D apply to Class I, and Groups E, F and G apply to Class II locations. The following definitions are from the NEC.

• **Group A:** Atmospheres containing acetylene.

• **Group B:** Atmospheres containing hydrogen, fuel and combustible process gases containing more than 30 percent hydrogen by volume, or gases or vapors of equivalent hazard such as butadiene, ethylene oxide, propylene oxide, and acrolein.

• **Group C:** Atmospheres such as ethyl ether, ethylene, or gases or vapors of equivalent hazard.

• **Group D:** Atmospheres such as acetone, ammonia, benzene, butane, cyclopropane, ethanol, gasoline, hexane, methanol, methane, natural gas, naphtha, propane, or gases or vapors of equivalent hazard.

• **Group E:** Atmospheres containing combustible metal dusts, including aluminum, magnesium, and their commercial alloy, or other combustible dusts whose particle size, abrasiveness, and conductivity present similar hazards in the use of electrical equipment.

• **Group F:** Atmospheres containing combustible carbonaceous dusts, including carbon black, charcoal, coal, or dusts that have been sensitized by other materials so that they present an explosion hazard.

• **Group G:** Atmospheres containing combustible dusts not included in Group E or F, including flour, grain, wood, plastic, and chemicals.

Temperature Code

A mixture of hazardous gases and air may be ignited by coming into contact with a hot surface. The conditions under which a hot surface will ignite a gas depend on surface area, temperature, and the concentration of the gas.

The approval agencies test and establish maximum temperature ratings for the different equipment submitted for approval. Equipment that has been tested receives a temperature code that indicates the maximum surface temperature attained by the equipment. The following is a list of the different temperature codes:

Class 1	Division 1	Groups ABCD	T4
Hazard Type	Area Classification	Gas or Dust Group	Temperature Code

North American Temperature Codes

TEMPER-ATURE CODE	MAXIMUM SURFACE TEMPERATURE	
	°C	°F
T1	450	842
T2	300	572
T2A	280	536
T2B	260	500
T2C	230	446
T2D	215	419
T3	200	392
T3A	180	356
T3B	165	329
T3C	160	320
T4	135	275
T4A	120	248
T5	100	212
T6	85	185

The NEC states that any equipment that does not exceed a maximum surface temperature of 100 °C (212 °F) [based on 40 °C (104 °F) ambient temperature] is not required to be marked with the temperature code. Therefore, when a temperature code is not specified on the approved apparatus, it is assumed to be T5.

NEMA Enclosure Rating

Enclosures may be tested to determine their ability to prevent the ingress of liquids and dusts. In the United States, equipment is tested to NEMA 250. Some of the more common enclosure ratings defined in NEMA 250 are as follows.

General Locations

• **Type 3 (Dust-tight, Rain-tight, or Ice-resistance, Outdoor enclosure):** Intended for outdoor use primarily to provide a degree of protection against rain, sleet, windblown dust, and damage from external ice formation.

• **Type 3R (Rain-proof, Ice-resistance, Outdoor enclosure):** Intended for outdoor use primarily to provide a degree of protection against rain, sleet, and damage from external ice formation.

• **Type 3S (Dust-tight, Rain-tight, Ice-proof, Outdoor enclosure):** Intended for outdoor use primarily to provide a degree of protection against rain, sleet, windblown dust, and to provide for operation of external mechanisms when ice ladened.

• **Type 4 (Water-tight, Dust-tight, Ice-resistant, Indoor or outdoor enclosure):** Intended for indoor or outdoor use primarily to provide a degree of protection against windblown dust and rain, splashing water, hose-directed water, and damage from external ice formation.

• **Type 4X (Water-tight, Dust-tight, Corrosion resistant, Indoor or outdoor enclosure):** Intended for indoor or outdoor use primarily to provide a degree of protection against corrosion, windblown dust and rain, splashing water, and hose-directed water, and damage from external ice formation.

Hazardous (Classified) Locations

Two of the four enclosure ratings for hazardous (classified) locations are described as follows in NEMA 250:

• **Type 7 (Class I, Division 1, Group A, B, C or D, Indoor hazardous location, Enclosure):** For indoor use in locations classified as Class I, Division 1, Groups A, B, C or D as defined in the NEC and shall be marked to show class, division, and group. Type 7 enclosures shall be capable of withstanding the pressures resulting from an internal explosion of specified gases, and contain such an explosion sufficient that an explosive gas-air mixture existing in the atmosphere surrounding the enclosure will not be ignited.

• **Type 9 (Class II, Division 1, Groups E, F or G, Indoor hazardous location, Enclosure):** Intended for use in indoor locations classified as Class II, Division 1, Groups E, F and G as defined in the NEC and shall be marked to show class, division, and group. Type 9 enclosures shall be capable of preventing the entrance of dust.

The above two NEMA ratings are often misunderstood. For example, the above definition of Type 7 is essentially the same as that for explosion–proof. Therefore, when an approval agency approves equipment as explosion–proof and suitable for Class I, Division 1, the equipment automatically satisfies the Type 7 requirement; however, the agency does not require that the equipment be labeled Type 7. Instead it is labeled as suitable for Class I, Division 1. Similarly, Type 9 enclosures would be labeled as suitable for Class II, Division 1.

CSA Enclosure Ratings

CSA enclosure ratings are defined in CSA C22.2, No. 94. They are similar to the NEMA ratings and are designated as type numbers; for example, Type 4. Previously they were designated with the prefix CSA ENC (for example, CSA ENC 4).

Intrinsically Safe Apparatus

Intrinsically safe apparatus must be installed with barriers that limit the electrical energy into the equipment. Two methods determine acceptable combinations of intrinsically safe apparatus and connected associated apparatus (for example, barriers) that have not been investigated in such combination: entity concept and system parameter concept.

Entity Concept

The entity concept specifies four parameters: voltage, current, capaci-

tance, and inductance. The length of cable connecting intrinsically safe equipment with associated equipment may be limited because of the energy storing characteristics of cable. The entity parameters are:

V_{max} = maximum voltage that may safely be applied to the intrinsically safe apparatus.

I_{max} = maximum current which may safely be applied to the terminals of the intrinsically safe apparatus

C_i = internal unprotected capacitance of the intrinsically safe apparatus that can appear at the terminals of the device under fault conditions

L_i = internal unprotected inductance of the intrinsically safe apparatus that can appear at the terminals of the device under fault conditions

Barriers used with the intrinsically safe apparatus must meet the following conditions, which are noted on the loop schematic (control drawing).

V_{max} must be greater than V_{oc} or V_t

I_{max} must be greater than I_{sc} or I_t

C_a must be less than $(C_i + C_{cable})$

L_a must be less than $(L_i + L_{cable})$

where:

V_{oc} or V_t = maximum open circuit voltage, under fault conditions, of the associated apparatus (barrier). For multiple associated apparatus, FM uses the maximum combination of voltage V_t in place of V_{oc}.

I_{sc} or I_t = maximum short circuit current that can be delivered under fault conditions by the associated apparatus. For multiple associated apparatus, FM uses the combination of current I_t in place of I_{sc}

C_a = maximum capacitance that can safely be connected to the associated apparatus

L_a = maximum inductance that can safely be connected to the associated apparatus

C_{cable} = capacitance of connecting cable

L_{cable} = inductance of connecting cable

The entity parameters are listed on the loop schematic (control drawing). The entity concept is used by FM and UL and will be used by CSA if requested.

CSA System Parameter Concept

The parametric concept is only used by CSA. For an intrinsically safe apparatus, the parameters are:

- The maximum hazardous location voltage that may be connected to the apparatus.

- The minimum resistance in ohms of the barrier that may be connected to the apparatus.

- CSA will also investigate specific barriers, which may be listed on the loop schematic along with the parametric rating.

Loop Schematic (Control Drawing)

Article 504 of the NEC specifically requires intrinsically safe and associated apparatus to have a control drawing that details the allowed interconnections between the intrinsically safe and associated apparatus. This drawing may also be referred to as a loop schematic. The drawing number is referenced on the apparatus nameplate and is available to the user. It must include the following information:

- **Wiring diagram:** The drawing shall contain a diagram of the apparatus showing all intrinsically safe terminal connections. For intrinsically safe apparatus, all associated apparatus must be defined either by specific equipment identification or by entity parameters.

- **Entity parameters:** The entity parameters (or system parameters in case of CSA) shall be supplied in a table showing allowable values for each applicable Class and Group.

- **Hazard location identification:** A demarcation line shall be provided on the drawing to show the equipment in the hazardous location and the non-hazardous location. The Class, Division, and Group of the hazardous location should be identified.

- **Equipment identification:** The equipment shall be identified by model, part number, etc. to permit positive identification.

- **Division 2:** Division 2 installation requirements for FM approved equipment shall be shown.

Comparison of Protection Techniques

Explosion–proof Technique:

This technique is implemented by enclosing all electrical circuits in housings and conduits strong enough to contain any explosion or fires that may take place inside the apparatus.

Advantages of this Technique

- Users are familiar with this technique and understand its principles and applications.

- Sturdy housing designs provide protection to the internal components of the apparatus and allow their application in hazardous environments.

- An explosion–proof housing is usually weather–proof as well.

Disadvantages of this Technique

- Circuits must be de-energized or location rendered nonhazardous before housing covers may be removed.

- Opening of the housing in a hazardous area voids all protection.

• Generally this technique requires use of heavy bolted or screwed enclosures.

Installation Requirements

• The user has responsibility for following proper installation procedures. (Refer to local and national electrical codes.)

• Installation requirements are listed in Article 501 of the NEC or Article 18-106 of the CEC.

• All electrical wiring leading to the field instrument must be installed using threaded rigid metal conduit, threaded steel intermediate metal conduit, or Type MI cable.

• Conduit seals may be required within 18 inches of the field instrument to maintain the explosion–proof rating and reduce the pressure piling effect on the housing.

Intrinsically Safe Technique:

This technique operates by limiting the electrical energy available in circuits and equipment to levels that are too low to ignite the most easily ignitable mixtures of a hazardous area.

Advantages of this Technique

• This technique offers lower cost. No rigid metal conduit or armored cable are required for field wiring of the instrument.

• Greater flexibility is offered since this technique permits simple components such as switches, contact closures, thermocouples, RTD's, and other non-energy-storing instruments to be used without certification but with appropriate barriers.

• Ease of field maintenance and repair are advantages. There is no need to remove power before adjustments or calibration are performed on the field instrument. The system re-

mains safe even if the instrument is damaged, because the energy level is too low to ignite most easily ignitable mixtures. Diagnostic and calibration instruments must have the appropriate approvals for hazardous areas.

Disadvantages of this Technique

• This technique requires the use of intrinsically safe barriers to limit the current and voltage between the hazardous and safe areas to avoid development of sparks or hot spots in the circuitry of the instrument under fault conditions.

• High energy consumption applications are not applicable to this technique, because the energy is limited at the source (or barrier). This technique is limited to low-energy applications such as DC circuits, electropneumatic converters, etc.

Dust Ignition–proof Technique:

This technique results in an enclosure that will exclude ignitable amounts of dusts and will not permit arcs, sparks, or heat otherwise generated inside the enclosure to cause ignition of exterior accumulations or atmospheric suspension of a specified dust on or near the enclosure.

Non–Incendive Technique:

This technique allows for the incorporation of circuits in electrical instruments that are not capable of igniting specific flammable gases or vapor-in-air mixtures under normal operating conditions.

Advantages of this Technique

• This technique uses electronic equipment that normally does not develop high temperatures or produce sparks strong enough to ignite the hazardous environment.

• There is lower cost than other hazardous environment protection techniques, because there is no need for explosion–proof housings or energy limiting barriers.

● For non–incendive circuits, the NEC permits any of the wiring methods suitable for wiring in ordinary locations.

Disadvantages of this Technique

● This technique is limited to Division 2 applications only.

● This technique places constraint on control room to limit energy to field wiring (normal operation is open, short or grounding of field wiring) so that

arcs or sparks under normal operation will not have enough energy to cause ignition.

● Both the field instrument and control room device may require more stringent labeling.

European and Asia/Pacific Approvals

Approval Agencies

Some of the common approval agencies in Europe and Asia/Pacific are listed below:

Approval Agencies

Location	Abbreviation	Agency
United Kingdom	BASEEFA	British Approvals Service for Electrical Equipment in Flammable Atmospheres
Germany	PTB	Physikalische-Technische Bundesanstalt
France	LCIE	Laboratorie Central des Industries Electriques
Australia	SAA	Standards Association of Australia
Japan	JTIISA	Japanese Technical Institution of Industry Safety Association

CENELEC Approvals

CENELEC is the acronym for European Committee for Electrotechnical Standardization. CENELEC standards are applicable to all European Union countries plus other countries that choose to use them. A piece of equipment that is successfully tested to the relevant CENELEC standard has CENELEC approval. The testing may be performed by any recognized testing laboratory in Europe. Approvals may be based on national standards, but CENELEC approvals are preferred.

Types of Protection

The types of protection commonly used outside North America are:

Flame–proof:

● A type of protection in which an enclosure can withstand the pressure developed during an internal explosion of an explosive mixture and that prevents the transmission of the ex-

plosion to the explosive atmosphere surrounding the enclosure and that operates at such an external temperature that a surrounding explosive gas or vapor will not be ignite there. This type of protection is similar to explosion–proof. It is referred to by IEC as Ex d.

Increased Safety:

● A type of protection in which various measures are applied to reduce the probability of excessive temperatures and the occurrence of arcs or sparks in the interior and on the external parts of electrical apparatus that do not produce them in normal service. Increased safety may be used with the flameproof type of protection. This type of protection is referred to by IEC as Ex e.

Intrinsically Safe:

● A type of protection in which the electrical equipment under normal or abnormal conditions is incapable of releasing sufficient electrical or ther-

186

mal energy to cause ignition of a specific hazardous atmospheric mixture in its most easily ignitable concentration. This type of protection is referred to by IEC as Ex i.

Non–Incendive:

• A type of protection in which the equipment is incapable, under normal conditions, of causing ignition of a specified flammable gas or vapor-in-air mixture due to arcing or thermal effect. This type of protection is referred to by IEC as Ex n.

Nomenclature

Approval agencies that use the IEC nomenclature (for example, BASE-EFA, LCIE, PTB, and SAA) classify equipment to be used in hazardous locations by specifying the type of protection, gas group, and temperature code as follows:

E	Ex	ia	IIC	T4
Denotes CENELEC Approval	Denotes Hazardous Area Approval	Types of Protection ia—Intrinsic safety (2 faults allowed) ib—Intrinsic safety (1 fault allowed) d—Flameproof e—Increased safety n—Type n (non–incendive) (SAA only) N—Type N (non–incendive) (BASEEFA only)	Group	Temperature Code

For CENELEC approvals, the nameplate must also include the following symbol to indicate explosion protection:

This mark indicates compliance with CENELEC requirements and is recognized by all European Union member countries.

Hazardous Location Classification

Hazardous locations outside North America are classified by gas group and zone.

Group

Electrical equipment is divided into two groups. Group I covers electrical equipment used in mines, and Group II covers all other electrical equipment. Group II is further subdivided into three subgroups: A, B, and C. The specific hazardous materials within each group can be found in CENELEC EN 50014, and the automatic ignition temperatures for some of these materials can be found in IEC 60079-4.

• **Group I (Mining):** Atmospheres containing methane, or gases or vapors of equivalent hazard.

• **Group IIA:** Atmospheres containing propane, or gases or vapors of equivalent hazard.

• **Group IIB:** Atmospheres containing ethylene, or gases or vapors of equivalent hazard.

• **Group IIC:** Atmospheres containing acetylene or hydrogen, or gases or vapors of equivalent hazard.

Note

An apparatus approved for one subgroup in Group II may be used in the subgroup below it; for example, Group IIC may be used in Group IIB locations.

Zone

The zone defines the probability of hazardous material being present in an ignitable concentration in the surrounding atmosphere:

• **Zone 0:** Location where an explosive concentration of a flammable gas or vapor mixture is continuously present or is present for long periods. The area classified as Zone 0, although not specifically defined, is contained within the United States and Canada classifications of a Division 1 location and constitutes an area with the highest probability that an ignitable mixture is present.

• **Zone 1:** Location where an explosive concentration of a flammable or explosive gas or vapor mixture is likely to occur in normal operation. The area classified as Zone 1 is contained within the United States and Canada classifications of a Division 1 location.

• **Zone 2:** Location in which an explosive concentration of a flammable or explosive gas or vapor mixture is unlikely to occur in normal operation and, if it does occur, will exist only for a short time. Zone 2 is basically equivalent to the United States and Canadian classifications of a Division 2 location.

Temperature Code

A mixture of hazardous gases and air may be ignited by coming into contact with a hot surface. The conditions under which a hot surface will ignite a gas depends on surface area, temperature, and the concentration of the gas.

The approval agencies test and establish maximum temperature ratings for the different equipment submitted for approval. Group II equipment that has been tested receives a temperature code that indicates the maximum surface temperature attained by the equipment. It is based on a 40 °C (104 °F) ambient temperature unless a higher ambient temperature is indicated.

IEC Temperature Codes

TEMPERATURE CODE	MAXIMUM SURFACE TEMPERATURE	
	°C	°F
T1	450	842
T2	300	572
T3	200	392
T4	135	275
T5	100	212
T6	85	185

IEC Enclosure Rating

According to IEC 60529, the degree of protection provided by an enclosure is indicated by the IP Code. The code consists of the letters IP (ingress protection) followed by two characteristic numerals indicating conformity with the degree of protection desired (for example, IP54). The first numeral indicates the degree of protection against the following: human contact with or approach to live parts; human contact with moving parts inside the enclosure; and ingress of solid foreign objects. The second numeral indicates the degree of protection provided by the enclosure against the ingress of water. The characteristic numerals are defined in the following table:

NEMA and IEC Enclosure Rating Comparison

The following table provides an equivalent conversion from NEMA type numbers to IEC IP designations. The

NEMA types meet or exceed the test requirements for the associated IEC classifications; for this reason, the table cannot be used to convert from IEC classification to NEMA types.

Conversion of NEMA Types to IEC IP Codes

NEMA Type	IEC IP
3	IP54
3R	IP14
3S	IP54
4 and 4X	IP65

Ingress Protection (IP) Codes

First Numeral Protection against solid bodies	Second Numeral Protection against liquid
0 No protection	0 No protection
1 Objects greater than 50 mm	1 Vertically dripping water
2 Objects greater than 12 mm	2 Angled dripping water (75° to 90°)
3 Objects greater than 2.5 mm	3 Sprayed water
4 Objects greater than 1.0 mm	4 Splashed water
5 Dust-protected	5 Water jets
6 Dust-tight	6 Heavy seas
- -	7 Effects of immersion
- -	8 Indefinite immersion

Comparison of Protection Techniques

Flame–proof Technique:

This technique is implemented by enclosing all electrical circuits in housing and conduits strong enough to contain any explosion or fires that may take place inside the apparatus.

Advantages of this Technique

• Users are familiar with this technique and understand its principles and applications.

• Sturdy housing designs provide protection to the internal components of the apparatus and allow their application in hazardous environments.

• A flame–proof housing is usually weather–proof as well.

Disadvantages of this Technique

• Circuits must be de-energized or location rendered nonhazardous before housing covers may be removed.

• Opening of the housing in a hazardous area voids all protection.

• This technique generally requires use of heavy bolted or screwed enclosures.

Increased Safety Technique:

The increased safety technique incorporates special measures to reduce the probability of excessive temperatures and the occurrence of arcs or sparks in normal service.

Advantages of this Technique

• Increased safety enclosures provide at least IP54 enclosure protection.

• Installation and maintenance are easier for flameproof enclosures.

• This technique offers significantly reduced wiring costs over flameproof installations.

Disadvantages of this Technique

• This technique is limited in the
apparatus for which it may be used. It
is normally used for apparatus such
as terminal boxes and compartments.

Intrinsically Safe Technique:

This technique requires the use of intrinsically safe barriers to limit the current and voltage between the hazardous and safe areas to avoid the
development of sparks or hot spots in
the circuitry of the instrument under
fault conditions.

Advantages of this Technique

• This technique costs less because of less stringent rules for field
wiring of the apparatus.

• Greater flexibility is offered because this technique permits simple
components such as switches, contact closures, thermocouples, RTD's,
and other non-energy-storing apparatus to be used without special certification but with appropriate barriers.

• Ease of field maintenance and
repair characterize this technique.
There is no need to remove power before adjustments or calibration are
performed on the field instrument. The
system remains safe even if the instrument is damaged, because the
energy level is too low to ignite most
easily ignitable mixtures. Diagnostics
and calibration instruments must have
the appropriate approvals for hazardous areas.

Disadvantages of this Technique

• High energy consumption applications are not applicable to this
technique because the energy is limited at the source (or barrier). This
technique is limited to low-energy applications such as DC circuits, electro-
pneumatic converters, etc.

Type n Technique:

This technique allows for the incorporation of circuits in electrical instruments that are not capable of igniting
specific flammable gases or vapor-in-
air mixtures under normal operating
conditions. This type of protection is
not available from CENELEC.

Advantages of this Technique

• This technique uses electronic
equipment that normally does not develop high temperatures or produce
sparks strong enough to ignite the
hazardous environment.

• Cost is lower than other hazardous environment protection techniques because there is no need for
flameproof housings or energy limiting
barriers.

• This technique provides a degree of protection of IP54.

Disadvantages of this Technique

• This technique is applicable to
Zone 2 locations only.

• Constraints are placed on control room to limit energy to field wiring
(normal operation is open, short or
grounding of field wiring) so that arcs
or sparks under normal operation will
not have enough energy to cause ignition.

Chapter 10

Engineering Data

Standard Specifications For Valve Materials

(See table following this listing for additional specifications, cross-referenced to Material Code numbers.)

1. Cast Carbon Steel
ASTM A216 Grade WCC
Temp. range = −20 to 800°F (−29 to 427°C)
Composition (Percent)
C	0.25 max
Mn	1.2 max
P	0.04 max
S	0.045 max
Si	0.6 max

2. Cast Carbon Steel
ASTM A352 Grade LCC
Temp. range = −50 to 700°F (−46 to 371°C)

Composition – Same as ASTM A216 grade WCC

3. Carbon Steel Bar
AISI 1018, UNS G10180
Temp. range = −20 to 800°F (−29 to 427°C)
Composition (Percent)
C	0.15 to 0.2
Mn	0.6 to 0.9
P	0.04 max
S	0.05 max

4. Leaded Steel Bar
AISI 12L14, UNS G12144
Temp. range = −20 to 800°F (−29 to 427°C)
Composition (Percent)
C	0.15 max
Mn	0.85 to 1.15
P	0.04 to 0.09
S	0.26 to 0.35
Pb	0.15 to 0.35

5. AISI 4140 Cr-Mo Steel (Similar to ASTM A193 Grade B7 bolt material)

Temp. range = −20°F (−29°C) to 100°F (56°C) less than tempering temperature to a maximum of 1000°F (593°C).

Composition (Percent)

C	0.38 to 0.43
Mn	0.75 to 1.0
P	0.035 max
S	0.035 max
Si	0.15 to 0.35
Cr	0.8 to 1.1
Mo	0.15 to 0.25
Fe	Remainder

6. Forged 3-1/2% Nickel Steel ASTM A352 Grade LC3

Temp. range = −150 to 650°F (−101 to 343°C)

Composition (Percent)

C	0.15 max
Mn	0.5 to 0.8
P	0.04 max
S	0.045 max
Si	0.6 max
Ni	3.0 to 4.0

7. Cast Cr-Mo Steel ASTM A217 Grade WC6

Temp. range = −20 to 1100°F (−29 to 593°C)

Composition (Percent)

C	0.05 to 0.2
Mn	0.5 to 0.8
P	0.04 max
S	0.045 max
Si	0.60 max
Cr	1.0 to 1.5
Mo	0.45 to 0.65

8. Cast Cr-Mo Steel ASTM A217 Grade WC9

Temp. range = −20 to 1100°F (−29 to 593°C)

Composition (Percent)

C	0.05 to 0.18
Mn	0.4 to 0.7
P	0.04 max
S	0.045 max
Si	0.6 max
Cr	2.0 to 2.75
Mo	0.9 to 1.2

9. Forged Cr-Mo Steel ASTM A182 Grade F22

Temp. range = −20 to 1100°F (−29 to 593°C)

Composition (Percent)

C	0.05 to 0.15
Mn	0.3 to 0.6
P	0.04 max
S	0.04 max
Si	0.5 max
Cr	2.0 to 2.5
Mo	0.87 to 1.13

10. Cast Cr-Mo Steel ASTM A217 Grade C5

Temp. range = −20 to 1200°F (−29 to 649°C)

Composition (Percent)

C	0.2 max
Mn	0.4 to 0.7
P	0.04 max
S	0.045 max
Si	0.75 max
Cr	4.0 to 6.5
Mo	0.45 to 0.65

11. Type 302 Stainless Steel ASTM A479 Grade UNS S30200

Temp. range = −325 to 1500°F (−198 to 816°C)

Composition (Percent)

C	0.15 max
Mn	2.0 max
P	0.045 max
S	0.03 max
Si	1.0 max
Cr	17.0 to 19.0
Ni	8.0 to 10.0
N	0.1 max
Fe	Remainder

12. Type 304L Stainless Steel ASTM A479 Grade UNS S30403

Temp. range = −425 to 800°F (−254 to 427°C)

Composition (Percent)

C	0.03 max
Mn	2.0 max
P	0.045 max
S	0.03 max
Si	1.0 max
Cr	18.0 to 20.0
Ni	8.0 to 12.0

N   0.1 max
Fe   Remainder

13. Cast Type 304L Stainless Steel ASTM A351 Grade CF3
Temp. range = −425 to 800°F (−254 to 427°C)
Composition (Percent)
C   0.03 max
Mn   1.5 max
Si   2.0 max
S   0.03 max
P   0.045 max
Cr   18.0 to 21.0
Ni   8.0 to 11.0
Mo   0.50 max

14. Type 316L Stainless Steel ASTM A479 Grade UNS S31603
Temp. range = −425 to 850°F (−254 to 454°C)
Composition (Percent)
C   0.03 max
Mn   2.0 max
P   0.045 max
S   0.03 max
Si   1.0 max
Cr   16.0 to 18.0
Ni   10.0 to 14.0
Mo   2.0 to 3.0
N   0.1 max
Fe   Remainder

15. Type 316 Stainless Steel ASTM A479 Grade UNS S31600
Temp. range = −425 to 1500°F (−254 to 816°C); above 1000°F (538C), 0.04 C required
Composition (Percent)
C   0.08 max
Mn   2.0 max
P   0.045 max
S   0.03 max
Si   1.0 max
Cr   16.0 to 18.0
Ni   10.0 to14.0
Mo   2.0 to 3.0
N   0.1 max
Fe   Remainder

16. Cast Type 316 Stainless Steel ASTM A351 Grade CF8M
Temp. range = −425 to 1500°F (−254 to 816°C); above 1000°F (538C), 0.04 C required
Composition (Percent)
C   0.08 max
Mn   1.5 max
Si   1.5 max
P   0.04 max
S   0.04 max
Cr   18.0 to 21.0
Ni   9.0 to 12.0
Mo   2.0 to 3.0

17. Type 317 Stainless Steel ASTM A479 Grade UNS S31700
Temp. range = −425 to 1500°F (−254 to 816°C); above 1000°F (538C), 0.04 C required
Composition (Percent)
C   0.08 max
Mn   2.0 max
P   0.045 max
S   0.03 max
Si   1.0 max
Cr   18.0 to 20.0
Ni   11.0 to15.0
Mo   3.0 to 4.0
N   0.1 max
Fe   Remainder

18. Cast Type 317 Stainless Steel ASTM A351 Grade CG8M
Temp. range = −325 to 1000°F (−198 to 538°C); above 1000°F (538C), 0.04 C required
Composition (Percent)
C   0.08 max
Mn   1.5 max
Si   1.5 max
P   0.04 max
S   0.04 max
Cr   18.0 to 21.0
Ni   9.0 to 13.0
Mo   2.0 to 3.0

19. Type 410 Stainless Steel
ASTM A276 Grade S41000

Temp. range = Annealed condition,–20 to 1200°F (–29 to 649°C); Heat treated 38 HRC, –20 to 800°F (–29 to 427°C)

Composition (Percent)

C	0.15 max
Mn	1.0 max
P	0.04 max
S	0.03 max
Si	1.0 max
Cr	11.5 to 13.5
Fe	Remainder

20. Type 17-4PH Stainless Steel
ASTM A564 Grade 630, UNS S17400

Temp. range = –20 to 650°F (–29 to 343°C). Can be used to 800°F (427°C) for applications, such as cages, where stresses are generally compressive, and there is no impact loading.

Composition (Percent)

C	0.07 max
Mn	1.0 max
Si	1.0 max
P	0.04 max
S	0.03 max
Cr	15.0 to 17.5
Nb	0.15 to 0.45
Cu	3.0 to 5.0
Ni	3.0 to 5.0
Fe	Remainder

20. Type 254 SMO Stainless Steel
ASTM A479 Grade UNS S31254

Temp. range = –325 to 750°F (–198 to 399)°C

Composition (Percent)

C	0.02 max
Mn	1.0 max
P	0.03 max
S	0.01 max
Si	0.8 max
Cr	18.5 to 20.5
Ni	17.5 to 18.5
Mo	6.0 to 6.5
N	0.18–0.22
Fe	Remainder

22. Cast Type 254 SMO Stainless Steel
ASTM A351 Grade CK3MCuN

Temp. range = –325 to 750°F (–198 to 399°C)

Composition (Percent)

C	0.025 max
Mn	1.2 max
Si	1.0 max
P	0.044 max
S	0.01 max
Cr	19.5 to 20.5
Ni	17.5 to 19.5
Mo	6.0 to 7.0

23. Type 2205, S31803 Duplex Stainless Steel
ASTM A279 Grade UNS S31803

Temp. range = –20 to 600°F (–29 to 316°C)

Composition (Percent)

C	0.03 max
Mn	2.0 max
P	0.03 max
S	0.02 max
Si	1.0 max
Cr	21.0 to 23.0
Ni	4.5 to 6.5
Mo	2.5 to 3.5
N	0.03 to 0.2
Fe	Remainder

24. Cast Type 2205, S31803 Stainless Steel
ASTM A890 Grade 4a, CD3MN

Temp. range = –20 to 600°F (–29 to 316°C)

Composition (Percent)

C	0.03 max
Mn	1.5 max
Si	1.0 max
P	0.04 max
S	0.02 max
Cr	21.0 to 23.5
Ni	4.5 to 6.5
Mo	2.5 to 3.5
N	0.1 to 0.3
Fe	Remainder

25. Cast Iron
ASTM A126 Class B, UNS F12102
Temp. range = Pressure Retaining
  Components, −20 to 450°F (−29 to
  232°C); Non-Pressure Retaining
  Components, −100 to 800°F (73 to
  427°C); ANSI B31.5 −150°F
  (−101°C) minimum if the maximum
  stress does not exceed 40% of the
  ambient allowable stress.
Composition (Percent)
  P   0.75 max
  S   0.15 max

26. Cast Iron
ASTM A126 Class C, UNS F12802
Temp. range = Pressure Retaining
  Components, −20 to 450°F (−29 to
  232°C); Non-Pressure Retaining
  Components, −100 to 800°F (73 to
  427°C); ANSI B31.5 −150°F
  (−101°C) minimum if the maximum
  stress does not exceed 40% of the
  ambient allowable stress.
Composition (Percent)
  P   0.75 max
  S   0.15 max

27. Ductile Iron
ASTM A395 Type 60-40-18
Temp. range = −20 to 650°F (−29 to
  343°C)
Composition (Percent)
  C   3.0 min
  Si   2.5 max
  P   0.08 max

28. Ductile Ni-Resist Iron
ASTM A439 Type D-2B, UNS F43001
Temp. range = −20 to 1400°F (−29 to
  760°C)
Composition (Percent)
  C   3.0 min
  Si   1.5 to 3.00
  Mn   0.70 to 1.25
  P   0.08 max
  Ni   18.0 to 22.0
  Cr   2.75 to 4.0

29. Valve Bronze
ASTM B61, UNS C92200
Temp. range = −325 to 550°F (−198 to
  288°C)

Composition (Percent)
  Cu   86.0 to 90.0
  Sn   5.5 to 6.5
  Pb   1.0 to 2.0
  Zn   3.0 to 5.0
  Ni   1.0 max
  Fe   0.25 max
  S   0.05 max
  P   0.05 max

30. Tin Bronze
ASTM B564 Grade UNS C90500
Temp. range = −325 to 400°F (−198 to
  204°C)
Composition (Percent)
  Cu   86.0 to 89.0
  Sn   9.0 to 11.0
  Pb   0.30 max
  Zn   1.0 to 3.0
  Ni   1.0 max
  Fe   0.2 max
  S   0.05 max
  P   0.05 max

31. Manganese Bronze
ASTM B584 Grade UNS C86500
Temp. range = −325 to 350°F (−198 to
  177°C)
Composition (Percent)
  Cu   55.0 to 60.0
  Sn   1.0 max
  Pb   0.4 max
  Ni   1.0 max
  Fe   0.4 to 2.0
  Al   0.5 to 1.5
  Mn   0.1 to 1.5
  Zn   36.0 to 42.0

32. Cast Aluminum Bronze
ASTM B148 Grade UNS C95400
Temp. range = ANSI B31.1, B31.3,
  −325 to 500°F (−198 to 260°C);
  ASME Section VIII, −325 to 600°F
  (−198 to 316°C)
Composition (Percent)
  Cu   83.0 min
  Al   10.0 to 11.5
  Fe   3.0 to 5.0
  Mn   0.50 max
  Ni   1.5 max

33. Cast Aluminum Bronze
ASTM B148 Grade UNS C95800

Temp. range = –325 to 500°F (–198 to 260°C)

Composition (Percent)

Cu	79.0 min
Al	8.5 to 9.5
Fe	3.5 to 4.5
Mn	0.8 to 1.5
Ni	4.0 to 5.0
Si	0.1 max

34. B16 Yellow Brass Bar
ASTM B16 Grade UNS C36000, 1/2 Hard

Temp. range = Non-Pressure Retaining Components, –325 to 400°F (–198 to 204°C)

Composition (Percent)

Cu	60.0 to 63.0
Pb	2.5 to 3.7
Fe	0.35 max
Zn	Remainder

35. Naval Brass Forgings
ASTM B283 Alloy UNS C46400

Temp. range = –325 to 400°F (–198 to 204°C)

Composition (Percent)

Cu	59.0 to 62.0
Sn	0.5 to 1.0
Pb	0.2 max
Fe	0.15 max
Zn	Remainder

36. Aluminum Bar
ASTM B211 Alloy UNS A96061-T6

Temp. range = –452 to 400°F (–269 to 204°C)

Composition (Percent)

Si	0.4 to 0.8
Fe	0.7 max
Cu	0.15 to 0.4
Zn	0.25 max
Mg	0.8 to 1.2
Mn	0.15 max
Cr	0.04 to 0.35
Ti	0.15 max
Other Elements 0.15 max	
Al	Remainder

37. Cobalt-base Alloy No.6
Cast UNS R30006, Weld filler CoCr-A

Temp. range = –325 to 1500°F (–198 to 816°C)

Composition (Percent)

C	0.9 to 1.4
Mn	1.0 max
W	3.0 to 6.0
Ni	3.0
Cr	26.0 to 32.0
Mo	1.0 max
Fe	3.0 max
Si	2.0 max
Co	Remainder

38. Ni-Cu Alloy Bar K500
B865 Grade N05500

Temp. range = –325°F to 900°F (–198°C to 482°C)

Composition (Percent)

Ni	63.0 to 70.0
Fe	2.0 max
Mn	1.5 max
Si	0.5 max
C	0.25 max
S	0.01 max
P	0.02 max
Al	2.3 to 3.15
Ti	0.35 to 0.85
Cu	Remainder

39. Cast Ni-Cu Alloy 400
ASTM A494 Grade M35-1

Temp. range = –325 to 900°F (–198 to 482°C)

Composition (Percent)

Cu	26.0 to 33.0
C	0.35 max
Mn	1.5 max
Fe	3.5 max
S	0.03 max
P	0.03 max
Si	1.35 max
Nb	0.5 max
Ni	Remainder

40. Ni-Cr-Mo Alloy C276 Bar
ASTM B574 Grade N10276

Temp. range = –325 to 1250°F (–198 to 677°C)

Composition (Percent)

Cr	14.5 to 16.5
Fe	4.0 to 7.0
W	3.0 to 4.5
C	0.01 max
Si	0.08 max
Co	2.5 max
Mn	1.0 max
V	0.35 max
Mo	15.0 to 17.0
P	0.04
S	0.03
Ni	Remainder

41. Ni-Cr-Mo Alloy C
ASTM A494 CW2M

Temp. range = −325 to 1000°F (−198 to 538°C)

Composition (Percent)

Cr	15.5 to 17.5
Fe	2.0 max
W	1.0 max
C	0.02 max
Si	0.8 max
Mn	1.0 max
Mo	15.0 to 17.5
P	0.03
S	0.03
Ni	Remainder

42. Ni-Mo Alloy B2 Bar
ASTM B335 Grade B2, UNS N10665

Temp. range = −325 to 800°F (−198 to 427°C)

Composition (Percent)

Cr	1.0 max
Fe	2.0 max
C	0.02 max
Si	0.1 max
Co	1.0 max
Mn	1.0 max
Mo	26.0 to 30.0
P	0.04 max
S	0.03 max
Ni	Remainder

43. Cast Ni-Mo Alloy B2
ASTM A494 N7M

Temp. range = −325 to 1000°F (−198 to 538°C)

Composition (Percent)

Cr	1.0 max
Fe	3.0 max
C	0.07 max
Si	1.0 max
Mn	1.0 max
Mo	30.0 to 33.0
P	0.04 max
S	0.03 max
Ni	Remainder

Valve Materials Properties for Pressure–Containing Components

(The material codes in this table correspond to the previous Standard Specifications for Valve Materials listing.)

MATER-IAL CODE	MINIMUM MECHANICAL PROPERTIES				MODULUS OF ELASTICITY AT 70°F (21°C) PSI (MPa)	TYPICAL BRINELL HARDNESS
	Tensile Strength ksi (MPa)	Yield Strength ksi (MPa)	Elongation in 2-inch (50 mm)	Reduction in Area (%)		
1	70-95 (485-655)	40 (275)	22	35	27.9E6 (19.2E4)	137-187
2	70-95 (485-655)	40 (275)	22	35	27.9E6 (19.2E4)	137-187
3	57 (390) typical	42 (290) typical	37 typical	67 typical	- - -	111
4	79 (545) typical	71 (490) typical	16 typical	52 typical	- - -	163
5[(1)]	135 (930) typical	115 (792) typical	22 typical	63 typical	29.9E6 (20.6E4)	255
6	70-95 (485-655)	40 (275)	24	35	27.9E6 (19.2E4)	137
7	70-95 (485-655)	40 (275)	20	35	29.9E6 (20.6E4)	147-200

(continued)

Valve Materials Properties for Pressure–Containing Components (continued)
(The material codes in this table correspond to the previous Standard Specifications for Valve Materials listing.)

| MATER-IAL CODE | MINIMUM MECHANICAL PROPERTIES | | | | MODULUS OF ELASTICITY AT 70°F (21 °C) PSI (MPa) | TYPICAL BRINELL HARDNESS |
	Tensile Strength ksi (MPa)	Yield Strength ksi (MPa)	Elongation in 2-inch (50 mm)	Reduction in Area (%)		
8	70-95 (485-655)	40 (275)	20	35	29.9E6 (20.6E4)	147-200
9	75 (515)	45(310)	20	30	29.9E6 (20.6E4)	156-207 required
10	90-115 (620-795)	60 (415)	18	35	27.4E6 (19.0E4)	176-255
11	75 (515)	30 (205)	30	40	28.3E6 (19.3E4)	150
12	70 (485)	25 (170)	30	40	29.0E6 (20.0E4)	149
13	70 (485)	25 (170)	30	40	29.0E6 (20.0E4)	149
14	70 (485)	25 (170)	30	40	28.3E6 (19.3E4)	150-170
15[2]	80 (551)	35 (240)	30	40	28.3E6 (19.5E4)	150
16	70 (485)	30 (205)	30	– – –	28.3E6 (19.5E4)	163
17	75 (515)	35 (240)	25	– – –	28.3E6 (19.5E4)	170
18	75 (515)	35 (240)	25	– – –	28.3E6 (19.5E4)	170
19	70 (480)	40 (275)	16	45	29.2E6 (20.1E4)	223
20	145 (1000)	125 (860)	13	45	29E6 (20.0E4)	302 min
21	95(665)	44(305)	35	50	29.0E6 (20.0E4)	90 HRB
22	80(550)	38(260)	35	- - -	29.0E6 (20.0E4)	82 HRB
23	90(620)	65(450)	25	- - -	30.5E6 (21.0E4)	290 max
24	90(620)	65(450)	25	- - -	30.5E6 (21.0E4)	98 HRB
25[3]	31 (214)	– – –	– – –	– – –	13.4E6 (9.2E4)	160-220
26[4]	41 (282)	– – –	– – –	– – –	13.4E6 (9.2E4)	160-220
27	60 (415)	40 (276)	18	– – –	23E6 (16E4)	143-187
28	58 (400)	30(205)	7	– – –	– – –	148-211
29	34 (234)	16(110)	24	– – –	14.0E6 (9.7E4)	65

(continued)

Valve Materials Properties for Pressure–Containing Components (continued)

(The material codes in this table correspond to the previous Standard Specifications for Valve Materials listing.)

| MATER-IAL CODE | MINIMUM MECHANICAL PROPERTIES | | | | MODULUS OF ELASTICITY AT 70°F (21 °C) PSI (MPa) | TYPICAL BRINELL HARDNESS |
	Tensile Strength ksi (MPa)	Yield Strength ksi (MPa)	Elongation in 2-inch (50 mm)	Reduction in Area (%)		
30	40 (275)	18(124)	20	– – –	14.0 (9.7E4)	75
31	65 (448)	25(172)	20	– – –	15.3E6 (10.5E4)	98
32	75 (515)	30(205)	12	– – –	16E6 (11.0E4)	150
33	85 (585)	35(240)	15	– – –	16E6 (11.0E4)	120–170
34	55 (380)	25(170)	10	– – –	14E6 (9.6E4)	60–80 HRB required
35	60 (415)	27(186)	22	– – –	15.0E6 (10.3E4)	131–142
36	42 (290)	35(241)	10	– – –	9.9E6 (6.8E4)	95
37[5]	154 (1060) typical	93(638) typical	17 typical	– – –	30E6 (21E4)	37 HRC
38	100 (689)	70(485)	20	– – –	26E6 (17.9E4)	250–325
39	65 (450)	25(170)	25	– – –	23E6 (15.8E4)	110–150
40	100 (689)	41(283)	40	– – –	29.8E6 (20.5E4)	210
41	72 (496)	40(275)	20	– – –	30.8E6 (21.2E4)	150–185
42	110 (760)	51(350)	40	– – –	31.4E6 (21.7E4)	238
43	76 (525)	40(275)	20	– – –	28.5E6 (19.7E4)	180

1. Tempered (1200°F (650°C).
2. Annealed.
3. A126 Cl.B 1.125 in. (95 mm) dia bar.
4. A126 Cl.C 1.125 in. (95 mm) dia bar.
5. Wrought.

Physical Constants of Hydrocarbons

NO.	COMPOUND	FORMULA	MOLECULAR WEIGHT	BOILING POINT AT 14.696 PSIA (°F)	VAPOR PRESSURE AT 100°F (PSIA)	FREEZING POINT AT 14.696 PSIA (°F)	CRITICAL CONSTANTS		SPECIFIC GRAVITY AT 14.696 PSIA	
							Critical Temperature (°F)	Critical Pressure (psia)	Liquid,[3],[4] 60°F/60°F	Gas at 60°F (Air=1)[1]
1	Methane	CH_4	16.043	-258.69	(5000)[2]	-296.46[5]	-116.63	667.8	0.3[8]	0.5539
2	Ethane	C_2H_6	30.070	-127.48	(800)[2]	-297.89[5]	90.09	707.8	0.3564[7]	1.0382
3	Propane	C_3H_8	44.097	-43.67	190.	-305.84[5]	206.01	616.3	0.5077[7]	1.5225
4	n–Butane	C_4H_{10}	58.124	31.10	51.6	-217.05	305.65	550.7	0.5844[7]	2.0068
5	Isobutane	C_4H_{10}	58.124	10.90	72.2	-255.29	274.98	529.1	0.5631[7]	2.0068
6	n–Pentane	C_5H_{12}	72.151	96.92	15.570	-201.51	385.7	488.6	0.6310	2.4911
7	Isopentane	C_5H_{12}	72.151	82.12	20.44	-255.83	369.10	490.4	0.6247	2.4911
8	Neopentane	C_5H_{12}	72.151	49.10	35.9	2.17	321.13	464.0	0.5967[7]	2.4911
9	n–Hexane	C_6H_{14}	86.178	155.72	4.956	-139.58	453.7	436.9	0.6640	2.9753
10	2–Methylpentane	C_6H_{14}	86.178	140.47	6.767	-244.63	435.83	436.6	0.6579	2.9753
11	3–Methylpentane	C_6H_{14}	86.178	145.89	6.098	- - -	448.3	453.1	0.6689	2.9753
12	Neohexane	C_6H_{14}	86.178	121.52	9.856	-147.72	420.13	446.8	0.6540	2.9753
13	2,3–Dimethylbutane	C_6H_{14}	86.178	136.36	7.404	-199.38	440.29	453.5	0.6664	2.9753
14	n–Heptane	C_7H_{16}	100.205	209.17	1.620	-131.05	512.8	396.8	0.6882	3.4596
15	2–Methylhexane	C_7H_{16}	100.205	194.09	2.271	-180.89	495.00	396.5	0.6830	3.4596
16	3–Methylhexane	C_7H_{16}	100.205	197.32	2.130	- - -	503.78	408.1	0.6917	3.4596
17	3–Ethylpentane	C_7H_{16}	100.205	200.25	2.012	-181.48	513.48	419.3	0.7028	3.4596
18	2,2–Dimethylpentane	C_7H_{16}	100.205	174.54	3.492	-190.86	477.23	402.2	0.6782	3.4596
19	2,4–Dimethylpentane	C_7H_{16}	100.205	176.89	3.292	-182.63	475.95	396.9	0.6773	3.4596
20	3,3–Dimethylpentane	C_7H_{16}	100.205	186.91	2.773	-210.01	505.85	427.2	0.6976	3.4596
21	Triptane	C_7H_{16}	100.205	177.58	3.374	-12.82	496.44	428.4	0.6946	3.4596

Physical Constants of Hydrocarbons (continued)

NO.	COMPOUND	FORMULA	MOLECULAR WEIGHT	BOILING POINT AT 14.696 PSIA (°F)	VAPOR PRESSURE AT 100°F (PSIA)	FREEZING POINT AT 14.696 PSIA (°F)	CRITICAL CONSTANTS		SPECIFIC GRAVITY AT 14.696 PSIA	
							Critical Temperature (°F)	Critical Pressure (psia)	Liquid,[3],[4] 60°F/60°F	Gas at 60°F (Air=1)[1]
22	n–Octane	C_8H_{18}	114.232	258.22	0.537	–70.18	564.22	360.6	0.7068	3.9439
23	Diisobutyl	C_8H_{18}	114.232	228.39	1.101	–132.07	530.44	360.6	0.6979	3.9439
24	Isooctane	C_8H_{18}	114.232	210.63	1.708	–161.27	519.46	372.4	0.6962	3.9439
25	n–Nonane	C_9H_{20}	128.259	303.47	0.179	–64.28	610.68	332.	0.7217	4.4282
26	n–Decane	$C_{10}H_{22}$	142.286	345.48	0.0597	–21.36	652.1	304.	0.7342	4.9125
27	Cyclopentane	C_5H_{10}	70.135	120.65	9.914	–136.91	461.5	653.8	0.7504	2.4215
28	Methylcyclopentane	C_6H_{12}	84.162	161.25	4.503	–224.44	499.35	548.9	0.7536	2.9057
29	Cyclohexane	C_6H_{12}	84.162	177.29	3.264	43.77	536.7	591.	0.7834	2.9057
30	Methylcyclohexane	C_7H_{14}	98.189	213.68	1.609	–195.87	570.27	503.5	0.7740	3.3900
31	Ethylene	C_2H_4	28.054	–154.62	– – –	–272.45[5]	48.58	729.8	– – –	0.9686
32	Propene	C_3H_6	42.081	–53.90	226.4	–301.45[5]	196.9	669.	0.5220[7]	1.4529
33	1–Butene	C_4H_8	56.108	20.75	63.05	–301.63[5]	295.6	583.	0.6013[7]	1.9372
34	Cis–2–Butene	C_4H_8	56.108	38.69	45.54	–218.06	324.37	610.	0.6271[7]	1.9372
35	Trans–2–Butene	C_4H_8	56.108	33.58	49.80	–157.96	311.86	595.	0.6100[7]	1.9372
36	Isobutene	C_4H_8	56.108	19.59	63.40	–220.61	292.55	580.	0.6004[7]	1.9372
37	1–Pentene	C_5H_{10}	70.135	85.93	19.115	–265.39	376.93	590.	0.6457	2.4215
38	1,2–Butadiene	C_4H_6	54.092	51.53	(20.)[2]	–213.16	(339.)[2]	(653.)[2]	0.658[7]	1.8676
39	1,3–Butadiene	C_4H_6	54.092	24.06	(60.)[2]	–164.02	306.	628.	0.6272[7]	1.8676
40	Isoprene	C_5H_8	68.119	93.30	16.672	–230.74	(412.)[2]	(558.4)[2]	0.6861	2.3519

Physical Constants of Hydrocarbons (continued)

NO.	COMPOUND	FORMULA	MOLECULAR WEIGHT	BOILING POINT AT 14.696 PSIA (°F)	VAPOR PRESSURE AT 100°F (PSIA)	FREEZING POINT AT 14.696 PSIA (°F)	CRITICAL CONSTANTS		SPECIFIC GRAVITY AT 14.696 PSIA	
							Critical Temperature (°F)	Critical Pressure (psia)	Liquid,[3]/[4] 60°F/60°F	Gas at 60°F (Air=1)[1]
41	Acetylene	C_2H_2	26.038	$-119.$[6]	$- - -$	$-114.$[5]	95.31	890.4	0.615[9]	0.8990
42	Benzene	C_6H_6	78.114	176.17	3.224	41.96	552.22	710.4	0.8844	2.6969
43	Toluene	C_7H_8	92.141	231.13	1.032	-138.94	605.55	595.9	0.8718	3.1812
44	Ethylbenzene	C_8H_{10}	106.168	277.16	0.371	-138.91	651.24	523.5	0.8718	3.6655
45	o–Xylene	C_8H_{10}	106.168	291.97	0.264	-13.30	675.0	541.4	0.8848	3.6655
46	m–Xylene	C_8H_{10}	106.168	282.41	0.326	-54.12	651.02	513.6	0.8687	3.6655
47	p–Xylene	C_8H_{10}	106.168	281.05	0.342	55.86	649.6	509.2	0.8657	3.6655
48	Styrene	C_8H_8	104.152	293.29	(0.24)[2]	-23.10	706.0	580.	0.9110	3.5959
49	Isopropylbenzene	C_9H_{12}	120.195	306.34	0.188	-140.82	676.4	465.4	0.8663	4.1498

1. Calculated values.
2. ( )=Estimated values.
3. Air saturated hydrocarbons.
4. Absolute values from weights in vacuum.
5. At saturation pressure (triple point).
6. Sublimation point.
7. Saturation pressure and 60°F.
8. Apparent value for methane at 60°F.
9. Specific gravity, 119°F/60°F (sublimation point).

Specific Heat Ratio (k)

Gas	Specific Heat Ratio (k)	Gas	Specific Heat Ratio (k)	Gas	Specific Heat Ratio (k)	Gas	Specific Heat Ratio (k)
Acetylene	1.38	Carbon Dioxide	1.29	0.6 Natural Gas	1.32	Steam[1]	1.33
Air	1.40	Ethane	1.25	Nitrogen	1.40		
Argon	1.67	Helium	1.66	Oxygen	1.40		
Butane	1.17	Hydrogen	1.40	Propane	1.21		
Carbon Monoxide	1.40	Methane	1.26	Propylene	1.15		

1. Use property tables if available for greater accuracy.

Physical Constants of Various Fluids

FLUID	FORMULA	MOLECULAR WEIGHT	BOILING POINT (°F AT 14.696 PSIA)	VAPOR PRESSURE @ 70°F (PSIG)	CRITICAL TEMP. (°F)	CRITICAL PRESSURE (PSIA)	SPECIFIC GRAVITY Liquid 60/60°F	SPECIFIC GRAVITY Gas
Acetic Acid	$HC_2H_3O_2$	60.05	245				1.05	
Acetone	C_3H_6O	58.08	133		455	691	0.79	2.01
Air	N_2O_2	28.97	−317		−221	547	0.86[3]	1.0
Alcohol, Ethyl	C_2H_6O	46.07	173	2.3[2]	470	925	0.794	1.59
Alcohol, Methyl	CH_4O	32.04	148	4.63[2]	463	1174	0.796	1.11
Ammonia	NH_3	17.03	−28	114	270	1636	0.62	0.59
Ammonium Chloride[1]	NH_4Cl						1.07	
Ammonium Hydroxide[1]	NH_4OH						0.91	
Ammonium Sulfate[1]	$(NH_4)_2SO_4$						1.15	
Aniline	C_6H_7N	93.12	365		798	770	1.02	
Argon	A	39.94	−302		−188	705	1.65	1.38
Beer							1.01	
Bromine	Br_2	159.84	138		575		2.93	5.52
Calcium Chloride[1]	$CaCl_2$						1.23	
Carbon Dioxide	CO_2	44.01	−109	839	88	1072	0.801[3]	1.52
Carbon Disulfide	CS_2	76.1	115				1.29	2.63
Carbon Monoxide	CO	28.01	−314		−220	507	0.80	0.97
Carbon Tetrachloride	CCl_4	153.84	170		542	661	1.59	5.31
Chlorine	Cl_2	70.91	−30	85	291	1119	1.42	2.45
Chromic Acid	H_2CrO_4	118.03					1.21	
Citric Acid	$C_6H_8O_7$	192.12					1.54	
Copper Sulfate[1]	$CuSO_4$						1.17	

(continued)

Physical Constants of Various Fluids (continued)

FLUID	FORMULA	MOLECULAR WEIGHT	BOILING POINT (°F AT 14.696 PSIA)	VAPOR PRESSURE @ 70°F (PSIG)	CRITICAL TEMP. (°F)	CRITICAL PRESSURE (PSIA)	SPECIFIC GRAVITY Liquid 60/60°F	SPECIFIC GRAVITY Gas
Ether	$(C_2H_5)_2O$	74.12	34				0.74	2.55
Ferric Chloride[1]	$FeCl_3$						1.23	
Fluorine	F_2	38.00	–305	300	–200	809	1.11	1.31
Formaldehyde	H_2CO	30.03	–6				0.82	1.08
Formic Acid	HCO_2H	46.03	214				1.23	
Furfural	$C_5H_4O_2$	96.08	324				1.16	
Glycerine	$C_3H_8O_3$	92.09	554				1.26	
Glycol	$C_2H_6O_2$	62.07	387				1.11	
Helium	He	4.003	–454		–450	33	0.18	0.14
Hydrochloric Acid	HCl	36.47	–115				1.64	
Hydrofluoric Acid	HF	20.01	66	0.9	446		0.92	
Hydrogen	H_2	2.016	–422		–400	188	0.07[3]	0.07
Hydrogen Chloride	HCl	36.47	–115	613	125	1198	0.86	1.26
Hydrogen Sulfide	H_2S	34.07	–76	252	213	1307	0.79	1.17
Isopropyl Alcohol	C_3H_8O	60.09	180				0.78	2.08
Linseed Oil			538				0.93	
Magnesium Chloride[1]	$MgCl_2$						1.22	
Mercury	Hg	200.61	670				13.6	6.93
Methyl Bromide	CH_3Br	94.95	38	13	376		1.73	3.27
Methyl Chloride	CH_3Cl	50.49	–11	59	290	969	0.99	1.74
Naphthalene	$C_{10}H_8$	128.16	424				1.14	4.43
Nitric Acid	HNO_3	63.02	187				1.5	

(continued)

Physical Constants of Various Fluids (continued)

FLUID	FORMULA	MOLECULAR WEIGHT	BOILING POINT (°F AT 14.696 PSIA)	VAPOR PRESSURE @ 70°F (PSIG)	CRITICAL TEMP. (°F)	CRITICAL PRESSURE (PSIA)	SPECIFIC GRAVITY Liquid 60/60°F	Gas
Nitrogen	N_2	28.02	–320		–233	493	0.81[3]	0.97
Oil, Vegetable							0.91–0.94	
Oxygen	O_2	32	–297		–181	737	1.14[3]	1.105
Phosgene	$COCl_2$	98.92	47	10.7	360	823	1.39	3.42
Phosphoric Acid	H_3PO_4	98.00	415				1.83	
Potassium Carbonate[1]	K_2CO_3						1.24	
Potassium Chloride[1]	KCl						1.16	
Potassium Hydroxide[1]	KOH						1.24	
Sodium Chloride[1]	NaCl						1.19	
Sodium Hydroxide[1]	NaOH						1.27	
Sodium Sulfate[1]	Na_2SO_4						1.24	
Sodium Thiosulfate[1]	$Na_2S_2O_3$						1.23	
Starch	$(C_6H_{10}O_5)x$						1.50	
Sugar Solutions[1]	$C_{12}H_{22}O_{11}$						1.10	
Sulfuric Acid	H_2SO_4	98.08	626				1.83	
Sulfur Dioxide	SO_2	64.6	14	34.4	316	1145	1.39	2.21
Turpentine			320				0.87	
Water	H_2O	18.016	212	0.9492[2]	706	3208	1.00	0.62
Zinc Chloride[1]	$ZnCl_2$						1.24	
Zinc Sulfate[1]	$ZnSO_4$						1.31	

1. Aqueous Solution – 25% by weight of compound.
2. Vapor pressure in psia at 100°F.
3. Vapor pressure in psia.

Refrigerant 717 (Ammonia)
Properties of Liquid and Saturated Vapor

TEMP (°F)	PRESSURE		VOLUME (CU. FT./LB.)	DENSITY (LB./CU. FT.)	ENTHALPY[1] (BTU/LB.)		ENTROPY[1] BTU/(LB.)(°R)	
	psia	psig	Vapor V_g	Liquid $1/v_f$	Liquid h_f	Vapor h_g	Liquid s_f	Vapor s_g
−105	0.996	27.9[2]	223.2	45.71	−68.5	570.3	−0.1774	1.6243
−104	1.041	27.8[2]	214.2	45.67	−67.5	570.7	−.1774	1.6205
−103	1.087	27.7[2]	205.7	45.63	−66.4	571.2	−.1714	1.6167
−102	1.135	27.6[2]	197.6	45.59	−65.4	571.6	−.1685	1.6129
−101	1.184	27.5[2]	189.8	45.55	−64.3	572.1	−.1655	1.6092
−100	1.24	27.4[2]	182.4	45.52	−63.3	572.5	−0.1626	1.6055
−99	1.29	27.3[2]	175.3	45.47	−62.2	572.9	−.1597	1.6018
−98	1.34	27.2[2]	168.5	45.43	−61.2	573.4	−.1568	1.5982
−97	1.40	27.1[2]	162.1	45.40	−60.1	573.8	−.1539	1.5945
−96	1.46	26.9[2]	155.9	45.36	−59.1	574.3	−.1510	1.5910
−95	1.52	26.8[2]	150.0	45.32	−58.0	574.7	−0.1481	1.5874
−94	1.59	26.7[2]	144.3	45.28	−57.0	575.1	−.1452	1.5838
−93	1.65	26.6[2]	138.9	45.24	−55.9	575.6	−.1423	1.5803
−92	1.72	26.4[2]	133.8	45.20	−54.9	576.0	−.1395	1.5768
−91	1.79	26.3[2]	128.9	45.16	−53.8	576.5	−.1366	1.5734
−90	1.86	26.1[2]	124.1	45.12	−52.8	576.9	−0.1338	1.5699
−89	1.94	26.0[2]	119.6	45.08	−51.7	577.3	−.1309	1.5665
−88	2.02	25.8[2]	115.3	45.04	−50.7	577.8	−.1281	1.5631
−87	2.10	25.6[2]	111.1	45.00	−49.6	578.2	−.1253	1.5597
−86	2.18	25.5[2]	107.1	44.96	−48.6	578.6	−.1225	1.5564
−85	2.27	25.3[2]	103.3	44.92	−47.5	579.1	−0.1197	1.5531
−84	2.35	25.1[2]	99.68	44.88	−46.5	579.5	−.1169	1.5498
−83	2.45	24.9[2]	96.17	44.84	−45.4	579.9	−.1141	1.5465
−82	2.54	24.7[2]	92.81	44.80	−44.4	580.4	−.1113	1.5432
−81	2.64	24.5[2]	89.59	44.76	−43.3	580.8	−.1085	1.5400
−80	2.74	24.3[2]	86.50	44.73	−42.2	581.2	0.1057	1.5368
−79	2.84	24.1[2]	83.54	44.68	−41.2	581.6	−.1030	1.5336
−78	2.95	23.9[2]	80.69	44.64	−40.1	582.1	−.1002	1.5304
−77	3.06	23.7[2]	77.96	44.60	−39.1	582.5	−.0975	1.5273
−76	3.18	23.5[2]	75.33	44.56	−38.0	582.9	−.0947	1.5242
−75	3.29	23.2[2]	72.81	44.52	−37.0	583.3	−0.0920	1.5211
−74	3.42	23.0[2]	70.39	44.48	−35.9	583.8	−.0892	1.5180
−73	3.54	22.7[2]	68.06	44.44	−34.9	584.2	−.0865	1.5149
−72	3.67	22.4[2]	65.82	44.40	−33.8	584.6	−.0838	1.5119
−71	3.80	22.2[2]	63.67	44.36	−32.8	585.0	−.0811	1.5089
−70	3.94	21.9[2]	61.60	44.32	−31.7	585.5	−0.0784	1.5059
−69	4.08	21.6[2]	59.61	44.28	−30.7	585.9	−.0757	1.5029
−68	4.23	21.3[2]	57.69	44.24	−29.6	586.3	−.0730	1.4999
−67	4.38	21.0[2]	55.85	44.19	−28.6	586.7	−.0703	1.4970
−66	4.53	20.7[2]	54.08	44.15	−27.5	587.1	−.0676	1.4940
−65	4.69	20.4[2]	52.37	44.11	−26.5	587.5	−0.0650	1.4911
−64	4.85	20.0[2]	50.73	44.07	−25.4	588.0	−.0623	1.4883
−63	5.02	19.7[2]	49.14	44.03	−24.4	588.4	−.0596	1.4854
−62	5.19	19.4[2]	47.62	43.99	−23.3	588.8	−.0570	1.4826
−61	5.37	19.0[2]	46.15	43.95	−22.2	589.2	−.0543	1.4797
−60	5.55	18.6[2]	44.73	43.91	−21.2	589.6	−.0517	1.4769

(continued)

Refrigerant 717 (Ammonia)
Properties of Liquid and Saturated Vapor (continued)

TEMP (°F)	PRESSURE		VOLUME (CU. FT./LB.)	DENSITY (LB./CU. FT.)	ENTHALPY[1] (BTU/LB.)		ENTROPY[1] BTU/(LB.)(°R)	
	psia	psig	Vapor V_g	Liquid $1/v_f$	Liquid h_f	Vapor h_g	Liquid s_f	Vapor s_g
−59	5.74	18.2[2]	43.37	43.87	−20.1	590.0	−0.0490	1.4741
−58	5.93	17.8[2]	42.05	43.83	−19.1	590.4	−.0464	1.4713
−57	6.13	17.4[2]	40.79	43.78	−18.0	590.8	−.0438	1.4686
−56	6.33	17.0[2]	39.56	43.74	−17.0	591.2	−.0412	1.4658
−55	6.54	16.6[2]	38.38	43.70	−15.9	591.6	−.0386	1.4631
−54	6.75	16.2[2]	37.24	43.66	−14.8	592.1	−0.0360	1.4604
−53	6.97	15.7[2]	36.15	43.62	−13.8	592.4	−.0334	1.4577
−52	7.20	15.3[2]	35.09	43.58	−12.7	592.9	−.0307	1.4551
−51	7.43	14.8[2]	34.06	43.54	−11.7	593.2	−.0281	1.4524
−50	7.67	14.3[2]	33.08	43.49	−10.6	593.7	−.0256	1.4497
−49	7.91	13.8[2]	32.12	43.45	−9.6	594.0	−0.0230	1.4471
−48	8.16	13.3[2]	31.20	43.41	−8.5	594.4	−.0204	1.4445
−47	8.42	12.8[2]	30.31	43.37	−7.4	594.9	−.0179	1.4419
−46	8.68	12.2[2]	29.45	43.33	−6.4	595.2	−.0153	1.4393
−45	8.95	11.7[2]	28.62	43.28	−5.3	595.6	−.0127	1.4368
−44	9.23	11.1[2]	27.82	43.24	−4.3	596.0	−0.0102	1.4342
−43	9.51	10.6[2]	27.04	43.20	−3.2	596.4	−.0076	1.4317
−42	9.81	10.0[2]	26.29	43.16	−2.1	596.8	−.0051	1.4292
−41	10.10	9.3[2]	25.56	43.12	−1.1	597.2	−.0025	1.4267
−40	10.41	8.7[2]	24.86	43.08	0.0	597.6	.0000	1.4242
−39	10.72	8.1[2]	24.18	43.04	1.1	598.0	0.0025	1.4217
−38	11.04	7.4[2]	23.53	42.99	2.1	598.3	.0051	1.4193
−37	11.37	6.8[2]	22.89	42.95	3.2	598.7	.0076	1.4169
−36	11.71	6.1[2]	22.27	42.90	4.3	599.1	.0101	1.4144
−35	12.05	5.4[2]	21.68	42.86	5.3	599.5	.0126	1.4120
−34	12.41	4.7[2]	21.10	42.82	6.4	599.9	0.0151	1.4096
−33	12.77	3.9[2]	20.54	42.78	7.4	600.2	.0176	1.4072
−32	13.14	3.2[2]	20.00	42.73	8.5	600.6	.0201	1.4048
−31	13.52	2.4[2]	19.48	42.69	9.6	601.0	.0226	1.4025
−30	13.90	1.6[2]	18.97	42.65	10.7	601.4	.0250	1.4001
−29	14.30	0.8[2]	18.48	42.61	11.7	601.7	0.0275	1.3978
−28	14.71	0.0	18.00	42.57	12.8	602.1	.0300	1.3955
−27	15.12	0.4	17.54	42.54	13.9	602.5	.0325	1.3932
−26	15.55	0.8	17.09	42.48	14.9	602.8	.0350	1.3909
−25	15.98	1.3	16.66	42.44	16.0	603.2	.0374	1.3886
−24	16.24	1.7	16.24	42.40	17.1	603.6	0.0399	1.3863
−23	16.88	2.2	15.83	42.35	18.1	603.9	.0423	1.3840
−22	17.34	2.6	15.43	42.31	19.2	604.3	.0448	1.3818
−21	17.81	3.1	15.05	42.26	20.3	604.6	.0472	1.3796
−20	18.30	3.6	14.68	42.22	21.4	605.0	.0497	1.3774
−19	18.79	4.1	14.32	42.18	22.4	605.3	0.0521	1.3752
−18	19.30	4.6	13.97	42.13	23.5	605.7	.0545	1.3729
−17	19.81	5.1	13.62	42.09	24.6	606.1	.0570	1.3708
−16	20.34	5.6	13.29	42.04	25.6	606.4	.0594	1.3686
−15	20.88	6.2	12.97	42.00	26.7	606.7	.0618	1.3664
−14	21.43	6.7	12.66	41.96	27.8	607.1	.0642	1.3642

(continued)

Refrigerant 717 (Ammonia)
Properties of Liquid and Saturated Vapor (continued)

TEMP (°F)	PRESSURE		VOLUME (CU. FT./LB.)	DENSITY (LB./CU. FT.)	ENTHALPY[1] (BTU/LB.)		ENTROPY[1] BTU/(LB.)(°R)	
	psia	psig	Vapor V_g	Liquid l/v_f	Liquid h_f	Vapor h_g	Liquid s_f	Vapor s_g
−13	21.99	7.3	12.36	41.91	28.9	607.5	0.0666	1.3624
−12	22.56	7.9	12.06	41.87	30.0	607.8	.0690	1.3600
−11	23.15	8.5	11.78	41.82	31.0	608.1	.0714	1.3579
−10	23.74	9.0	11.50	41.78	32.1	608.5	.0738	1.3558
−9	24.35	9.7	11.23	41.74	33.2	608.8	.0762	1.3537
−8	24.97	10.3	10.97	41.69	34.3	609.2	0.0786	1.3516
−7	25.61	10.9	10.71	41.65	35.4	609.5	.0809	1.3493
−6	26.26	11.6	10.47	41.60	36.4	609.8	.0833	1.3474
−5	26.92	12.2	10.23	41.56	37.5	610.1	.0857	1.3454
−4	27.59	12.9	9.991	41.52	38.6	610.5	.0880	1.3433
−3	28.28	13.6	9.763	41.47	39.7	610.8	0.0909	1.3413
−2	28.98	14.3	9.541	41.43	40.7	611.1	.0928	1.3393
−1	29.69	15.0	9.326	41.38	41.8	611.4	.0951	1.3372
0	30.42	15.7	9.116	41.34	42.9	611.8	.0975	1.3352
1	31.16	16.5	8.912	41.29	44.0	612.1	.0998	1.3332
2	31.92	17.2	8.714	41.25	45.1	612.4	0.1022	1.3312
3	32.69	18.0	8.521	41.20	46.2	612.7	.1045	1.3292
4	33.47	18.8	8.333	41.16	47.2	613.0	.1069	1.3273
5[3]	34.27	19.6	8.150	41.11	48.3	613.3	.1092	1.3253
6	35.09	20.4	7.971	41.07	49.4	613.6	.1115	1.3234
7	35.92	21.2	7.798	41.01	50.5	613.9	0.1138	1.3214
8	36.77	22.1	7.629	40.98	51.6	614.3	.1162	1.3195
9	37.63	22.9	7.464	40.93	52.7	614.6	.1185	1.3176
10	38.51	23.8	7.304	40.89	53.8	614.9	.1208	1.3157
11	39.40	24.7	7.148	40.84	54.9	615.2	.1231	1.3137
12	40.31	25.6	6.996	40.80	56.0	615.5	0.1254	1.3118
13	41.24	26.5	6.847	40.75	57.1	615.8	.1277	1.3099
14	42.18	27.5	6.703	40.71	58.2	616.1	.1300	1.3081
15	43.14	28.4	6.562	40.66	59.2	616.3	.1323	1.3062
16	44.12	29.4	6.425	40.61	60.3	616.6	.1346	1.3043
17	45.12	30.4	6.291	40.57	61.4	616.9	0.1369	1.3025
18	46.13	31.4	6.161	40.52	62.5	617.2	.1392	1.3006
19	47.16	32.5	6.034	40.48	63.6	617.5	.1415	1.2988
20	48.21	33.5	5.910	40.43	64.7	617.8	.1437	1.2969
21	49.28	34.6	5.789	40.38	65.8	618.0	.1460	1.2951
22	50.36	35.7	5.671	40.34	66.9	618.3	0.1483	1.2933
23	51.47	36.8	5.556	40.29	68.0	618.6	.1505	1.2915
24	52.59	37.9	5.443	40.25	69.1	618.9	.1528	1.2897
25	53.73	39.0	5.334	40.20	70.2	619.1	.1551	1.2879
26	54.90	40.2	5.227	40.15	71.3	619.4	.1573	1.2861
27	56.08	41.4	5.123	40.10	72.4	619.7	0.1596	1.2843
28	57.28	42.6	5.021	40.06	73.5	619.9	.1618	1.2823
29	58.50	43.8	4.922	40.01	74.6	620.2	.1641	1.2809
30	59.74	45.0	4.825	39.96	75.7	620.5	.1663	1.2790
31	61.00	46.3	4.730	39.91	76.8	620.7	.1686	1.2773
32	62.29	47.6	4.637	39.86	77.9	621.0	.1708	1.2755

(continued)

Refrigerant 717 (Ammonia)
Properties of Liquid and Saturated Vapor (continued)

TEMP (°F)	PRESSURE		VOLUME (CU. FT./LB.)	DENSITY (LB./CU. FT.)	ENTHALPY[1] (BTU/LB.)		ENTROPY[1] BTU/(LB.)(°R)	
	psia	psig	Vapor V_g	Liquid l/v_f	Liquid h_f	Vapor h_g	Liquid s_f	Vapor s_g
33	63.59	48.9	4.547	39.82	79.0	621.2	0.1730	1.2738
34	64.91	50.2	4.459	39.77	80.1	621.5	.1753	1.2721
35	66.26	51.6	4.373	39.72	81.2	621.7	.1775	1.2704
36	67.63	52.9	4.289	39.67	82.3	622.0	.1797	1.2686
37	69.02	54.3	4.207	39.63	83.4	622.2	.1819	1.2669
38	70.43	55.7	4.126	39.58	84.6	622.5	0.1841	1.2652
39	71.87	57.2	4.048	39.54	85.7	622.7	.1863	1.2635
40	73.32	58.6	3.971	39.49	86.8	623.0	.1885	1.2618
41	74.80	60.1	3.897	39.44	87.9	623.2	.1908	1.2602
42	76.31	61.6	3.823	39.39	89.0	623.4	.1930	1.2585
43	77.83	63.1	3.752	39.34	90.1	623.7	0.1952	1.2568
44	79.38	64.7	3.682	39.29	91.2	623.9	.1974	1.2552
45	80.96	66.3	3.614	39.24	92.3	624.1	.1996	1.2535
46	82.55	67.9	3.547	39.19	93.5	624.4	.2018	1.2518
47	84.18	69.5	3.481	39.14	94.6	624.6	.2040	1.2492
48	85.82	71.1	3.418	39.10	95.7	624.8	0.2062	1.2484
49	87.49	72.8	3.355	39.05	96.8	625.0	.2083	1.2469
50	89.19	74.5	3.294	39.00	97.9	625.2	.2105	1.2453
51	90.91	76.2	3.234	38.95	99.1	625.5	.2127	1.2437
52	92.66	78.0	3.176	38.90	100.2	625.7	.2149	1.2421
53	94.43	79.7	3.119	38.85	101.3	625.9	0.2171	1.2405
54	96.23	81.5	3.063	38.80	102.4	626.1	.2192	1.2382
55	98.06	83.4	3.008	38.75	103.5	626.3	.2214	1.2372
56	99.91	85.2	2.954	38.70	104.7	626.5	.2236	1.2357
57	101.8	87.1	2.902	38.65	105.8	626.7	.2257	1.2341
58	103.7	89.0	2.851	38.60	106.9	626.9	0.2279	1.2325
59	105.6	90.9	2.800	38.55	108.1	627.1	.2301	1.2310
60	107.6	92.9	2.751	38.50	109.2	627.3	.2322	1.2294
61	109.6	94.9	2.703	38.45	110.3	627.5	.2344	1.2273
62	111.6	96.9	2.656	38.40	111.5	627.7	.2365	1.2263
63	113.6	98.9	2.610	38.35	112.6	627.9	0.2387	1.2247
64	115.7	101.0	2.565	38.30	113.7	628.0	.2408	1.2231
65	117.8	103.1	2.520	38.25	114.8	628.2	.2430	1.2213
66	120.0	105.3	2.477	38.20	116.0	628.4	.2451	1.2201
67	122.1	107.4	2.435	38.15	117.1	628.6	.2473	1.2183
68	124.3	109.6	2.393	38.10	118.3	628.8	0.2494	1.2179
69	126.5	111.8	2.352	38.05	119.4	628.9	.2515	1.2155
70	128.8	114.1	2.312	38.00	120.5	629.1	.2537	1.2140
71	131.1	116.4	2.273	37.95	121.7	629.3	.2558	1.2125
72	133.4	118.7	2.235	37.90	122.8	629.4	.2579	1.2110
73	135.7	121.0	2.197	37.84	124.0	629.6	0.2601	1.2095
74	138.1	123.4	2.161	37.79	125.1	629.8	.2622	1.2080
75	140.5	125.8	2.125	37.74	126.2	629.9	.2643	1.2065
76	143.0	128.3	2.089	37.69	127.4	630.1	.2664	1.2050
77	145.4	130.7	2.055	37.64	128.5	630.2	.2685	1.2035
78	147.9	133.2	2.021	37.58	129.7	630.4	.2706	1.2020

(continued)

Refrigerant 717 (Ammonia)
Properties of Liquid and Saturated Vapor (continued)

TEMP (°F)	PRESSURE		VOLUME (CU. FT./LB.)	DENSITY (LB./CU. FT.)	ENTHALPY[1] (BTU/LB.)		ENTROPY[1] BTU/(LB.)(°R)	
	psia	psig	Vapor V_g	Liquid $1/v_f$	Liquid h_f	Vapor h_g	Liquid s_f	Vapor s_g
79	150.5	135.8	1.988	37.53	130.8	630.5	0.2728	1.2006
80	153.0	138.3	1.955	37.48	132.0	630.7	.2749	1.1991
81	155.6	140.9	1.923	37.43	133.1	630.8	.2769	1.1976
82	158.3	143.6	1.892	37.37	134.3	631.0	.2791	1.1962
83	161.0	146.3	1.861	37.32	135.4	631.1	.2812	1.1947
84	163.7	149.0	1.831	37.26	136.6	631.3	0.2833	1.1933
85	166.4	151.7	1.801	37.21	137.8	631.4	.2854	1.1918
86[3]	169.2	154.5	1.772	37.16	138.9	631.5	.2875	1.1904
87	172.0	157.3	1.744	37.11	140.1	631.7	.2895	1.1889
88	174.8	160.1	1.716	37.05	141.2	631.8	.2917	1.1875
89	177.7	163.0	1.688	37.00	142.4	631.9	0.2937	1.1860
90	180.6	165.9	1.661	36.95	143.5	632.0	.2958	1.1846
91	183.6	168.9	1.635	36.89	144.7	632.1	.2979	1.1832
92	186.6	171.9	1.609	36.84	145.8	632.2	.3000	1.1818
93	189.6	174.9	1.584	36.78	147.0	632.3	.3021	1.1804
94	192.7	178.0	1.559	36.73	148.2	632.5	0.3041	1.1789
95	195.8	181.1	1.534	36.67	149.4	632.6	.3062	1.1775
96	198.9	184.2	1.510	36.62	150.5	632.6	.3083	1.1761
97	202.1	187.4	1.487	36.56	151.7	632.8	.3104	1.1747
98	205.3	190.6	1.464	36.51	152.9	632.9	.3125	1.1733
99	208.6	193.9	1.441	36.45	154.0	632.9	0.3145	1.1719
100	211.9	197.2	1.419	36.40	155.2	633.0	.3166	1.1705
101	215.2	200.5	1.397	36.34	156.4	633.1	.3187	1.1691
102	218.6	203.9	1.375	36.29	157.6	633.2	.3207	1.1677
103	222.0	207.3	1.354	36.23	158.7	633.3	.3228	1.1663
104	225.4	210.7	1.334	36.18	159.9	633.4	0.3248	1.1649
105	228.9	214.2	1.313	36.12	161.1	633.4	.3269	1.1635
106	232.5	217.8	1.293	36.06	162.3	633.5	.3289	1.1621
107	236.0	221.3	1.274	36.01	163.5	633.6	.3310	1.1607
108	239.7	225.0	1.254	35.95	164.6	633.6	.3330	1.1593
109	243.3	228.6	1.235	35.90	165.8	633.7	0.3351	1.1580
110	247.0	232.3	1.217	35.84	167.0	633.7	.3372	1.1566
111	250.8	236.1	1.198	35.78	168.2	633.8	.3392	1.1552
112	254.5	239.8	1.180	35.72	169.4	633.8	.3413	1.1538
113	258.4	243.7	1.163	35.67	170.6	633.9	.3433	1.1524
114	262.2	247.5	1.145	35.61	171.8	633.9	0.3453	1.1510
115	266.2	251.5	1.128	35.55	173.0	633.9	.3474	1.1497
116	270.1	255.4	1.112	35.49	174.2	634.0	.3495	1.1483
117	274.1	259.4	1.095	35.43	175.4	634.0	.3515	1.1469
118	278.2	263.5	1.079	35.38	176.6	634.0	.3535	1.1455
119	282.3	267.6	1.063	35.32	177.8	634.0	3556	1.1441
120	286.4	271.7	1.047	35.26	179.0	634.0	0.3576	1.1427
121	290.6	275.9	1.032	35.20	180.2	634.0	.3597	1.1414
122	294.8	280.1	1.017	35.14	181.4	634.0	.3618	1.1400
123	299.1	284.4	1.002	35.08	182.6	634.0	.3638	1.1386
124	303.4	288.7	0.987	35.02	183.9	634.0	.3659	1.1372
125	307.8	293.1	0.973	34.96	185.1	634.0	.3679	1.1358

1. Based on 0 for the saturated liquid at –40° F.
2. Inches of mercury below one standard atmosphere.
3. Standard cycle temperatures.

Properties of Water

Temperature (°F)	Saturation Pressure (Pounds Per Square Inch Absolute)	Weight (Pounds Per Gallon)	Specific Gravity 60/60 °F	Conversion Factor,[1] lbs./hr. to GPM
32	.0885	8.345	1.0013	.00199
40	.1217	8.345	1.0013	.00199
50	.1781	8.340	1.0007	.00199
60	.2653	8.334	1.0000	.00199
70	.3631	8.325	.9989	.00200
80	.5069	8.314	.9976	.00200
90	.6982	8.303	.9963	.00200
100	.9492	8.289	.9946	.00201
110	1.2748	8.267	.9919	.00201
120	1.6924	8.253	.9901	.00201
130	2.2225	8.227	.9872	.00202
140	2.8886	8.207	.9848	.00203
150	3.718	8.182	.9818	.00203
160	4.741	8.156	.9786	.00204
170	5.992	8.127	.9752	.00205
180	7.510	8.098	.9717	.00205
190	9.339	8.068	.9681	.00206
200	11.526	8.039	.9646	.00207
210	14.123	8.005	.9605	.00208
212	14.696	7.996	.9594	.00208
220	17.186	7.972	.9566	.00209
240	24.969	7.901	.9480	.00210
260	35.429	7.822	.9386	.00211
280	49.203	7.746	.9294	.00215
300	67.013	7.662	.9194	.00217
350	134.63	7.432	.8918	.00224
400	247.31	7.172	.8606	.00232
450	422.6	6.892	.8270	.00241
500	680.8	6.553	.7863	.00254
550	1045.2	6.132	.7358	.00271
600	1542.9	5.664	.6796	.00294
700	3093.7	3.623	.4347	.00460

1. Multiply flow in pounds per hour by the factor to get equivalent flow in gallons per minute.
Weight per gallon is based on 7.48 gallons per cubic foot.

Properties of Saturated Steam

ABSOLUTE PRESSURE		VACUUM (INCHES OF Hg)	TEMPER–ATURE t (°F)	HEAT OF THE LIQUID (BTU/LB)	LATENT HEAT OF EVAPOR–ATION (BTU/LB)	TOTAL HEAT OF STEAM H_g (BTU/LB)	SPECIFIC VOLUME ∇ (CU FT PER LB)
Lbs Per Sq In. P'	Inches of Hg						
0.20	0.41	29.51	53.14	21.21	1063.8	1085.0	1526.0
0.25	0.51	29.41	59.30	27.36	1060.3	1087.7	1235.3
0.30	0.61	29.31	64.47	32.52	1057.4	1090.0	1039.5
0.35	0.71	29.21	68.93	36.97	1054.9	1091.9	898.5
0.40	0.81	29.11	72.86	40.89	1052.7	1093.6	791.9
0.45	0.92	29.00	76.38	44.41	1050.7	1095.1	708.5
0.50	1.02	28.90	79.58	47.60	1048.8	1096.4	641.4
0.60	1.22	28.70	85.21	53.21	1045.7	1098.9	540.0
0.70	1.43	28.49	90.08	58.07	1042.9	1101.0	466.9
0.80	1.63	28.29	94.38	62.36	1040.4	1102.8	411.7
0.90	1.83	28.09	98.24	66.21	1038.3	1104.5	368.4
1.0	2.04	27.88	101.74	69.70	1036.3	1106.0	333.6
1.2	2.44	27.48	107.92	75.87	1032.7	1108.6	280.9
1.4	2.85	27.07	113.26	81.20	1029.6	1110.8	243.0
1.6	3.26	26.66	117.99	85.91	1026.9	1112.8	214.3
1.8	3.66	26.26	122.23	90.14	1024.5	1114.6	191.8
2.0	4.07	25.85	126.08	93.99	1022.2	1116.2	173.73
2.2	4.48	25.44	129.62	97.52	1020.2	1117.7	158.85
2.4	4.89	25.03	132.89	100.79	1018.3	1119.1	146.38
2.6	5.29	24.63	135.94	103.83	1016.5	1120.3	135.78
2.8	5.70	24.22	138.79	106.68	1014.8	1121.5	126.65
3.0	6.11	23.81	141.48	109.37	1013.2	1122.6	118.71
3.5	7.13	22.79	147.57	115.46	1009.6	1125.1	102.72
4.0	8.14	21.78	152.97	120.86	1006.4	1127.3	90.63
4.5	9.16	20.76	157.83	125.71	1003.6	1129.3	81.16
5.0	10.18	19.74	162.24	130.13	1001.0	1131.1	73.52
5.5	11.20	18.72	166.30	134.19	998.5	1132.7	67.24
6.0	12.22	17.70	170.06	137.96	996.2	1134.2	61.98
6.5	13.23	16.69	173.56	141.47	994.1	1135.6	57.50
7.0	14.25	15.67	176.85	144.76	992.1	1136.9	53.64
7.5	15.27	14.65	179.94	147.86	990.2	1138.1	50.29
8.0	16.29	13.63	182.86	150.79	988.5	1139.3	47.34
8.5	17.31	12.61	185.64	153.57	986.8	1140.4	44.73
9.0	18.32	11.60	188.28	156.22	985.2	1141.4	42.40
9.5	19.34	10.58	190.80	158.75	983.6	1142.3	40.31
10.0	20.36	9.56	193.21	161.17	982.1	1143.3	38.42
11.0	22.40	7.52	197.75	165.73	979.3	1145.0	35.14
12.0	24.43	5.49	201.96	169.96	976.6	1146.6	32.40
13.0	26.47	3.45	205.88	173.91	974.2	1148.1	30.06
14.0	28.50	1.42	209.56	177.61	971.9	1149.5	28.04

Properties of Saturated Steam

PRESSURE (LBS. PER SQ IN.)		TEMPER- ATURE t (°F)	HEAT OF THE LIQUID (BTU/LB)	LATENT HEAT OF EVAPOR- ATION (BTU/LB)	TOTAL HEAT OF STEAM H_g (BTU/LB)	SPECIFIC VOLUME ▽ (CU FT PER LB)
Absolute P'	Gauge P					
14.696	0.0	212.00	180.07	970.3	1150.4	26.80
15.0	0.3	213.03	181.11	969.7	1150.8	26.29
16.0	1.3	216.32	184.42	967.6	1152.0	24.75
17.0	2.3	219.44	187.56	965.5	1153.1	23.39
18.0	3.3	222.41	190.56	963.6	1154.2	22.17
19.0	4.3	225.24	193.42	961.9	1155.3	21.08
20.0	5.3	227.96	196.16	960.1	1156.3	20.089
21.0	6.3	230.57	198.79	958.4	1157.2	19.192
22.0	7.3	233.07	201.33	956.8	1158.1	18.375
23.0	8.3	235.49	203.78	955.2	1159.0	17.627
24.0	9.3	237.82	206.14	953.7	1159.8	16.938
25.0	10.3	240.07	208.42	952.1	1160.6	16.303
26.0	11.3	242.25	210.62	950.7	1161.3	15.715
27.0	12.3	244.36	212.75	949.3	1162.0	15.170
28.0	13.3	246.41	214.83	947.9	1162.7	14.663
29.0	14.3	248.40	216.86	946.5	1163.4	14.189
30.0	15.3	250.33	218.82	945.3	1164.1	13.746
31.0	16.3	252.22	220.73	944.0	1164.7	13.330
32.0	17.3	254.05	222.59	942.8	1165.4	12.940
33.0	18.3	255.84	224.41	941.6	1166.0	12.572
34.0	19.3	257.58	226.18	940.3	1166.5	12.226
35.0	20.3	259.28	227.91	939.2	1167.1	11.898
36.0	21.3	260.95	229.60	938.0	1167.6	11.588
37.0	22.3	262.57	231.26	936.9	1168.2	11.294
38.0	23.3	264.16	232.89	935.8	1168.7	11.015
39.0	24.3	265.72	234.48	934.7	1169.2	10.750
40.0	25.3	267.25	236.03	933.7	1169.7	10.498
41.0	26.3	268.74	237.55	932.6	1170.2	10.258
42.0	27.3	270.21	239.04	931.6	1170.7	10.029
43.0	28.3	271.64	240.51	930.6	1171.1	9.810
44.0	29.3	273.05	241.95	929.6	1171.6	9.601
45.0	30.3	274.44	243.36	928.6	1172.0	9.401
46.0	31.3	275.80	244.75	927.7	1172.4	9.209
47.0	32.3	277.13	246.12	926.7	1172.9	9.025
48.0	33.3	278.45	247.47	925.8	1173.3	8.848
49.0	34.3	279.74	248.79	924.9	1173.7	8.678
50.0	35.3	281.01	250.09	924.0	1174.1	8.515
51.0	36.3	282.26	251.37	923.0	1174.4	8.359
52.0	37.3	283.49	252.63	922.2	1174.8	8.208
53.0	38.3	284.70	253.87	921.3	1175.2	8.062
54.0	39.3	285.90	255.09	920.5	1175.6	7.922

(continued)

Properties of Saturated Steam (continued)

PRESSURE (LBS. PER SQ IN.)		TEMPER- ATURE t (°F)	HEAT OF THE LIQUID (BTU/LB)	LATENT HEAT OF EVAPOR- ATION (BTU/LB)	TOTAL HEAT OF STEAM H$_g$ (BTU/LB)	SPECIFIC VOLUME ▽ (CU FT PER LB)
Absolute P'	Gauge P					
55.0	40.3	287.07	256.30	919.6	1175.9	7.787
56.0	41.3	288.23	257.50	918.8	1176.3	7.656
57.0	42.3	289.37	258.67	917.9	1176.6	7.529
58.0	43.3	290.50	259.82	917.1	1176.9	7.407
59.0	44.3	291.61	260.96	916.3	1177.3	7.289
60.0	45.3	292.71	262.09	915.5	1177.6	7.175
61.0	46.3	293.79	263.20	914.7	1177.9	7.064
62.0	47.3	294.85	264.30	913.9	1178.2	6.957
63.0	48.3	295.90	265.38	913.1	1178.5	6.853
64.0	49.3	296.94	266.45	912.3	1178.8	6.752
65.0	50.3	297.97	267.50	911.6	1179.1	6.655
66.0	51.3	298.99	268.55	910.8	1179.4	6.560
67.0	52.3	299.99	269.58	910.1	1179.7	6.468
68.0	53.3	300.98	270.60	909.4	1180.0	6.378
69.0	54.3	301.96	291.61	908.7	1180.3	6.291
70.0	55.3	302.92	272.61	907.9	1180.6	6.206
71.0	56.3	303.88	273.60	907.2	1180.8	6.124
72.0	57.3	304.83	274.57	906.5	1181.1	6.044
73.0	58.3	305.76	275.54	905.8	1181.3	5.966
74.0	59.3	306.68	276.49	905.1	1181.6	5.890
75.0	60.3	307.60	277.43	904.5	1181.9	5.816
76.0	61.3	308.50	278.37	903.7	1182.1	5.743
77.0	62.3	309.40	279.30	903.1	1182.4	5.673
78.0	63.3	310.29	280.21	902.4	1182.6	5.604
79.0	64.3	311.16	281.12	901.7	1182.8	5.537
80.0	65.3	312.03	282.02	901.1	1183.1	5.472
81.0	66.3	312.89	282.91	900.4	1183.3	5.408
82.0	67.3	313.74	283.79	899.7	1183.5	5.346
83.0	68.3	314.59	284.66	899.1	1183.8	5.285
84.0	69.3	315.42	285.53	898.5	1184.0	5.226
85.0	70.3	316.25	286.39	897.8	1184.2	5.168
86.0	71.3	317.07	287.24	897.2	1184.4	5.111
87.0	72.3	317.88	288.08	896.5	1184.6	5.055
88.0	73.3	318.68	288.91	895.9	1184.8	5.001
89.0	74.3	319.48	289.74	895.3	1185.1	4.948
90.0	75.3	320.27	290.56	894.7	1185.3	4.896
91.0	76.3	321.06	291.38	894.1	1185.5	4.845
92.0	77.3	321.83	292.18	893.5	1185.7	4.796
93.0	78.3	322.60	292.98	892.9	1185.9	4.747
94.0	79.3	323.36	293.78	892.3	1186.1	4.699
95.0	80.3	324.12	294.56	891.7	1186.2	4.652
96.0	81.3	324.87	295.34	891.1	1186.4	4.606
97.0	82.3	325.61	296.12	890.5	1186.6	4.561
98.0	83.3	326.35	296.89	889.9	1186.8	4.517
99.0	84.3	327.08	297.65	889.4	1187.0	4.474

(continued)

Properties of Saturated Steam (continued)

PRESSURE (LBS. PER SQ IN.)		TEMPER–ATURE t (°F)	HEAT OF THE LIQUID (BTU/LB)	LATENT HEAT OF EVAPOR–ATION (BTU/LB)	TOTAL HEAT OF STEAM H$_g$ (BTU/LB)	SPECIFIC VOLUME ▽ (CU FT PER LB)
Absolute P'	Gauge P					
100.0	85.3	327.81	298.40	888.8	1187.2	4.432
101.0	86.3	328.53	299.15	888.2	1187.4	4.391
102.0	87.3	329.25	299.90	887.6	1187.5	4.350
103.0	88.3	329.96	300.64	887.1	1187.7	4.310
104.0	89.3	330.66	301.37	886.5	1187.9	4.271
105.0	90.3	331.36	302.10	886.0	1188.1	4.232
106.0	91.3	332.05	302.82	885.4	1188.2	4.194
107.0	92.3	332.74	303.54	884.9	1188.4	4.157
108.0	93.3	333.42	304.26	884.3	1188.6	4.120
109.0	94.3	334.10	304.97	883.7	1188.7	4.084
110.0	95.3	334.77	305.66	883.2	1188.9	4.049
111.0	96.3	335.44	306.37	882.6	1189.0	4.015
112.0	97.3	336.11	307.06	882.1	1189.2	3.981
113.0	98.3	336.77	307.75	881.6	1189.4	3.947
114.0	99.3	337.42	308.43	881.1	1189.5	3.914
115.0	100.3	338.07	309.11	880.6	1189.7	3.882
116.0	101.3	338.72	309.79	880.0	1189.8	3.850
117.0	102.3	339.36	310.46	879.5	1190.0	3.819
118.0	103.3	339.99	311.12	879.0	1190.1	3.788
119.0	104.3	340.62	311.78	878.4	1190.2	3.758
120.0	105.3	341.25	312.44	877.9	1190.4	3.728
121.0	106.3	341.88	313.10	877.4	1190.5	3.699
122.0	107.3	342.50	313.75	876.9	1190.7	3.670
123.0	108.3	343.11	314.40	876.4	1190.8	3.642
124.0	109.3	343.72	315.04	875.9	1190.9	3.614
125.0	110.3	344.33	315.68	875.4	1191.1	3.587
126.0	111.3	344.94	316.31	874.9	1191.2	3.560
127.0	112.3	345.54	316.94	874.4	1191.3	3.533
128.0	113.3	346.13	317.57	873.9	1191.5	3.507
129.0	114.3	346.73	318.19	873.4	1191.6	3.481
130.0	115.3	347.32	318.81	872.9	1191.7	3.455
131.0	116.3	347.90	319.43	872.5	1191.9	3.430
132.0	117.3	348.48	320.04	872.0	1192.0	3.405
133.0	118.3	349.06	320.65	871.5	1192.1	3.381
134.0	119.3	349.64	321.25	871.0	1192.2	3.357
135.0	120.3	350.21	321.85	870.6	1192.4	3.333
136.0	121.3	350.78	322.45	870.1	1192.5	3.310
137.0	122.3	351.35	323.05	869.6	1192.6	3.287
138.0	123.3	351.91	323.64	869.1	1192.7	3.264
139.0	124.3	352.47	324.23	868.7	1192.9	3.242
140.0	125.3	353.02	324.82	868.2	1193.0	3.220
141.0	126.3	353.57	325.40	867.7	1193.1	3.198
142.0	127.3	354.12	325.98	867.2	1193.2	3.177
143.0	128.3	354.67	326.56	866.7	1193.3	3.155
144.0	129.3	355.21	327.13	866.3	1193.4	3.134

(continued)

Properties of Saturated Steam (continued)

PRESSURE (LBS. PER SQ IN.)		TEMPER– ATURE t (°F)	HEAT OF THE LIQUID (BTU/LB)	LATENT HEAT OF EVAPOR– ATION (BTU/LB)	TOTAL HEAT OF STEAM H$_g$ (BTU/LB)	SPECIFIC VOLUME ▽ (CU FT PER LB)
Absolute P'	Gauge P					
145.0	130.3	355.76	327.70	865.8	1193.5	3.114
146.0	131.3	356.29	328.27	865.3	1193.6	3.094
147.0	132.3	356.83	328.83	864.9	1193.8	3.074
148.0	133.3	357.36	329.39	864.5	1193.9	3.054
149.0	134.3	357.89	329.95	864.0	1194.0	3.034
150.0	135.3	358.42	330.51	863.6	1194.1	3.015
152.0	137.3	359.46	331.61	862.7	1194.3	2.977
154.0	139.3	360.49	332.70	861.8	1194.5	2.940
156.0	141.3	361.52	333.79	860.9	1194.7	2.904
158.0	143.3	362.53	334.86	860.0	1194.9	2.869
160.0	145.3	363.53	335.93	859.2	1195.1	2.834
162.0	147.3	364.53	336.98	858.3	1195.3	2.801
164.0	149.3	365.51	338.02	857.5	1195.5	2.768
166.0	151.3	366.48	339.05	856.6	1195.7	2.736
168.0	153.3	367.45	340.07	855.7	1195.8	2.705
170.0	155.3	368.41	341.09	854.9	1196.0	2.675
172.0	157.3	369.35	342.10	854.1	1196.2	2.645
174.0	159.3	370.29	343.10	853.3	1196.4	2.616
176.0	161.3	371.22	344.09	852.4	1196.5	2.587
178.0	163.3	372.14	345.06	851.6	1196.7	2.559
180.0	165.3	373.06	346.03	850.8	1196.9	2.532
182.0	167.3	373.96	347.00	850.0	1197.0	2.505
184.0	169.3	374.86	347.96	849.2	1197.2	2.479
186.0	171.3	375.75	348.92	848.4	1197.3	2.454
188.0	173.3	376.64	349.86	847.6	1197.5	2.429
190.0	175.3	377.51	350.79	846.8	1197.6	2.404
192.0	177.3	378.38	351.72	846.1	1197.8	2.380
194.0	179.3	379.24	352.64	845.3	1197.9	2.356
196.0	181.3	380.10	353.55	844.5	1198.1	2.333
198.0	183.3	380.95	354.46	843.7	1198.2	2.310
200.0	185.3	381.79	355.36	843.0	1198.4	2.288
205.0	190.3	383.86	357.58	841.1	1198.7	2.234
210.0	195.3	385.90	359.77	839.2	1199.0	2.183
215.0	200.3	387.89	361.91	837.4	1199.3	2.134
220.0	205.3	389.86	364.02	835.6	1199.6	2.087
225.0	210.3	391.79	366.09	833.8	1199.9	2.0422
230.0	215.3	393.68	368.13	832.0	1200.1	1.9992
235.0	220.3	395.54	370.14	830.3	1200.4	1.9579
240.0	225.3	397.37	372.12	828.5	1200.6	1.9183
245.0	230.3	399.18	374.08	826.8	1200.9	1.8803
250.0	235.3	400.95	376.00	825.1	1201.1	1.8438
255.0	240.3	402.70	377.89	823.4	1201.3	1.8086
260.0	245.3	404.42	379.76	821.8	1201.5	1.7748
265.0	250.3	406.11	381.60	820.1	1201.7	1.7422
270.0	255.3	407.78	383.42	818.5	1201.9	1.7107

(continued)

Properties of Saturated Steam (continued)

PRESSURE (LBS. PER SQ IN.)		TEMPER-ATURE t (°F)	HEAT OF THE LIQUID (BTU/LB)	LATENT HEAT OF EVAPOR-ATION (BTU/LB)	TOTAL HEAT OF STEAM H_g (BTU/LB)	SPECIFIC VOLUME ▽ (CU FT PER LB)
Absolute P'	Gauge P					
275.0	260.3	409.43	385.21	816.9	1202.1	1.6804
280.0	265.3	411.05	386.98	815.3	1202.3	1.6511
285.0	270.3	412.65	388.73	813.7	1202.4	1.6228
290.0	275.3	414.23	390.46	812.1	1202.6	1.5954
295.0	280.3	415.79	392.16	810.5	1202.7	1.5689
300.0	285.3	417.33	393.84	809.0	1202.8	1.5433
320.0	305.3	423.29	400.39	803.0	1203.4	1.4485
340.0	325.3	428.97	406.66	797.1	1203.7	1.3645
360.0	345.3	434.40	412.67	791.4	1204.1	1.2895
380.0	365.3	439.60	418.45	785.8	1204.3	1.2222
400.0	385.3	444.59	424.0	780.5	1204.5	1.1613
420.0	405.3	449.39	429.4	775.2	1204.6	1.1061
440.0	425.3	454.02	434.6	770.0	1204.6	1.0556
460.0	445.3	458.50	439.7	764.9	1204.6	1.0094
480.0	465.3	462.82	444.6	759.9	1204.5	0.9670
500.0	485.3	467.01	449.4	755.0	1204.4	0.9278
520.0	505.3	471.07	454.1	750.1	1204.2	0.8915
540.0	525.3	475.01	458.6	745.4	1204.0	0.8578
560.0	545.3	478.85	463.0	740.8	1203.8	0.8265
580.0	565.3	482.58	467.4	736.1	1203.5	0.7973
600.0	585.3	486.21	471.6	731.6	1203.2	0.7698
620.0	605.3	489.75	475.7	727.2	1202.9	0.7440
640.0	625.3	493.21	479.8	722.7	1202.5	0.7198
660.0	645.3	496.58	483.8	718.3	1202.1	0.6971
680.0	665.3	499.88	487.7	714.0	1201.7	0.6757
700.0	685.3	503.10	491.5	709.7	1201.2	0.6554
720.0	705.3	506.25	495.3	705.4	1200.7	0.6362
740.0	725.3	509.34	499.0	701.2	1200.2	0.6180
760.0	745.3	512.36	502.6	697.1	1199.7	0.6007
780.0	765.3	515.33	506.2	692.9	1199.1	0.5843
800.0	785.3	518.23	509.7	688.9	1198.6	0.5687
820.0	805.3	521.08	513.2	684.8	1198.0	0.5538
840.0	825.3	523.88	516.6	680.8	1197.4	0.5396
860.0	845.3	526.63	520.0	676.8	1196.8	0.5260
880.0	865.3	529.33	523.3	672.8	1196.1	0.5130
900.0	885.3	531.98	526.6	668.8	1195.4	0.5006
920.0	905.3	534.59	529.8	664.9	1194.7	0.4886
940.0	925.3	537.16	533.0	661.0	1194.0	0.4772
960.0	945.3	539.68	536.2	657.1	1193.3	0.4663
980.0	965.3	542.17	539.3	653.3	1192.6	0.4557
1000.0	985.3	544.61	542.4	649.4	1191.8	0.4456
1050.0	1035.3	550.57	550.0	639.9	1189.9	0.4218
1100.0	1085.3	556.31	557.4	630.4	1187.8	0.4001
1150.0	1135.3	561.86	564.6	621.0	1185.6	0.3802
1200.0	1185.3	567.22	571.7	611.7	1183.4	0.3619

(continued)

Properties of Saturated Steam (continued)

PRESSURE (LBS. PER SQ IN.)		TEMPER–ATURE t (°F)	HEAT OF THE LIQUID (BTU/LB)	LATENT HEAT OF EVAPOR–ATION (BTU/LB)	TOTAL HEAT OF STEAM H_g (BTU/LB)	SPECIFIC VOLUME ∇ (CU FT PER LB)
Absolute P'	Gauge P					
1250.0	1235.3	572.42	578.6	602.4	1181.0	0.3450
1300.0	1285.3	577.46	585.4	593.2	1178.6	0.3293
1350.0	1335.3	582.35	592.1	584.0	1176.1	0.3148
1400.0	1385.3	587.10	598.7	574.7	1173.4	0.3012
1450.0	1435.3	591.73	605.2	565.5	1170.7	0.2884
1500.0	1485.3	596.23	611.6	556.3	1167.9	0.2765
1600.0	1585.3	604.90	624.1	538.0	1162.1	0.2548
1700.0	1685.3	613.15	636.3	519.6	1155.9	0.2354
1800.0	1785.3	621.03	648.3	501.1	1149.4	0.2179
1900.0	1885.3	628.58	660.1	482.4	1142.4	0.2021
2000.0	1985.3	635.82	671.7	463.4	1135.1	0.1878
2100.0	2085.3	642.77	683.3	444.1	1127.4	0.1746
2200.0	2185.3	649.46	694.8	424.4	1119.2	0.1625
2300.0	2285.3	655.91	706.5	403.9	1110.4	0.1513
2400.0	2385.3	662.12	718.4	382.7	1101.1	0.1407
2500.0	2485.3	668.13	730.6	360.5	1091.1	0.1307
2600.0	2585.3	673.94	743.0	337.2	1080.2	0.1213
2700.0	2685.3	679.55	756.2	312.1	1068.3	0.1123
2800.0	2785.3	684.99	770.1	284.7	1054.8	0.1035
2900.0	2885.3	690.26	785.4	253.6	1039.0	0.0947
3000.0	2985.3	695.36	802.5	217.8	1020.3	0.0858
3100.0	3085.3	700.31	825.0	168.1	993.1	0.0753
3200.0	3185.3	705.11	872.4	62.0	934.4	0.0580
3206.2	3191.5	705.40	902.7	0.0	902.7	0.0503

Properties of Superheated Steam

∇ = specific volume, cubic feet per pound
h_g = total heat of steam, Btu per pound

PRESSURE (LBS PER SQ IN)		SAT. TEMP. t		TOTAL TEMPERATURE—DEGREES FAHRENHEIT (t)										
Absolute P'	Gauge P			360°	400°	440°	480°	500°	600°	700°	800°	900°	1000°	1200°
14.696	0.0	212.00	∇	33.03	34.68	36.32	37.96	38.78	42.86	46.94	51.00	55.07	59.13	67.25
			h_g	1221.1	1239.9	1258.8	1277.6	1287.1	1334.8	1383.2	1432.3	1482.3	1533.1	1637.5
20.0	5.3	227.96	∇	24.21	25.43	26.65	27.86	28.46	31.47	34.47	37.46	40.45	43.44	49.41
			h_g	1220.3	1239.2	1258.2	1277.1	1286.6	1334.4	1382.9	1432.1	1482.1	1533.0	1637.4
30.0	15.3	250.33	∇	16.072	16.897	17.714	18.528	18.933	20.95	22.96	24.96	26.95	28.95	32.93
			h_g	1218.6	1237.9	1257.0	1276.2	1285.7	1333.8	1382.4	1431.7	1481.8	1532.7	1637.2
40.0	25.3	267.25	∇	12.001	12.628	13.247	13.862	14.168	15.688	17.198	18.702	20.20	21.70	24.69
			h_g	1216.9	1236.5	1255.9	1275.2	1284.8	1333.1	1381.9	1431.3	1481.4	1532.4	1637.0
50.0	35.3	281.01	∇	9.557	10.065	10.567	11.062	11.309	12.532	13.744	14.950	16.152	17.352	19.747
			h_g	1215.2	1235.1	1254.7	1274.2	1283.9	1332.5	1381.4	1430.9	1481.1	1532.1	1636.8
60.0	45.3	292.71	∇	7.927	8.357	8.779	9.196	9.403	10.427	11.441	12.449	13.452	14.454	16.451
			h_g	1213.4	1233.6	1253.5	1273.2	1283.0	1331.8	1380.9	1430.5	1480.8	1531.9	1636.6
70.0	55.3	302.92	∇	6.762	7.136	7.502	7.863	8.041	8.924	9.796	10.662	11.524	12.383	14.097
			h_g	1211.5	1232.1	1252.3	1272.2	1282.0	1331.1	1380.4	1430.1	1480.5	1531.6	1636.3
80.0	65.3	312.03	∇	5.888	6.220	6.544	6.862	7.020	7.797	8.562	9.322	10.077	10.830	12.332
			h_g	1209.7	1230.7	1251.1	1271.1	1281.1	1330.5	1379.9	1429.7	1480.1	1531.3	1636.2
90.0	75.3	320.27	∇	5.208	5.508	5.799	6.084	6.225	6.920	7.603	8.279	8.952	9.623	10.959
			h_g	1207.7	1229.1	1249.8	1270.1	1280.1	1329.8	1379.4	1429.3	1479.8	1531.0	1635.9
100.0	85.3	327.81	∇	4.663	4.937	5.202	5.462	5.589	6.218	6.835	7.446	8.052	8.656	9.860
			h_g	1205.7	1227.6	1248.6	1269.0	1279.1	1329.1	1378.9	1428.9	1479.5	1530.8	1635.7

– Continued –

Properties of Superheated Steam (continued)

▽ = specific volume, cubic feet per pound
h_g = total heat of steam, Btu per pound

PRESSURE (LBS PER SQ IN)		SAT. TEMP. t		TOTAL TEMPERATURE—DEGREES FAHRENHEIT (t)										
Absolute P'	Gauge P			360°	400°	440°	480°	500°	600°	700°	800°	900°	1000°	1200°
120.0	105.3	341.25	▽	3.844	4.081	4.307	4.527	4.636	5.165	5.683	6.195	6.702	7.207	8.212
			h_g	1201.6	1224.4	1246.0	1266.90	1277.2	1327.7	1377.8	1428.1	1478.8	1530.2	1635.3
140.0	125.3	353.02	▽	3.258	3.468	3.667	3.860	3.954	4.413	4.861	5.301	5.738	6.172	7.035
			h_g	1197.3	1221.1	1243.3	1264.7	1275.2	1326.4	1376.8	1427.3	1478.2	1529.7	1634.9
160.0	145.3	363.53	▽	- -	3.008	3.187	3.359	3.443	3.849	4.244	4.631	5.015	5.396	6.152
			h_g	- -	1217.6	1240.6	1262.4	1273.1	1325.0	1375.7	1426.4	1477.5	1529.1	1634.5
180.0	165.3	373.06	▽	- -	2.649	2.813	2.969	3.044	3.411	3.764	4.110	4.452	4.792	5.466
			h_g	- -	1214.0	1237.8	1260.2	1271.0	1323.5	1374.7	1425.6	1476.8	1528.6	1634.1
200.0	185.3	381.79	▽	- -	2.361	2.513	2.656	2.726	3.060	3.380	3.693	4.002	4.309	4.917
			h_g	- -	1210.3	1234.9	1257.8	1268.9	1322.1	1373.6	1424.8	1476.2	1528.0	1633.7
220.0	205.3	389.86	▽	- -	2.125	2.267	2.400	2.465	2.772	3.066	3.352	3.634	3.913	4.467
			h_g	- -	1206.5	1231.9	1255.4	1266.7	1320.7	1372.6	1424.0	1475.5	1527.5	1633.3
240.0	225.3	397.37	▽	- -	1.9276	2.062	2.187	2.247	2.533	2.804	3.068	3.327	3.584	4.093
			h_g	- -	1202.5	1228.8	1253.0	1264.5	1319.2	1371.5	1423.2	1474.8	1526.9	1632.9
260.0	245.3	404.42	▽	- -	- -	1.8882	2.006	2.063	2.330	2.582	2.827	3.067	3.305	3.776
			h_g	- -	- -	1225.7	1250.5	1262.3	1317.7	1370.4	1422.3	1474.2	1526.3	1632.5
280.0	265.3	411.05	▽	- -	- -	1.7388	1.8512	1.9047	2.156	2.392	2.621	2.845	3.066	3.504
			h_g	- -	- -	1222.4	1247.9	1260.0	1316.2	1369.4	1421.5	1473.5	1525.8	1632.1
300.0	285.3	417.33	▽	- -	- -	1.6090	1.7165	1.7675	2.005	2.227	2.442	2.652	2.859	3.269
			h_g	- -	- -	1219.1	1245.3	1257.6	1314.7	1368.3	1420.6	1472.8	1525.2	1631.7

– Continued –

Properties of Superheated Steam (continued)

∇ = specific volume, cubic feet per pound
h_g = total heat of steam, Btu per pound

PRESSURE (LBS PER SQ IN)		SAT. TEMP. t		TOTAL TEMPERATURE—DEGREES FAHRENHEIT (t)										
Absolute P'	Gauge P			360°	400°	440°	480°	500°	600°	700°	800°	900°	1000°	1200°
320.0	305.3	423.29	∇	- - -	- - -	1.4950	1.5985	1.6472	1.8734	2.083	2.285	2.483	2.678	3.063
			h_g	- - -	- - -	1215.6	1242.6	1255.2	1313.2	1367.2	1419.8	1472.1	1524.7	1631.3
340.0	325.3	428.97	∇	- - -	- - -	1.3941	1.4941	1.5410	1.7569	1.9562	2.147	2.334	2.518	2.881
			h_g	- - -	- - -	1212.1	1239.9	1252.8	1311.6	1366.1	1419.0	1471.5	1524.1	1630.9
360.0	345.3	434.40	∇	- - -	- - -	1.3041	1.4012	1.4464	1.6533	1.8431	2.025	2.202	2.376	2.719
			h_g	- - -	- - -	1208.4	1237.1	1250.3	1310.1	1365.0	1418.1	1470.8	1523.5	1630.5

– Continued –

Properties of Superheated Steam (continued)

∇ = specific volume, cubic feet per pound
h_g = total heat of steam, Btu per pound

PRESSURE (LBS PER SQ IN)		SAT. TEMP. t		TOTAL TEMPERATURE—DEGREES FAHRENHEIT (t)										
Absolute P'	Gauge P			500°	540°	600°	640°	660°	700°	740°	800°	900°	1000°	1200°
380.0	365.3	439.60	∇	1.3616	1.444	1.5605	1.6345	1.6707	1.7419	1.8118	1.9149	2.083	2.249	2.575
			h_g	1247.7	1273.1	1308.5	1331.0	1342.0	1363.8	1385.3	1417.3	1470.1	1523.0	1630.0
400.0	385.3	444.59	∇	1.2851	1.3652	1.4770	1.5480	1.5827	1.6508	1.7177	1.8161	1.9767	2.134	2.445
			h_g	1245.1	1271.0	1306.9	1329.6	1340.8	1362.7	1384.3	1416.4	1469.4	1522.4	1629.6
420.0	405.3	449.39	∇	1.2158	1.2935	1.4014	1.4697	1.5030	1.5684	1.6324	1.7267	1.8802	2.031	2.327
			h_g	1242.5	1268.9	1305.3	1328.3	1339.5	1361.6	1383.3	1415.5	1468.7	1521.9	1629.2
440.0	425.3	454.02	∇	1.1526	1.2282	1.3327	1.3984	1.4306	1.4934	1.5549	1.6454	1.7925	1.9368	2.220
			h_g	1239.8	1266.7	1303.6	1326.9	1338.2	1360.4	1382.3	1414.7	1468.1	1521.3	1628.8
460.0	445.3	458.50	∇	1.0948	1.1685	1.2698	1.3334	1.3644	1.4250	1.4842	1.5711	1.7124	1.8508	2.122
			h_g	1237.0	1264.5	1302.0	1325.4	1336.9	1359.3	1381.3	1413.8	1467.4	1520.7	1628.4
480.0	465.3	462.82	∇	1.0417	1.1138	1.2122	1.2737	1.3038	1.3622	1.4193	1.5031	1.6390	1.7720	2.033
			h_g	1234.2	1262.3	1300.3	1324.0	1335.6	1358.2	1380.3	1412.9	1466.7	1520.2	1628.0
500.0	485.3	467.01	∇	0.9927	1.0633	1.1591	1.2188	1.2478	1.3044	1.3596	1.4405	1.5715	1.6996	1.9504
			h_g	1231.3	1260.0	1298.6	1322.6	1334.2	1357.0	1379.3	1412.1	1466.0	1519.6	1627.6
520.0	505.3	471.07	∇	0.9473	1.0166	1.1101	1.1681	1.1962	1.2511	1.3045	1.3826	1.5091	1.6326	1.8743
			h_g	1228.3	1257.7	1296.9	1321.1	1332.9	1355.8	1378.2	1411.2	1465.3	1519.0	1627.2
540.0	525.3	475.01	∇	0.9052	0.9733	1.0646	1.1211	1.1485	1.2017	1.2535	1.3291	1.4514	1.5707	1.8039
			h_g	1225.3	1255.4	1295.2	1319.7	1331.5	1354.6	1377.2	1410.3	1464.6	1518.5	1626.8
560.0	545.3	478.85	∇	0.8659	0.9330	1.0224	1.0775	1.1041	1.1558	1.2060	1.2794	1.3978	1.5132	1.7385
			h_g	1222.2	1253.0	1293.4	1318.2	1330.2	1353.5	1376.1	1409.4	1463.9	1517.9	1626.4
580.0	565.3	482.58	∇	0.8291	0.8954	0.9830	1.0368	1.0627	1.1331	1.1619	1.2331	1.3479	1.4596	1.6776
			h_g	1219.0	1250.5	1291.7	1316.7	1328.8	1352.3	1375.1	1408.6	1463.2	1517.3	1626.0
600.0	585.3	486.21	∇	0.7947	0.8602	0.9463	0.9988	1.0241	1.0732	1.1207	1.1899	1.3013	1.4096	1.6208
			h_g	1215.7	1248.1	1289.9	1315.2	1327.4	1351.1	1374.0	1407.7	1462.5	1516.7	1625.5

Properties of Superheated Steam (continued)

∇ = specific volume, cubic feet per pound
h_g = total heat of steam, Btu per pound

PRESSURE (LBS PER SQ IN)		SAT. TEMP.		TOTAL TEMPERATURE—DEGREES FAHRENHEIT (t)										
Absolute P'	Gauge P	t		500°	540°	600°	640°	660°	700°	740°	800°	900°	1000°	1200°
620.0	605.3	489.75	∇	0.7624	0.8272	0.9118	0.9633	0.9880	1.0358	1.0821	1.1494	1.2577	1.3628	1.5676
			h_g	1212.4	1245.5	1288.1	1313.7	1326.0	1349.9	1373.0	1406.8	1461.8	1516.2	1625.1
640.0	625.3	493.21	∇	0.7319	0.7963	0.8795	0.9299	0.9541	1.0008	1.0459	1.1115	1.2168	1.3190	1.5178
			h_g	1209.0	1243.0	1286.2	1312.2	1324.6	1348.6	1371.9	1405.9	1461.1	1515.6	1624.7
660.0	645.3	496.58	∇	0.7032	0.7670	0.8491	0.8985	0.9222	0.9679	1.0119	1.0759	1.1784	1.2778	1.4709
			h_g	1205.4	1240.4	1284.4	1310.6	1323.2	1347.4	1370.8	1405.0	1460.4	1515.0	1624.3
680.0	665.3	499.88	∇	0.6759	0.7395	0.8205	0.8690	0.8922	0.9369	0.9800	1.0424	1.1423	1.2390	1.4269
			h_g	1201.8	1237.7	1282.5	1309.1	1321.7	1346.2	1369.8	1404.1	1459.7	1514.5	1623.9
700.0	685.3	503.10	∇	- - -	0.7134	0.7934	0.8411	0.8639	0.9077	0.9498	1.0108	1.1082	1.2024	1.3853
			h_g	- - -	1235.0	1280.6	1307.5	1320.3	1345.0	1368.7	1403.2	1459.0	1513.9	1623.5
750.0	735.3	510.86	∇	- - -	0.6540	0.7319	0.7778	0.7996	0.8414	0.8813	0.9391	1.0310	1.1196	1.2912
			h_g	- - -	1227.9	1275.7	1303.5	1316.6	1341.8	1366.0	1400.9	1457.2	1512.4	1622.4
800.0	785.3	518.23	∇	- - -	0.6015	0.6779	0.7223	0.7433	0.7833	0.8215	0.8763	0.9633	1.0470	1.2088
			h_g	- - -	1220.5	1270.7	1299.4	1312.9	1338.6	1363.2	1398.6	1455.4	1511.0	1621.4
850.0	835.3	525.26	∇	- - -	0.5546	0.6301	0.6732	0.6934	0.7320	0.7685	0.8209	0.9037	0.9830	1.1360
			h_g	- - -	1212.7	1265.5	1295.2	1309.0	1335.4	1360.4	1396.3	1453.6	1509.5	1620.4
900.0	885.3	531.98	∇	- - -	0.5124	0.5873	0.6294	0.6491	0.6863	0.7215	0.7716	0.8506	0.9262	1.0714
			h_g	- - -	1204.4	1260.1	1290.9	1305.1	1332.1	1357.5	1393.9	1451.8	1508.1	1619.3
950.0	935.3	538.42	∇	- - -	0.4740	0.5489	0.5901	0.6092	0.6453	0.6793	0.7275	0.8031	0.8753	1.0136
			h_g	- - -	1195.5	1254.6	1286.4	1301.1	1328.7	1354.7	1391.6	1450.0	1506.6	1618.3
1000.0	985.3	544.61	∇	- - -	- - -	0.5140	0.5546	0.5733	0.6084	0.6413	0.6878	0.7604	0.8294	0.9615
			h_g	- - -	- - -	1248.8	1281.9	1297.0	1325.3	1351.7	1389.2	1448.2	1505.1	1617.3

– Continued –

Properties of Superheated Steam (continued)

∇ = specific volume, cubic feet per pound
h_g = total heat of steam, Btu per pound

PRESSURE (LBS PER SQ IN)		SAT. TEMP. t		TOTAL TEMPERATURE—DEGREES FAHRENHEIT (t)										
Absolute P'	Gauge P			660°	700°	740°	760°	780°	800°	860°	900°	1000°	1100°	1200°
1100.0	1085.3	556.31	∇	0.5110	0.5445	0.5755	0.5904	0.6049	0.6191	0.6601	0.6866	0.7503	0.8177	0.8716
			h_g	1288.5	1318.3	1345.8	1358.9	1371.7	1384.3	1420.8	1444.5	1502.2	1558.8	1615.2
1200.0	1185.3	567.22	∇	0.4586	0.4909	0.5206	0.5347	0.5484	0.5617	0.6003	0.6250	0.6843	0.7412	07967
			h_g	1279.6	1311.0	1339.6	1353.2	1366.4	1379.3	1416.7	1440.7	1499.2	1556.4	1613.1
1300.0	1285.3	577.46	∇	0.4139	0.4454	0.4739	0.4874	0.5004	0.5131	0.5496	0.5728	0.6284	0.6816	0.7333
			h_g	1270.2	1303.4	1333.3	1347.3	1361.0	1374.3	1412.5	1437.0	1496.2	1553.9	1611.0
1400.0	1385.3	587.10	∇	0.3753	0.4062	0.4338	0.4468	0.4593	0.4714	0.5061	0.5281	0.5805	0.6305	0.6789
			h_g	1260.3	1295.5	1326.7	1341.3	1355.4	1369.1	1408.2	1433.1	1493.2	1551.4	1608.9
1500.0	1485.3	596.23	∇	0.3413	0.3719	0.3989	0.4114	0.4235	0.4352	0.4684	0.4893	0.5390	0.5862	0.6318
			h_g	1249.8	1287.2	1320.0	1335.2	1349.7	1363.8	1403.9	1429.3	1490.1	1548.9	1606.8
1600.0	1585.3	604.90	∇	0.3112	0.3417	0.3682	0.3804	0.3921	0.4034	0.4353	0.4553	0.5027	0.5474	0.5906
			h_g	1238.7	1278.7	1313.0	1328.8	1343.9	1358.4	1399.5	1425.3	1487.0	1546.4	1604.6
1700.0	1685.3	613.15	∇	0.2842	0.3148	0.3410	0.3529	0.3643	0.3753	0.4061	0.4253	0.4706	0.5132	0.5542
			h_g	1226.8	1269.7	1305.8	1322.3	1337.9	1352.9	1395.0	1421.4	1484.0	1543.8	1602.5
1800.0	1785.3	621.03	∇	0.2597	0.2907	0.3166	0.3284	0.3395	0.3502	0.3801	0.3986	0.4421	0.4828	0.5218
			h_g	1214.0	1260.3	1298.4	1315.5	1331.8	1347.2	1390.4	1417.4	1480.8	1541.3	1600.4
1900.0	1885.3	628.58	∇	0.2371	0.2688	0.2947	0.3063	0.3173	0.3277	0.3568	0.3747	0.4165	0.4556	0.4929
			h_g	1200.2	1250.4	1290.6	1308.6	1325.4	1341.5	1385.8	1413.3	1477.7	1538.8	1598.2
2000.0	1985.3	635.82	∇	0.2161	0.2489	0.2748	0.2863	0.2972	0.3074	0.3358	0.3532	0.3935	0.4311	0.4668
			h_g	1184.9	1240.0	1282.6	1301.4	1319.0	1335.5	1381.2	1409.2	1474.5	1536.2	1596.1
2100.0	2085.3	642.77	∇	0.1962	0.2306	0.2567	0.2682	0.2789	0.2890	0.3167	0.3337	0.3727	0.4089	0.4433
			h_g	1167.7	1229.0	1274.3	1294.0	1312.3	1329.5	1376.4	1405.0	1471.4	1533.6	1593.9
2200.0	2185.3	649.46	∇	0.1768	0.2135	0.2400	0.2514	0.2621	0.2721	0.2994	0.3159	0.3538	0.3837	0.4218
			h_g	1147.8	1217.4	1265.7	1286.3	1305.4	1323.3	1371.5	1400.8	1468.2	1531.1	1591.8

Properties of Superheated Steam (continued)

∇ = specific volume, cubic feet per pound
h_g = total heat of steam, Btu per pound

PRESSURE (LBS PER SQ IN)		SAT. TEMP.		TOTAL TEMPERATURE—DEGREES FAHRENHEIT (t)										
Absolute P'	Gauge P	t		660°	700°	740°	760°	780°	800°	860°	900°	1000°	1100°	1200°
2300.0	2285.3	655.91	∇	0.1575	0.1978	0.2247	0.2362	0.2468	0.2567	0.2835	0.2997	0.3365	0.3703	0.4023
			h_g	1123.8	1204.9	1256.7	1278.4	1298.4	1316.9	1366.6	1396.5	1464.9	1528.5	1589.6
2400.0	2385.3	662.12	∇	- - -	0.1828	0.2105	0.2221	0.2327	0.2425	0.2689	0.2848	0.3207	0.3534	0.3843
			h_g	- - -	1191.5	1247.3	1270.2	1291.1	1310.3	1361.6	1392.2	1461.7	1525.9	1587.4
2500.0	2485.3	668.13	∇	- - -	0.1686	0.1973	0.2090	0.2196	0.2294	0.2555	0.2710	0.3061	0.3379	0.3678
			h_g	- - -	1176.8	1237.6	1261.8	1283.6	1303.6	1356.5	1387.8	1458.4	1523.2	1585.3
2600.0	2585.3	673.94	∇	- - -	0.1549	0.1849	0.1967	0.2074	0.2172	0.2431	0.2584	0.2926	0.3236	0.3526
			h_g	- - -	1160.6	1227.3	1252.9	1275.8	1296.8	1351.4	1383.4	1455.1	1520.6	1583.1
2700.0	2685.3	679.55	∇	- - -	0.1415	0.1732	0.1853	0.1960	0.2059	0.2315	0.2466	0.2801	0.3103	0.3385
			h_g	- - -	1142.5	1216.5	1243.8	1267.9	1289.7	1346.1	1378.9	1451.8	1518.0	1580.9
2800.0	2785.3	684.99	∇	- - -	0.1281	0.1622	0.1745	0.1854	0.1953	0.2208	0.2356	0.2685	0.2979	0.3254
			h_g	- - -	1121.4	1205.1	1234.2	1259.6	1282.4	1340.8	1374.3	1448.5	1515.4	1578.7
2900.0	2885.3	690.26	∇	- - -	0.1143	0.1517	0.1644	0.1754	0.1853	0.2108	0.2254	0.2577	0.2864	0.3132
			h_g	- - -	1095.9	1193.0	1224.3	1251.1	1274.9	1335.3	1369.7	1445.1	1512.7	1576.5
3000.0	2985.3	695.36	∇	- - -	0.0984	0.1416	0.1548	0.1660	0.1760	0.2014	0.2159	0.2476	0.2757	0.3018
			h_g	- - -	1060.7	1180.1	1213.8	1242.2	1267.2	1329.7	1365.0	1441.8	1510.0	1574.3
3100.0	3085.3	700.31	∇	- - -	- - -	0.1320	0.1456	0.1571	0.1672	0.1926	0.2070	0.2382	0.2657	0.2911
			h_g	- - -	- - -	1166.2	1202.9	1233.0	1259.3	1324.1	1360.3	1438.4	1507.4	1572.1
3200.0	3185.3	705.11	∇	- - -	- - -	0.1226	0.1369	0.1486	0.1589	0.1843	0.1986	0.2293	0.2563	0.2811
			h_g	- - -	- - -	1151.1	1191.4	1223.5	1251.1	1318.3	1355.5	1434.9	1504.7	1569.9
3206.2	3191.5	705.40	∇	- - -	- - -	0.1220	0.1363	0.1480	0.1583	0.1838	0.1981	0.2288	0.2557	0.2806
			h_g	- - -	- - -	1150.2	1190.6	1222.9	1250.5	1317.9	1355.2	1434.7	1504.5	1569.8

Velocity of Liquids in Pipe

The mean velocity of any flowing liquid can be calculated from the following formula or from the nomograph on the opposite page. The nomograph is a graphical solution of the formula.

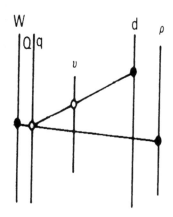

$$v = 183.3\frac{q}{d^2} = 0.408\frac{Q}{d^2} = 0.0509\frac{W}{d^2\,p}$$

(For values of d, see Pipe Data Carbon and Alloy Steel–Stainless Steel table in Chapter 11.)

The pressure drop per 100 feet and the velocity in Schedule 40 pipe, for water at 60°F, have been calculated for commonly used flow rates for pipe sizes of 1/8 to 24–inch; these values are tabulated on following pages.

Example 1

Given: No. 3 Fuel Oil of 0.898 specific gravity at 60°F flows through a 2–inch Schedule 40 pipe at the rate of 45,000 pounds per hour.

Find: The rate of flow in gallons per minute and the mean velocity in the pipe.

Solution:

p = 56.02 = weight density in pounds per cubic foot (specific gravity of fluid times weight density of water at same temperature.)

Connect		Read
W = 45,000	p = 56.02	Q = 100
Q = 100	2" Sched 40	v = 10

Example 2

Given: Maximum flow rate of a liquid will be 300 gallons per minute with maximum velocity limited to 12 feet per second through Schedule 40 pipe.

Find: The smallest suitable pipe size and the velocity through the pipe.

Solution:

Connect		Read
Q = 300	v = 12	d = 3.2
3–1/2" Schedule 40 pipe suitable		
Q = 300	3–1/2" Sched 40	v = 10

Reasonable Velocities for the Flow of Water through Pipe

Service Condition	Reasonable Velocity (feet per second)
Boiler Feed	8 to 15
Pump Suction and Drain Lines	4 to 7
General Service	4 to 10
City	to 7

Extracted from Technical Paper No. 410, *Flow of Fluids*, with permission of Crane Co.

Velocity of Liquids in Pipe (Continued)

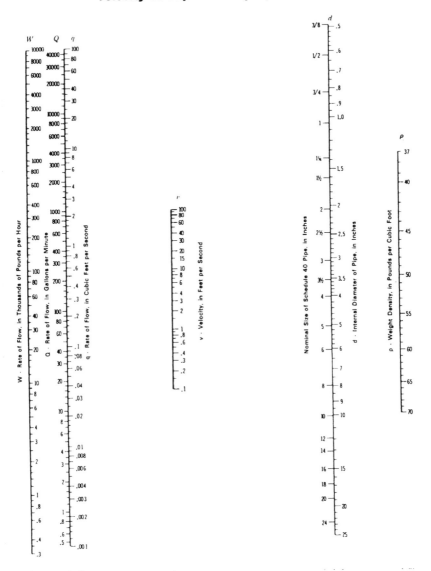

Flow of Water Through Schedule 40 Steel Pipe

PRESSURE DROP PER 100 FEET AND VELOCITY IN SCHEDULE 40 PIPE FOR WATER AT 60°F

Gallons per Minute	Cubic Ft. per Second	1/8" Velocity (Feet per Sec.)	1/8" Press. Drop (PSI)	1/4" Velocity (Feet per Sec.)	1/4" Press. Drop (PSI)	3/8" Velocity (Feet per Sec.)	3/8" Press. Drop (PSI)	1/2" Velocity (Feet per Sec.)	1/2" Press. Drop (PSI)	3/4" Velocity (Feet per Sec.)	3/4" Press. Drop (PSI)	1" Velocity (Feet per Sec.)	1" Press. Drop (PSI)	1-1/4" Velocity (Feet per Sec.)	1-1/4" Press. Drop (PSI)	1-1/2" Velocity (Feet per Sec.)	1-1/2" Press. Drop (PSI)	2" Velocity (Feet per Sec.)	2" Press. Drop (PSI)	2-1/2" Velocity (Feet per Sec.)	2-1/2" Press. Drop (PSI)	3" Velocity (Feet per Sec.)	3" Press. Drop (PSI)	3-1/2" Velocity (Feet per Sec.)	3-1/2" Press. Drop (PSI)	4" Velocity (Feet per Sec.)	4" Press. Drop (PSI)
.2	0.000446	1.13	1.86	0.616	0.359																						
.3	0.000668	1.69	4.22	0.924	0.903	0.504	0.159	0.317	0.061																		
.4	0.000891	2.26	6.98	1.23	1.61	0.672	0.345	0.422	0.086																		
.5	0.00111	2.82	10.5	1.54	2.39	0.840	0.539	0.528	0.167	0.301	0.033																
.6	0.00134	3.39	14.7	1.85	3.29	1.01	0.751	0.633	0.240	0.361	0.041																
.8	0.00178	4.52	25.0	2.46	5.44	1.34	1.25	0.844	0.408	0.481	0.102																
1	0.00223	5.65	37.2	3.08	8.28	1.68	1.85	1.06	0.600	0.602	0.155	0.371	0.048														
2	0.00446	11.29	134.4	6.16	30.1	3.36	6.58	2.11	2.10	1.20	0.526	0.743	0.164	0.429	0.044												
3	0.00668			9.25	64.1	5.04	13.9	3.17	4.33	1.81	1.09	1.114	0.336	0.644	0.090	0.473	0.043										
4	0.00891			12.33	111.2	6.72	23.9	4.22	7.42	2.41	1.83	1.49	0.565	0.858	0.150	0.630	0.071										
5	0.01114					8.40	36.7	5.28	11.2	3.01	2.75	1.86	0.835	1.073	0.223	0.788	0.104										
6	0.01337					10.08	51.9	6.33	15.8	3.61	3.84	2.23	1.17	1.29	0.309	0.946	0.145	0.574	0.044								
8	0.01782					13.44	91.1	8.45	27.7	4.81	6.60	2.97	1.99	1.72	0.518	1.26	0.241	0.765	0.073								
10	0.02228							10.56	42.4	6.02	9.99	3.71	2.99	2.15	0.774	1.58	0.361	0.956	0.108	0.670	0.046						
15	0.03342									9.03	21.6	5.57	6.36	3.22	1.63	2.37	0.755	1.43	0.224	1.01	0.094						
20	0.04456									12.03	37.8	7.43	10.9	4.29	2.78	3.16	1.28	1.91	0.375	1.34	0.158	0.868	0.056				
25	0.05570											9.28	16.7	5.37	4.22	3.94	1.93	2.39	0.561	1.68	0.234	1.09	0.083	0.812	0.041		
30	0.06684											11.14	23.8	6.44	5.92	4.73	2.72	2.87	0.786	2.01	0.327	1.30	0.114	0.974	0.056		
35	0.07798											12.99	32.2	7.51	7.90	5.52	3.64	3.35	1.05	2.35	0.436	1.52	0.151	1.14	0.071	0.882	0.041
40	0.08912											14.85	41.5	8.59	10.24	6.30	4.65	3.83	1.35	2.68	0.556	1.74	0.192	1.30	0.095	1.01	0.052
45	0.1003													9.67	12.80	7.09	5.85	4.30	1.67	3.02	0.668	1.95	0.239	1.46	0.117	1.13	0.064
50	0.1114													10.74	15.66	7.88	7.15	4.78	2.03	3.35	0.839	2.17	0.288	1.62	0.142	1.26	0.076

(continued)

Flow of Water Through Schedule 40 Steel Pipe (continued)

PRESSURE DROP PER 100 FEET AND VELOCITY IN SCHEDULE 40 PIPE FOR WATER AT 60°F

Gallons per Minute	Cubic Ft. per Second	Velocity (Ft/Sec) [10"]	Press. Drop (PSI)	Velocity	Press. Drop	Velocity	Press. Drop	Velocity	Press. Drop	Velocity	Press. Drop	Velocity [5"]	Press. Drop	Velocity [6"]	Press. Drop	Velocity [8"]	Press. Drop
60	0.1337	5.74	2.87	4.02	1.18	2.60	0.46	1.95	0.204	1.51	0.107	---	---	---	---	9.47	10.21
70	0.1560	6.70	3.84	4.69	1.59	3.04	0.540	2.27	0.261	1.76	0.143	1.12	0.047	---	---	11.05	13.71
80	0.1782	7.65	4.97	5.36	2.03	3.47	0.687	2.60	0.334	2.02	0.180	1.28	0.060	---	---	12.62	17.59
90	0.2005	8.60	6.20	6.03	2.53	3.91	0.861	2.92	0.416	2.27	0.224	1.44	0.074	---	---	14.20	22.0
100	0.2228	9.56	7.59	6.70	3.09	4.34	1.05	3.25	0.509	2.52	0.272	1.60	0.090	1.11	0.036	15.78	26.9
125	0.2785	11.97	11.76	8.38	4.71	5.43	1.61	4.06	0.769	3.15	0.415	2.01	0.135	1.39	0.055	19.72	41.4
150	0.3342	14.36	16.70	10.05	6.69	6.51	2.24	4.87	1.08	3.78	0.580	2.41	0.190	1.67	0.077	---	---
175	0.3899	16.75	22.3	11.73	8.97	7.60	3.00	5.68	1.44	4.41	0.774	2.81	0.253	1.94	0.102	---	---
200	0.4456	19.14	28.8	13.42	11.68	8.68	3.87	6.49	1.85	5.04	0.985	3.21	0.323	2.22	0.130	---	---
225	0.5013	---	---	15.09	14.63	9.77	4.83	7.30	2.32	5.67	1.23	3.61	0.401	2.50	0.162	1.44	0.043
250	0.557	---	---	---	---	10.85	5.93	8.12	2.84	6.30	1.46	4.01	0.495	2.78	0.195	1.60	0.051
275	0.6127	---	---	---	---	11.94	7.14	8.93	3.40	6.93	1.79	4.41	0.583	3.05	0.234	1.76	0.061
300	0.6684	---	---	---	---	13.00	8.36	9.74	4.02	7.56	2.11	4.81	0.683	3.33	0.275	1.92	0.072
325	0.7241	---	---	---	---	14.12	9.89	10.53	4.69	8.19	2.47	5.21	0.797	3.61	0.320	2.08	0.083
350	0.7798	---	---	---	---	---	---	11.36	5.41	8.82	2.84	5.62	0.919	3.89	0.367	2.24	0.095
375	0.8355	---	---	---	---	---	---	12.17	6.18	9.45	3.25	6.02	1.05	4.16	0.416	2.40	0.108
400	0.8912	---	---	---	---	---	---	12.98	7.03	10.08	3.68	6.42	1.19	4.44	0.471	2.56	0.121
425	0.9469	---	---	---	---	---	---	13.80	7.89	10.71	4.12	6.82	1.33	4.72	0.529	2.73	0.136
450	1.003	---	---	---	---	---	---	14.61	8.80	11.34	4.60	7.22	1.48	5.00	0.590	2.89	0.151
475	1.059	1.93	0.054	---	---	---	---	---	---	11.97	5.12	7.62	1.64	5.27	0.653	3.04	0.166
500	1.114	2.03	0.059	---	---	---	---	---	---	12.60	5.65	8.02	1.81	5.55	0.720	3.21	0.182
550	1.225	2.24	0.071	---	---	---	---	---	---	13.85	6.79	8.82	2.17	6.11	0.861	3.53	0.219

(continued)

Flow of Water Through Schedule 40 Steel Pipe (continued)

PRESSURE DROP PER 100 FEET AND VELOCITY IN SCHEDULE 40 PIPE FOR WATER AT 60°F

Velocity in Feet per Sec. / Press. Drop (PSI) for each pipe size.

Gallons per Minute	Cubic Ft. per Second	4" Vel	4" Press	5" Vel	5" Press	6" Vel	6" Press	8" Vel	8" Press	10" Vel	10" Press	12" Vel	12" Press	14" Vel	14" Press	16" Vel	16" Press	18" Vel	18" Press	20" Vel	20" Press	24" Vel	24" Press
600	1.337	15.12	8.04	9.63	2.55	6.66	1.02	3.85	0.258	2.44	0.083												
650	1.448	---	---	10.43	2.98	7.22	1.18	4.17	0.301	2.64	0.097												
700	1.560			11.23	3.43	7.78	1.35	4.49	0.343	2.85	0.112	2.01	0.047										
750	1.671			12.03	3.92	8.33	1.55	4.81	0.392	3.05	0.127	2.15	0.054										
800	1.782			12.83	4.43	8.88	1.75	5.13	0.443	3.25	0.143	2.29	0.061										
850	1.894			13.64	5.00	9.44	1.96	5.45	0.497	3.46	0.160	2.44	0.068	2.02	0.042								
900	2.005			14.44	5.58	9.99	2.18	5.77	0.554	3.66	0.179	2.58	0.075	2.13	0.047								
950	2.117			15.24	6.21	10.55	2.42	6.09	0.613	3.86	0.198	2.72	0.083	2.25	0.052								
1000	2.228			16.04	6.84	11.10	2.68	6.41	0.675	4.07	0.218	2.87	0.091	2.37	0.057								
1100	2.451			17.65	8.23	12.22	3.22	7.05	0.807	4.48	0.260	3.15	0.110	2.61	0.068								
1200	2.674			---	---	13.33	3.81	7.70	.948	4.88	0.306	3.44	0.128	2.85	0.080	2.18	0.042						
1300	2.896			---	---	14.43	4.45	8.33	1.11	5.29	0.355	3.73	0.150	3.08	0.093	2.36	0.048						
1400	3.119					15.55	5.13	8.98	1.28	5.70	0.409	4.01	0.171	3.32	0.107	2.54	0.055						
1500	3.342					16.66	5.85	9.62	1.46	6.10	0.466	4.30	0.195	3.56	0.122	2.72	0.063						
1600	3.565					17.77	6.61	10.26	1.65	6.51	0.527	4.59	0.219	3.79	0.138	2.90	0.071						
1800	4.010					19.99	8.37	11.54	2.08	7.32	0.663	5.16	0.276	4.27	0.172	3.27	0.088	2.58	0.050				
2000	4.456					22.21	10.3	12.82	2.55	8.14	0.808	5.73	0.339	4.74	0.209	3.63	0.107	2.87	0.060				
2500	5.570							16.03	3.94	10.17	1.24	7.17	0.515	5.93	0.321	4.54	0.163	3.59	0.091				
3000	6.684							19.24	5.59	12.20	1.76	8.60	0.731	7.11	0.451	5.45	0.232	4.30	0.129	3.46	0.075		
3500	7.798							22.44	7.56	14.24	2.38	10.03	0.982	8.30	0.607	6.35	0.312	5.02	0.173	4.04	0.101		
4000	8.912							25.65	9.80	16.27	3.08	11.47	1.27	9.48	0.787	7.26	0.401	5.74	0.222	4.62	0.129	3.19	0.052
4500	10.03							28.87	12.2	18.31	3.87	12.90	1.60	10.67	0.990	8.17	0.503	6.46	0.280	5.20	0.162	3.59	0.065
5000	11.14							---	---	20.35	4.71	14.33	1.95	11.85	1.21	9.08	0.617	7.17	0.340	5.77	0.199	3.99	0.079

(continued)

Flow of Water Through Schedule 40 Steel Pipe (continued)

PRESSURE DROP PER 100 FEET AND VELOCITY IN SCHEDULE 40 PIPE FOR WATER AT 60°F

DISCHARGE		Velocity (Feet per Sec.)	Press. Drop (PSI)	Velocity (Feet per Sec.)	Press. Drop (PSI)	Velocity (Feet per Sec.)	Press. Drop (PSI)	Velocity (Feet per Sec.)	Press. Drop (PSI)	Velocity (Feet per Sec.)	Press. Drop (PSI)	Velocity (Feet per Sec.)	Press. Drop (PSI)	Velocity (Feet per Sec.)	Press. Drop (PSI)	Velocity (Feet per Sec.)	Press. Drop (PSI)
Gallons per Minute	Cubic Ft. per Second																
6000	13.37	24.41	6.74	17.20	2.77	14.23	1.71	10.89	0.877	8.61	0.483	6.93	0.280	4.79	0.111	---	---
7000	15.60	28.49	9.11	20.07	3.74	16.60	2.31	12.71	1.18	10.04	0.652	8.08	0.376	5.59	0.150	---	---
8000	17.82	---	---	22.93	4.84	18.96	2.99	14.52	1.51	11.47	0.839	9.23	0.488	6.38	0.192	---	---
9000	20.05	---	---	25.79	6.09	21.34	3.76	16.34	1.90	12.91	1.05	10.39	0.608	7.18	0.242	---	---
10,000	22.28	---	---	28.66	7.46	23.71	4.61	18.15	2.34	14.34	1.28	11.54	0.739	7.98	0.294	---	---
12,000	26.74	---	---	34.40	10.7	28.45	6.59	21.79	3.33	17.21	1.83	13.85	1.06	9.58	0.416	---	---
14,000	31.19	---	---	---	---	33.19	8.89	25.42	4.49	20.08	2.45	16.16	1.43	11.17	0.562	---	---
16,000	35.65	---	---	---	---	---	---	29.05	5.83	22.95	3.18	18.47	1.85	12.77	0.723	---	---
18,000	40.10	---	---	---	---	---	---	32.68	7.31	25.82	4.03	20.77	2.32	14.36	0.907	---	---
20,000	44.56	---	---	---	---	---	---	36.31	9.03	28.69	4.93	23.08	2.86	15.96	1.12	---	---

For pipe lengths other than 100 feet, the pressure drop is proportional to the length. Thus, for 50 feet of pipe, the pressure drop is approximately one–half the value given in the table—for 300 feet, three times the given value, etc.
Velocity is a function of the cross sectional flow area; thus it is constant for a given flow rate and is independent of pipe length.

For calculations for pipe other than Schedule 40, see explanation later in this chapter.

Extracted from Technical Paper No. 410, *Flow of Fluids*, with permission of Crane Co.

Flow of Air Through Schedule 40 Steel Pipe

PRESSURE DROP OF AIR IN POUNDS PER SQUARE INCH PER 100 FEET OF SCHEDULE 40 PIPE FOR AIR AT 100 POUNDS PER SQUARE INCH GAUGE PRESSURE AND 60°F TEMPERATURE

FREE AIR q'm Cubic Feet Per Minute at 60°F and 14.7 psia	COMPRESSED AIR Cubic Feet Per Minute at 60°F and 100 psig	1/8"	1/4"	3/8"	1/2"	3/4"	1"	1-1/4"	1-1/2"	2"	2-1/2"
1	0.128	0.361	0.083	0.018							
2	0.256	1.31	0.285	0.064	0.020						
3	0.384	3.06	0.605	0.133	0.042						
4	0.513	4.83	1.04	0.226	0.071						
5	0.641	7.45	1.58	0.343	0.106	0.027					
6	0.769	10.6	2.23	0.408	0.148	0.037					
8	1.025	18.6	3.89	0.848	0.255	0.062	0.019				
10	1.282	28.7	5.96	1.26	0.356	0.094	0.029				
15	1.922	---	13.0	2.73	0.834	0.201	0.062				
20	2.563	---	22.8	4.76	1.43	0.345	0.102	0.026			
25	3.204	---	35.6	7.34	2.21	0.526	0.156	0.039	0.019		
30	3.845	---	---	10.5	3.15	0.748	0.219	0.055	0.026		
35	4.486	---	---	14.2	4.24	1.00	0.293	0.073	0.035		
40	5.126	---	---	18.4	5.49	1.30	0.379	0.095	0.044		
45	5.767	---	---	23.1	6.90	1.62	0.474	0.116	0.055		
50	6.408			28.5	8.49	1.99	0.578	0.149	0.067	0.019	
60	7.690			40.7	12.2	2.85	0.819	0.200	0.094	0.027	
70	8.971			---	16.5	3.83	1.10	0.270	0.126	0.036	
80	10.25			---	21.4	4.96	1.43	0.350	0.162	0.046	0.019

(continued)

Flow of Air Through Schedule 40 Steel Pipe (continued)

PRESSURE DROP OF AIR IN POUNDS PER SQUARE INCH PER 100 FEET OF SCHEDULE 40 PIPE FOR AIR AT 100 POUNDS PER SQUARE INCH GAUGE PRESSURE AND 60°F TEMPERATURE

FREE AIR q'_m — Cubic Feet Per Minute at 60°F and 14.7 psia	COMPRESSED AIR — Cubic Feet Per Minute at 60°F and 100 psig		3"	3-1/2"	4"	5"				
90	11.53	0.023	- - -	- - -	27.0	6.25	1.80	0.437	0.203	0.058
100	12.82	0.029	- - -	- - -	33.2	7.69	2.21	0.534	0.247	0.070
125	16.02	0.044	- - -	- - -	- - -	11.9	3.39	0.825	0.380	0.107
150	19.22	0.062	0.021	- - -	- - -	17.0	4.87	1.17	0.537	0.151
175	22.43	0.083	0.028	- - -	- - -	23.1	6.60	1.58	0.727	0.205
200	25.63	0.107	0.036	- - -	- - -	30.0	8.54	2.05	0.937	0.264
225	28.84	0.134	0.045	0.022	- - -	37.9	10.8	2.59	1.19	0.331
250	32.04	0.164	0.055	0.027	- - -	- - -	13.3	3.18	1.45	0.404
275	35.24	0.191	0.066	0.032	- - -	- - -	16.0	3.83	1.75	0.484
300	38.45	0.232	0.078	0.037	- - -	- - -	19.0	4.56	2.07	0.573
325	41.65	0.270	0.090	0.043	- - -	- - -	22.3	5.32	2.42	0.673
350	44.87	0.313	0.104	0.050	- - -	- - -	25.8	6.17	2.80	0.776
375	48.06	0.356	0.119	0.057	0.030	- - -	29.6	7.05	3.20	0.887
400	51.26	0.402	0.134	0.064	0.034	- - -	33.6	8.02	3.64	1.00
425	54.47	0.452	0.151	0.072	0.038	- - -	37.9	9.01	4.09	1.13
450	57.67	0.507	0.168	0.081	0.042	- - -	- - -	10.2	4.59	1.26
475	60.88	0.562	0.187	0.089	0.047	- - -	- - -	11.3	5.09	1.40
500	64.08	0.623	0.206	0.099	0.052	- - -	- - -	12.5	5.61	1.55
550	70.49	0.749	0.248	0.118	0.062	- - -	- - -	15.1	6.79	1.87
600	76.90	0.887	0.293	0.139	0.073	- - -	- - -	18.0	8.04	2.21
650	83.30	1.04	0.342	0.163	0.086	- - -	- - -	21.1	9.43	2.60
700	89.71	1.19	0.395	0.188	0.099	0.032	- - -	24.3	10.9	3.00

(continued)

Flow of Air Through Schedule 40 Steel Pipe (continued)

PRESSURE DROP OF AIR IN POUNDS PER SQUARE INCH PER 100 FEET OF SCHEDULE 40 PIPE FOR AIR AT 100 POUNDS PER SQUARE INCH GAUGE PRESSURE AND 60° F TEMPERATURE

FREE AIR q'_m Cubic Feet Per Minute at 60° F and 14.7 psia	COMPRESSED AIR Cubic Feet Per Minute at 60° F and 100 psig						6"	8"	10"	12"
750	96.12	1.36	0.451	0.214	0.113	0.036		27.9	12.6	3.44
800	102.5	1.55	0.513	0.244	0.127	0.041		31.8	14.2	3.90
850	108.9	1.74	0.576	0.274	0.144	0.046		35.9	16.0	4.40
900	115.3	1.95	0.642	0.305	0.160	0.051		40.2	18.0	4.91
950	121.8	2.18	0.715	0.340	0.178	0.057	0.023	- - -	20.0	5.47
1,000	128.2	2.40	0.788	0.375	0.197	0.063	0.025	- - -	22.1	6.06
1,100	141.0	2.89	0.948	0.451	0.236	0.075	0.030	- - -	26.7	7.29
1,200	153.8	3.44	1.13	0.533	0.279	0.089	0.035	- - -	31.8	8.63
1,300	166.6	4.01	1.32	0.626	0.327	0.103	0.041	- - -	37.3	10.1
1,400	179.4	4.65	1.52	0.718	0.377	0.119	0.047			11.8
1,500	192.2	5.31	1.74	0.824	0.431	0.136	0.054			13.5
1,600	205.1	6.04	1.97	0.932	0.490	0.154	0.061			15.3
1,800	230.7	7.65	2.50	1.18	0.616	0.193	0.075			19.3
2,000	256.3	9.44	3.06	1.45	0.757	0.237	0.094	0.023		23.9
2,500	320.4	14.7	4.76	2.25	1.17	0.366	0.143	0.035		37.3
3,000	384.5	21.1	6.82	3.20	1.67	0.524	0.204	0.051	0.016	
3,500	448.6	28.8	9.23	4.33	2.26	0.709	0.276	0.068	0.022	
4,000	512.6	37.6	12.1	5.66	2.94	0.919	0.358	0.088	0.028	
4,500	576.7	47.6	15.3	7.16	3.69	1.16	0.450	0.111	0.035	
5,000	640.8	- - -	18.8	8.85	4.56	1.42	0.552	0.136	0.043	0.018
6,000	769.0	- - -	27.1	12.7	6.57	2.03	0.794	0.195	0.061	0.025
7,000	897.1	- - -	36.9	17.2	8.94	2.76	1.07	0.262	0.082	0.034

(continued)

Flow of Air Through Schedule 40 Steel Pipe (continued)

PRESSURE DROP OF AIR IN POUNDS PER SQUARE INCH PER 100 FEET OF SCHEDULE 40 PIPE FOR AIR AT 100 POUNDS PER SQUARE INCH GAUGE PRESSURE AND 60°F TEMPERATURE

FREE AIR q'm — Cubic Feet Per Minute at 60°F and 14.7 psia	COMPRESSED AIR — Cubic Feet Per Minute at 60°F and 100 psig								
8,000	1025	- - -	- - -	22.5	11.7	3.59	1.39	0.339	0.107	0.044
9,000	1153	- - -	- - -	28.5	14.9	4.54	1.76	0.427	0.134	0.055
10,000	1282	- - -	- - -	35.2	18.4	5.60	2.16	0.526	0.164	0.067
11,000	1410	- - -	- - -	- - -	22.2	6.78	2.62	0.633	0.197	0.081
12,000	1538	- - -	- - -	- - -	26.4	8.07	3.09	0.753	0.234	0.096
13,000	1666	- - -	- - -	- - -	31.0	9.47	3.63	0.884	0.273	0.112
14,000	1794	- - -	- - -	- - -	36.0	11.0	4.21	1.02	0.316	0.129
15,000	1922	- - -	- - -	- - -	- - -	12.6	4.84	1.17	0.364	0.148
16,000	2051	- - -	- - -	- - -	- - -	14.3	5.50	1.33	0.411	0.167
18,000	2307	- - -	- - -	- - -	- - -	18.2	6.96	1.68	0.520	0.213
20,000	2563	- - -	- - -	- - -	- - -	22.4	8.60	2.01	0.642	0.260
22,000	2820	- - -	- - -	- - -	- - -	27.1	10.4	2.50	0.771	0.314
24,000	3076	- - -	- - -	- - -	- - -	32.3	12.4	2.97	0.918	0.371
26,000	3332	- - -	- - -	- - -	- - -	37.9	14.5	3.49	1.12	0.435
28,000	3588	- - -	- - -	- - -	- - -	- - -	16.9	4.04	1.25	0.505
30,000	3845	- - -	- - -	- - -	- - -	- - -	19.3	4.64	1.42	0.520

For lengths of pipe other than 100 feet, the pressure drop is proportional to the length. Thus, for 50 feet of pipe, the pressure drop is approximately one–half the value given in the table—for 300 feet, three times the given value, etc.

The pressure drop is also inversely proportional to the absolute pressure and directly proportional to the absolute temperature.

Therefore, to determine the pressure drop for inlet or average pressures other than 100 psi and at temperatures other than 60°F, multiply the values given in the table by the ratio:

$$\left(\frac{100 + 14.7}{P + 14.7}\right) \left(\frac{460 + t}{520}\right)$$

where:

P is the inlet or average gauge pressure in pounds per square inch, and,

t is the temperature in degrees Fahrenheit under consideration.

The cubic feet per minute of compressed air at any pressure is inversely proportional to the absolute pressure and directly proportional to the absolute temperature.

To determine the cubic feet per minute of compressed air at any temperature and pressure other than standard conditions, multiply the value of cubic feet per minute of free air by the ratio:

$$\left(\frac{14.7}{14.7 + P}\right) \left(\frac{460 + t}{520}\right)$$

Calculations for Pipe Other than Schedule 40

To determine the velocity of water, or the pressure drop of water or air, through pipe other than Schedule 40, use to following formulas:

$$v_a = v_{40}\left(\frac{d_{40}}{d_a}\right)^2$$

$$\Delta P_a = \Delta P_{40}\left(\frac{d_{40}}{d_a}\right)^5$$

Subscript a refers to the Schedule of pipe through which velocity or pressure drop is desired.

Subscript 40 refers to the velocity or pressure drop through Schedule 40 pipe, as given in the tables earlier in this chapter titled Flow of Water Through Schedule 40 Steel Pipe.

Extracted from Technical Paper No. 410, *Flow of Fluids*, with permission of Crane Co.

Chapter 11

Pipe Data

Pipe Engagement
Length of Thread on Pipe to Make a Tight Joint

	Nominal Pipe Size (Inches)	Dimension A (Inches)	Nominal Pipe Size (Inches)	Dimension A (Inches)
	1/8	0.27	1–1/2	0.68
	1/4	0.39	2	0.70
	3/8	0.41	2–1/2	0.93
	1/2	0.53	3	1.02
	3/4	0.55	4	1.09
	1	0.66	5	1.19
	1–1/4	0.68	6	1.21

Dimension A is the sum of L_1 (handtight engagement) and L_3 (wrench makeup length for internal thread) from ASME B1.20.1–1992.

Pipe Data
Carbon and Alloy Steel – Stainless Steel

Identification, wall thickness and weights are extracted from ASME B36.10M and B36.19M. The notations STD, XS and XXS indicate Standard, Extra Strong, and Double Extra Strong pipe, respectively.

Transverse internal area values listed in "sq.ft" also represent volume in cubic feet per foot of pipe length.

NOMINAL PIPE SIZE (INCHES)	OUTSIDE DIAMETER (Inches)	IDENTIFICATION			WALL THICKNESS (t) (INCHES)	INSIDE DIAMETER (d) (INCHES)	AREA OF METAL (SQUARE INCHES)	TRANSVERSE INTERNAL AREA		WEIGHT PIPE (LB/FT)	WATER WEIGHT (LB/FT PIPE)
		Iron Pipe Size (Steel)	Sched. No. (Steel)	Stainless Steel Sched. No.				(a) (Square Inches)	(A) (Square Feet)		
1/8	0.405	--	--	10S	0.049	0.307	0.0548	0.0740	0.00051	0.19	0.032
		--	30	--	0.057	0.291	0.0623	0.0665	0.00046	0.21	0.029
		STD	40	40S	0.068	0.269	0.0720	0.0568	0.00039	0.24	0.025
		XS	80	80S	0.095	0.215	0.0925	0.0363	0.00025	0.31	0.016
1/4	0.540	--	--	10S	0.065	0.410	0.0970	0.1320	0.00092	0.33	0.057
		--	30	--	0.073	0.394	0.1071	0.1219	0.00085	0.36	0.053
		STD	40	40S	0.088	0.364	0.1250	0.1041	0.00072	0.42	0.045
		XS	80	80S	0.119	0.302	0.1574	0.0716	0.00050	0.54	0.031
3/8	0.675	--	--	10S	0.065	0.545	0.1246	0.2333	0.00162	0.42	0.101
		--	30	--	0.073	0.529	0.1381	0.2198	0.00153	0.47	0.095
		STD	40	40S	0.091	0.493	0.1670	0.1909	0.00133	0.57	0.083
		XS	80	80S	0.126	0.423	0.2173	0.1405	0.00098	0.74	0.061
1/2	0.840	--	--	5S	0.065	0.710	0.1583	0.3959	0.00275	0.54	0.172
		--	--	10S	0.083	0.674	0.1974	0.3568	0.00248	0.67	0.155
		--	30	--	0.095	0.650	0.2223	0.3318	0.00230	0.76	0.144
		STD	40	40S	0.109	0.622	0.2503	0.3039	0.00211	0.85	0.132
		XS	80	80S	0.147	0.546	0.3200	0.2341	0.00163	1.09	0.101
		--	160	--	0.188	0.464	0.3851	0.1691	0.00117	1.31	0.073
		XXS	--	--	0.294	0.252	0.5043	0.0499	0.00035	1.71	0.022

(continued)

Pipe Data (continued)
Carbon and Alloy Steel – Stainless Steel

Identification, wall thickness and weights are extracted from ASME B36.10M and B36.19M. The notations STD, XS and XXS indicate Standard, Extra Strong, and Double Extra Strong pipe, respectively.

Transverse internal area values listed in "sq.ft" also represent volume in cubic feet per foot of pipe length.

NOMINAL PIPE SIZE (INCHES)	OUTSIDE DIAMETER (Inches)	IDENTIFICATION			WALL THICKNESS (t) (INCHES)	INSIDE DIAMETER (d) (INCHES)	AREA OF METAL (SQUARE INCHES)	TRANSVERSE INTERNAL AREA		WEIGHT PIPE (LB/FT)	WATER WEIGHT (LB/FT PIPE)
		Steel		Stainless Steel Sched. No.				(a) (Square Inches)	(A) (Square Feet)		
		Iron Pipe Size	Sched. No.								
3/4	1.050	– –	– –	5S	0.065	0.920	0.2011	0.6648	0.00462	0.69	0.288
		– –	– –	10S	0.083	0.884	0.2521	0.6138	0.00426	0.86	0.266
		– –	30	– –	0.095	0.860	0.2850	0.5809	0.00403	0.97	0.252
		STD	40	40S	0.113	0.824	0.3326	0.5333	0.00370	1.13	0.231
		XS	80	80S	0.154	0.742	0.4335	0.4324	0.00300	1.47	0.187
		– –	160	– –	0.219	0.612	0.5717	0.2942	0.00204	1.94	0.127
		XXS	– –	– –	0.308	0.434	0.7180	0.1479	0.00103	2.44	0.064
1	1.315	– –	– –	5S	0.065	1.185	0.2553	1.103	0.00766	0.87	0.478
		– –	– –	10S	0.109	1.097	0.4130	0.9452	0.00656	1.40	0.410
		– –	30	– –	0.114	1.087	0.4301	0.9280	0.00644	1.46	0.402
		STD	40	40S	0.133	1.049	0.4939	0.8643	0.00600	1.68	0.375
		XS	80	80S	0.179	0.957	0.6388	0.7193	0.00500	2.17	0.312
		– –	160	– –	0.250	0.815	0.8365	0.5217	0.00362	2.84	0.226
		XXS	– –	– –	0.358	0.599	1.0763	0.2818	0.00196	3.66	0.122
1–1/4	1.660	– –	– –	5S	0.065	1.530	0.3257	1.839	0.01277	1.11	0.797
		– –	– –	10S	0.109	1.442	0.5311	1.633	0.01134	1.81	0.708
		– –	30	– –	0.117	1.426	0.5672	1.597	0.01109	1.93	0.692
		STD	40	40S	0.140	1.380	0.6685	1.496	0.01039	2.27	0.648
		XS	80	80S	0.191	1.278	0.8815	1.283	0.00891	3.00	0.556
		– –	160	– –	0.250	1.160	1.1070	1.057	0.00734	3.76	0.458
		XXS	– –	– –	0.382	0.896	1.5340	0.6305	0.00438	5.21	0.273

(continued)

Pipe Data (continued)
Carbon and Alloy Steel – Stainless Steel

Identification, wall thickness and weights are extracted from ASME B36.10M and B36.19M. The notations STD, XS and XXS indicate Standard, Extra Strong, and Double Extra Strong pipe, respectively. **Transverse internal area** values listed in "sq.ft" also represent volume in cubic feet per foot of pipe length.

NOMINAL PIPE SIZE (INCHES)	OUTSIDE DIAMETER (Inches)	IDENTIFICATION			WALL THICKNESS (t) (INCHES)	INSIDE DIAMETER (d) (INCHES)	AREA OF METAL (SQUARE INCHES)	TANSVERSE INTERNAL AREA		WEIGHT PIPE (LB/FT)	WATER WEIGHT (LB/FT PIPE)
		Steel		Stainless Steel Sched. No.				(a) (Square Inches)	(A) (Square Feet)		
		Iron Pipe Size	Sched. No.								
1–1/2	1.900	--	--	5S	0.065	1.770	0.3747	2.461	0.01709	1.28	1.066
		--	--	10S	0.109	1.682	0.6133	2.222	0.01543	2.09	0.963
		--	30	--	0.125	1.650	0.6970	2.138	0.01485	2.37	0.927
		STD	40	40S	0.145	1.610	0.7995	2.036	0.01414	2.72	0.882
		XS	80	80S	0.200	1.500	1.068	1.767	0.01227	3.63	0.766
		--	160	--	0.281	1.338	1.429	1.406	0.00976	4.86	0.609
		XXS	--	--	0.400	1.100	1.885	0.9503	0.00660	6.41	0.412
2	2.375	--	--	5S	0.065	2.245	0.4717	3.958	0.02749	1.61	1.715
		--	--	10S	0.109	2.157	0.7760	3.654	0.02538	2.64	1.583
		--	30	--	0.125	2.125	0.8836	3.547	0.02463	3.00	1.537
		STD	40	40S	0.154	2.067	1.075	3.356	0.02330	3.65	1.454
		XS	80	80S	0.218	1.939	1.477	2.953	0.02051	5.02	1.280
		--	160	--	0.344	1.687	2.195	2.235	0.01552	7.46	0.969
		XXS	--	--	0.436	1.503	2.656	1.774	0.01232	9.03	0.769
2–1/2	2.875	--	--	5S	0.083	2.709	0.7280	5.764	0.04003	2.48	2.498
		--	--	10S	0.120	2.635	1.039	5.453	0.03787	3.53	2.363
		--	30	--	0.188	2.499	1.587	4.905	0.03406	5.40	2.125
		STD	40	40S	0.203	2.469	1.704	4.788	0.03325	5.79	2.075
		XS	80	80S	0.276	2.323	2.254	4.238	0.02943	7.66	1.837
		--	160	--	0.375	2.125	2.945	3.547	0.02463	10.01	1.537
		XXS	--	--	0.552	1.771	4.028	2.463	0.01711	13.69	1.067

(continued)

Pipe Data (continued)
Carbon and Alloy Steel – Stainless Steel

Identification, wall thickness and weights are extracted from ASME B36.10M and B36.19M. The notations STD, XS and XXS indicate Standard, Extra Strong, and Double Extra Strong pipe, respectively.

Transverse internal area values listed in "sq.ft" also represent volume in cubic feet per foot of pipe length.

NOMINAL PIPE SIZE (INCHES)	OUTSIDE DIAMETER (Inches)	IDENTIFICATION			WALL THICKNESS (t) (INCHES)	INSIDE DIAMETER (d) (INCHES)	AREA OF METAL (SQUARE INCHES)	TRANSVERSE INTERNAL AREA		WEIGHT PIPE (LB/FT)	WATER WEIGHT (LB/FT PIPE)
		Steel		Stainless Steel Sched. No.				(a) (Square Inches)	(A) (Square Feet)		
		Iron Pipe Size	Sched. No.								
3	3.500	---	---	5S	0.083	3.334	0.8910	8.730	0.06063	3.03	3.783
		---	---	10S	0.120	3.260	1.274	8.347	0.05796	4.33	3.617
		30	---	---	0.188	3.124	1.956	7.665	0.05323	6.65	3.322
		STD	40	40S	0.216	3.068	2.228	7.393	0.05134	7.58	3.203
		XS	80	80S	0.300	2.900	3.016	6.605	0.04587	10.25	2.862
		---	160	---	0.438	2.624	4.213	5.408	0.03755	14.32	2.343
		XXS	---	---	0.600	2.300	5.466	4.155	0.02885	18.58	1.800
3-1/2	4.000	---	---	5S	0.083	3.834	1.021	11.55	0.08017	3.48	5.003
		---	---	10S	0.120	3.760	1.463	11.10	0.07711	4.97	4.812
		30	---	---	0.188	3.624	2.251	10.31	0.07163	7.65	4.470
		STD	40	40S	0.226	3.548	2.680	9.887	0.06866	9.11	4.284
		XS	80	80S	0.318	3.364	3.678	8.888	0.06172	12.50	3.851
4	4.500	---	---	5S	0.083	4.334	1.152	14.75	0.10245	3.92	6.393
		---	---	10S	0.120	4.260	1.651	14.25	0.09898	5.61	6.176
		30	---	---	0.188	4.124	2.547	13.36	0.09276	8.66	5.788
		STD	40	40S	0.237	4.026	3.174	12.73	0.08840	10.79	5.516
		XS	80	80S	0.337	3.826	4.407	11.50	0.07984	14.98	4.982
		---	120	---	0.438	3.624	5.589	10.31	0.07163	19.00	4.470
		---	160	---	0.531	3.438	6.621	9.283	0.06447	22.51	4.023
		XXS	---	---	0.674	3.152	8.101	7.803	0.05419	27.54	3.381

(continued)

Pipe Data (continued)
Carbon and Alloy Steel – Stainless Steel

Identification, wall thickness and weights are extracted from ASME B36.10M and B36.19M. The notations STD, XS and XXS indicate Standard, Extra Strong, and Double Extra Strong pipe, respectively.

Transverse internal area values listed in "sq.ft" also represent volume in cubic feet per foot of pipe length.

NOMINAL PIPE SIZE (INCHES)	OUTSIDE DIAMETER (Inches)	IDENTIFICATION			WALL THICKNESS (t) (INCHES)	INSIDE DIAMETER (d) (INCHES)	AREA OF METAL (SQUARE INCHES)	TRANSVERSE INTERNAL AREA		WEIGHT PIPE (LB/FT)	WATER WEIGHT (LB/FT PIPE)
		Steel		Stainless Steel Sched. No.				(a) (Square Inches)	(A) (Square Feet)		
		Iron Pipe Size	Sched. No.								
5	5.563	---	---	5S	0.109	5.345	1.868	22.44	0.15582	6.36	9.723
		---	---	10S	0.134	5.295	2.285	22.02	0.15292	7.77	9.542
		STD	40	40S	0.258	5.047	4.300	20.01	0.13893	14.62	8.669
		XS	80	80S	0.375	4.813	6.112	18.19	0.12635	20.78	7.884
		---	120	---	0.500	4.563	7.953	16.35	0.11356	27.04	7.086
		---	160	---	0.625	4.313	9.696	14.61	0.10146	32.96	6.331
		XXS	---	---	0.750	4.063	11.34	12.97	0.09004	38.55	5.618
6	6.625	---	---	5S	0.109	6.407	2.231	32.24	0.22389	7.60	13.97
		---	---	10S	0.134	6.357	2.733	31.74	0.22041	9.29	13.75
		STD	40	40S	0.28	6.065	5.581	28.89	0.20063	18.97	12.52
		XS	80	80S	0.432	5.761	8.405	26.07	0.18102	28.57	11.30
		---	120	---	0.562	5.501	10.70	23.77	0.16505	36.39	10.30
		---	160	---	0.719	5.187	13.34	21.13	0.14674	45.35	9.157
		XXS	---	---	0.864	4.897	15.64	18.83	0.13079	53.16	8.162

(continued)

Pipe Data (continued)
Carbon and Alloy Steel – Stainless Steel

Identification, wall thickness and weights are extracted from ASME B36.10M and B36.19M. The notations STD, XS and XXS indicate Standard, Extra Strong, and Double Extra Strong pipe, respectively.

Transverse internal area values listed in "sq.ft" also represent volume in cubic feet per foot of pipe length.

NOMINAL PIPE SIZE (INCHES)	OUTSIDE DIAMETER (Inches)	IDENTIFICATION Steel Iron Pipe Size	IDENTIFICATION Steel Sched. No.	IDENTIFICATION Stainless Steel Sched. No.	WALL THICKNESS (t) (INCHES)	INSIDE DIAMETER (d) (INCHES)	AREA OF METAL (SQUARE INCHES)	TRANSVERSE INTERNAL AREA (a) (Square Inches)	TRANSVERSE INTERNAL AREA (A) (Square Feet)	WEIGHT PIPE (LB/FT)	WATER WEIGHT (LB/FT PIPE)
8	8.625	– –	– –	5S	0.109	8.407	2.916	55.51	0.38549	9.93	24.05
		– –	– –	10S	0.148	8.329	3.941	54.48	0.37837	13.40	23.61
		– –	20	– –	0.25	8.125	6.578	51.85	0.36006	22.36	22.47
		– –	30	– –	0.277	8.071	7.265	51.16	0.35529	24.70	22.17
		STD	40	40S	0.322	7.981	8.399	50.03	0.34741	28.55	21.68
		– –	60	– –	0.406	7.813	10.48	47.94	0.33294	35.64	20.78
		XS	80	80S	0.5	7.625	12.76	45.66	0.31711	43.39	19.79
		– –	100	– –	0.594	7.437	14.99	43.44	0.30166	50.95	18.82
		– –	120	– –	0.719	7.187	17.86	40.57	0.28172	60.71	17.58
		– –	140	– –	0.812	7.001	19.93	38.50	0.26733	67.76	16.68
		XXS	– –	– –	0.875	6.875	21.30	37.12	0.25779	72.42	16.09
		– –	160	– –	0.906	6.813	21.97	36.46	0.25317	74.69	15.80
10	10.750	– –	– –	5S	0.134	10.482	4.469	86.29	0.59926	15.19	37.39
		– –	– –	10S	0.165	10.420	5.487	85.28	0.59219	18.65	36.95
		– –	20	– –	0.250	10.250	8.247	82.52	0.57303	28.04	35.76
		– –	30	– –	0.307	10.136	10.07	80.69	0.56035	34.24	34.97
		STD	40	40S	0.365	10.020	11.91	78.85	0.54760	40.48	34.17
		XS	60	80S	0.500	9.750	16.10	74.66	0.51849	54.74	32.35
		– –	80	– –	0.594	9.562	18.95	71.81	0.49868	64.43	31.12
		– –	100	– –	0.719	9.312	22.66	68.10	0.47295	77.03	29.51
		– –	120	– –	0.844	9.062	26.27	64.50	0.44790	89.29	27.95
		XXS	140	– –	1.000	8.750	30.63	60.13	0.41758	104.13	26.06
		– –	160	– –	1.125	8.500	34.02	56.75	0.39406	115.64	24.59

(continued)

Pipe Data (continued)
Carbon and Alloy Steel – Stainless Steel

Identification, wall thickness and weights are extracted from ASME B36.10M and B36.19M. The notations STD, XS and XXS indicate Standard, Extra Strong, and Double Extra Strong pipe, respectively.

Transverse internal area values listed in "sq.ft" also represent volume in cubic feet per foot of pipe length.

NOMINAL PIPE SIZE (INCHES)	OUTSIDE DIAMETER (Inches)	IDENTIFICATION			WALL THICKNESS (t) (INCHES)	INSIDE DIAMETER (d) (INCHES)	AREA OF METAL (SQUARE INCHES)	TANSVERSE INTERNAL AREA		WEIGHT PIPE (LB/FT)	WATER WEIGHT (LB/FT PIPE)
		Steel		Stainless Steel Sched. No.				(a) (Square Inches)	(A) (Square Feet)		
		Iron Pipe Size	Sched. No.								
		– –	– –	5S	0.156	12.438	6.172	121.5	0.84378	20.98	52.65
		– –	– –	10S	0.180	12.390	7.108	120.6	0.83728	24.17	52.25
		– –	20	– –	0.250	12.250	9.818	117.9	0.81847	33.38	51.07
		– –	30	– –	0.330	12.090	12.88	114.8	0.79723	43.77	49.75
		STD	– –	40S	0.375	12.000	14.58	113.1	0.78540	49.56	49.01
12	12.750	– –	40	– –	0.406	11.938	15.74	111.9	0.77731	53.52	48.50
		XS	– –	80S	0.500	11.750	19.24	108.4	0.75302	65.42	46.99
		– –	60	– –	0.562	11.626	21.52	106.2	0.73721	73.15	46.00
		– –	80	– –	0.688	11.374	26.07	101.6	0.70559	88.63	44.03
		– –	100	– –	0.844	11.062	31.57	96.11	0.66741	107.32	41.65
		XXS	120	– –	1.000	10.750	36.91	90.76	0.63030	125.49	39.33
		– –	140	– –	1.125	10.500	41.09	86.59	0.60132	139.67	37.52
		– –	160	– –	1.312	10.126	47.14	80.53	0.55925	160.27	34.90

(continued)

Pipe Data (continued)
Carbon and Alloy Steel – Stainless Steel

Identification, wall thickness and weights are extracted from ASME B36.10M and B36.19M. The notations STD, XS and XXS indicate Standard, Extra Strong, and Double Extra Strong pipe, respectively.

Transverse internal area values listed in "sq.ft" also represent volume in cubic feet per foot of pipe length.

NOMINAL PIPE SIZE (INCHES)	OUTSIDE DIAMETER (Inches)	IDENTIFICATION			WALL THICKNESS (t) (INCHES)	INSIDE DIAMETER (d) (INCHES)	AREA OF METAL (SQUARE INCHES)	TANSVERSE INTERNAL AREA		WEIGHT PIPE (LB/FT)	WATER WEIGHT (LB/FT PIPE)
		Steel		Stainless Steel Sched. No.				(a) (Square Inches)	(A) (Square Feet)		
		Iron Pipe Size	Sched. No.								
14	14.000	– – –	– – –	5S	0.156	13.688	6.785	147.2	1.02190	23.07	63.77
		– – –	– – –	10S	0.188	13.624	8.158	145.8	1.01237	27.73	63.17
		– – –	10	– – –	0.250	13.500	10.80	143.1	0.99402	36.71	62.03
		– – –	20	– – –	0.312	13.376	13.42	140.5	0.97585	45.61	60.89
		STD	30	– – –	0.375	13.250	16.05	137.9	0.95755	54.57	59.75
		– – –	40	– – –	0.438	13.124	18.66	135.3	0.93942	63.44	58.62
		XS	– – –	– – –	0.500	13.000	21.21	132.7	0.92175	72.09	57.52
		– – –	60	– – –	0.594	12.812	25.02	128.9	0.89529	85.05	55.87
		– – –	80	– – –	0.750	12.500	31.22	122.7	0.85221	106.13	53.18
		– – –	100	– – –	0.938	12.124	38.49	115.4	0.80172	130.85	50.03
		– – –	120	– – –	1.094	11.812	44.36	109.6	0.76098	150.79	47.49
		– – –	140	– – –	1.250	11.500	50.07	103.9	0.72131	170.21	45.01
		– – –	160	– – –	1.406	11.188	55.63	98.31	0.68271	189.11	42.60

(continued)

Pipe Data (continued)
Carbon and Alloy Steel – Stainless Steel

Identification, wall thickness and weights are extracted from ASME B36.10M and B36.19M. The notations STD, XS and XXS indicate Standard, Extra Strong, and Double Extra Strong pipe, respectively.

Transverse internal area values listed in "sq.ft" also represent volume in cubic feet per foot of pipe length.

NOMINAL PIPE SIZE (INCHES)	OUTSIDE DIAMETER (Inches)	IDENTIFICATION				WALL THICKNESS (t) (INCHES)	INSIDE DIAMETER (d) (INCHES)	AREA OF METAL (SQUARE INCHES)	TRANSVERSE INTERNAL AREA		WEIGHT PIPE (LB/FT)	WATER WEIGHT (LB/FT PIPE)
		Steel			Stainless Steel Sched. No.				(a) (Square Inches)	(A) (Square Feet)		
		Iron Pipe Size	Sched. No.									
16	16.000	- - -	- - -	5S		0.165	15.670	8.208	192.9	1.33926	27.90	83.57
		- - -	- - -	10S		0.188	15.624	9.339	191.7	1.33141	31.75	83.08
		- - -	10	- - -		0.250	15.500	12.37	188.7	1.31036	42.05	81.77
		- - -	20	- - -		0.312	15.376	15.38	185.7	1.28948	52.27	80.46
		STD	30	- - -		0.375	15.250	18.41	182.7	1.26843	62.58	79.15
		XS	40	- - -		0.500	15.000	24.35	176.7	1.22719	82.77	76.58
		- - -	60	- - -		0.656	14.688	31.62	169.4	1.17667	107.50	73.42
		- - -	80	- - -		0.844	14.312	40.19	160.9	1.11720	136.61	69.71
		- - -	100	- - -		1.031	13.938	48.48	152.6	1.05957	164.82	66.12
		- - -	120	- - -		1.219	13.562	56.61	144.5	1.00317	192.43	62.60
		- - -	140	- - -		1.438	13.124	65.79	135.3	0.93942	223.64	58.62
		- - -	160	- - -		1.594	12.812	72.14	128.9	0.89529	245.25	55.87

(continued)

Pipe Data (continued)
Carbon and Alloy Steel – Stainless Steel

Identification, wall thickness and weights are extracted from ASME B36.10M and B36.19M. The notations STD, XS and XXS indicate Standard, Extra Strong, and Double Extra Strong pipe, respectively.

Transverse internal area values listed in "sq.ft" also represent volume in cubic feet per foot of pipe length.

NOMINAL PIPE SIZE (INCHES)	OUTSIDE DIAMETER (Inches)	IDENTIFICATION			WALL THICKNESS (t) (INCHES)	INSIDE DIAMETER (d) (INCHES)	AREA OF METAL (SQUARE INCHES)	TRANSVERSE INTERNAL AREA		WEIGHT PIPE (LB/FT)	WATER WEIGHT (LB/FT PIPE)
		Steel		Stainless Steel Sched. No.				(a) (Square Inches)	(A) (Square Feet)		
		Iron Pipe Size	Sched. No.								
18	18.000	– –	– –	5S	0.165	17.670	9.245	245.2	1.70295	31.43	106.3
		– –	– –	10S	0.188	17.624	10.52	243.9	1.69409	35.76	105.7
		– –	10	– –	0.250	17.500	13.94	240.5	1.67034	47.39	104.2
		– –	20	– –	0.312	17.376	17.34	237.1	1.64675	58.94	102.8
		STD	30	– –	0.375	17.250	20.76	233.7	1.62296	70.59	101.3
		– –	– –	– –	0.438	17.124	24.17	230.3	1.59933	82.15	99.80
		XS	– –	– –	0.500	17.000	27.49	227.0	1.57625	93.45	98.36
		– –	40	– –	0.562	16.876	30.79	223.7	1.55334	104.67	96.93
		– –	60	– –	0.750	16.500	40.64	213.8	1.48490	138.17	92.66
		– –	80	– –	0.938	16.124	50.28	204.2	1.41799	170.92	88.48
		– –	100	– –	1.156	15.688	61.17	193.3	1.34234	207.96	83.76
		– –	120	– –	1.375	15.250	71.82	182.7	1.26843	244.14	79.15
		– –	140	– –	1.562	14.876	80.66	173.8	1.20698	274.22	75.32
		– –	160	– –	1.781	14.438	90.75	163.7	1.13695	308.50	70.95

(continued)

Pipe Data (continued)
Carbon and Alloy Steel – Stainless Steel

Identification, wall thickness and weights are extracted from ASME B36.10M and B36.19M. The notations STD, XS and XXS indicate Standard, Extra Strong, and Double Extra Strong pipe, respectively.

Transverse internal area values listed in "sq.ft" also represent volume in cubic feet per foot of pipe length.

NOMINAL PIPE SIZE (INCHES)	OUTSIDE DIAMETER (Inches)	IDENTIFICATION			WALL THICKNESS (t) (INCHES)	INSIDE DIAMETER (d) (INCHES)	AREA OF METAL (SQUARE INCHES)	TRANSVERSE INTERNAL AREA		WEIGHT PIPE (LB/FT)	WATER WEIGHT (LB/FT PIPE)
		Steel		Stainless Steel Sched. No.				(a) (Square Inches)	(A) (Square Feet)		
		Iron Pipe Size	Sched. No.								
20	20.000	– –	– –	5S	0.188	19.624	11.70	302.5	2.10041	39.78	131.1
		– –	– –	10S	0.218	19.564	13.55	300.6	2.08758	46.06	130.3
		– –	10	– –	0.250	19.500	15.51	298.6	2.07395	52.73	129.4
		STD	20	– –	0.375	19.250	23.12	291.0	2.02111	78.60	126.1
		XS	30	– –	0.500	19.000	30.63	283.5	1.96895	104.13	122.9
		– –	40	– –	0.594	18.812	36.21	277.9	1.93018	123.11	120.4
		– –	60	– –	0.812	18.376	48.95	265.2	1.84175	166.40	114.9
		– –	80	– –	1.031	17.938	61.44	252.7	1.75500	208.87	109.5
		– –	100	– –	1.281	17.438	75.33	238.8	1.65852	256.10	103.5
		– –	120	– –	1.500	17.000	87.18	227.0	1.57625	296.37	98.36
		– –	140	– –	1.750	16.500	100.3	213.8	1.48490	341.09	92.66
		– –	160	– –	1.969	16.062	111.5	202.6	1.40711	379.17	87.80
22	22.000	– –	– –	5S	0.188	21.624	12.88	367.3	2.55035	43.80	159.1
		– –	– –	10S	0.218	21.564	14.92	365.2	2.53622	50.71	158.3
		– –	10	– –	0.250	21.500	17.08	363.1	2.52119	58.07	157.3
		STD	20	– –	0.375	21.250	25.48	354.7	2.46290	86.61	153.7
		XS	30	– –	0.500	21.000	33.77	346.4	2.40529	114.81	150.1
		– –	60	– –	0.875	20.250	58.07	322.1	2.23655	197.41	139.6
		– –	80	– –	1.125	19.750	73.78	306.4	2.12747	250.81	132.8
		– –	100	– –	1.375	19.250	89.09	291.0	2.02111	302.88	126.1
		– –	120	– –	1.625	18.750	104.0	276.1	1.91748	353.61	119.7
		– –	140	– –	1.875	18.250	118.5	261.6	1.81658	403.00	113.4
		– –	160	– –	2.125	17.750	132.7	247.5	1.71840	451.06	107.2

(continued)

Pipe Data (continued)
Carbon and Alloy Steel – Stainless Steel

Identification, wall thickness and weights are extracted from ASME B36.10M and B36.19M. The notations STD, XS and XXS indicate Standard, Extra Strong, and Double Extra Strong pipe, respectively.

Transverse internal area values listed in "sq.ft" also represent volume in cubic feet per foot of pipe length.

NOMINAL PIPE SIZE (INCHES)	OUTSIDE DIAMETER (Inches)	IDENTIFICATION			WALL THICKNESS (t) (INCHES)	INSIDE DIAMETER (d) (INCHES)	AREA OF METAL (SQUARE INCHES)	TRANSVERSE INTERNAL AREA		WEIGHT PIPE (LB/FT)	WATER WEIGHT (LB/FT PIPE)
		Steel		Stainless Steel Sched. No.				(a) (Square Inches)	(A) (Square Feet)		
		Iron Pipe Size	Sched. No.								
24	24.000	— —	— —	5S	0.218	23.564	16.29	436.1	3.02849	55.37	189.0
		10	— —	10S	0.250	23.500	18.65	433.7	3.01206	63.41	188.0
		STD	20	— —	0.375	23.250	27.83	424.6	2.94832	94.62	184.0
		XS	— —	— —	0.500	23.000	36.91	415.5	2.88525	125.49	180.0
		— —	30	— —	0.562	22.876	41.38	411.0	2.85423	140.68	178.1
		— —	40	— —	0.688	22.624	50.39	402.0	2.79169	171.29	174.2
		— —	60	— —	0.969	22.062	70.11	382.3	2.65472	238.35	165.7
		— —	80	— —	1.219	21.562	87.24	365.1	2.53575	296.58	158.2
		— —	100	— —	1.531	20.938	108.1	344.3	2.39111	367.39	149.2
		— —	120	— —	1.812	20.376	126.3	326.1	2.26447	429.39	141.3
		— —	140	— —	2.062	19.876	142.1	310.3	2.15470	483.12	134.5
		— —	160	— —	2.344	19.312	159.5	292.9	2.03415	542.13	126.9
26	26.000	— —	10	— —	0.312	25.376	25.18	505.8	3.51216	85.60	219.2
		STD	— —	— —	0.375	25.250	30.19	500.7	3.47737	102.63	217.0
		XS	20	— —	0.500	25.000	40.06	490.9	3.40885	136.17	212.7
28	28.000	— —	10	— —	0.312	27.376	27.14	588.6	4.08760	92.26	255.1
		STD	— —	— —	0.375	27.250	32.55	583.2	4.05006	110.64	252.7
		XS	20	— —	0.500	27.000	43.20	572.6	3.97609	146.85	248.1
		— —	30	— —	0.625	26.750	53.75	562.0	3.90280	182.73	243.5

(continued)

Pipe Data (continued)
Carbon and Alloy Steel – Stainless Steel

Identification, wall thickness and weights are extracted from ASME B36.10M and B36.19M. The notations STD, XS and XXS indicate Standard, Extra Strong, and Double Extra Strong pipe, respectively.

Transverse internal area values listed in "sq.ft" also represent volume in cubic feet per foot of pipe length.

| NOMINAL PIPE SIZE (INCHES) | OUTSIDE DIAMETER (Inches) | IDENTIFICATION | | | WALL THICKNESS (t) (INCHES) | INSIDE DIAMETER (d) (INCHES) | AREA OF METAL (SQUARE INCHES) | TRANSVERSE INTERNAL AREA | | WEIGHT PIPE (LB/FT) | WATER WEIGHT (LB/FT PIPE) |
| | | Steel | | Stainless Steel | | | | | | | |
		Iron Pipe Size	Sched. No.	Steel Sched. No.				(a) (Square Inches)	(A) (Square Feet)		
30	30.000	– –	– –	5S	0.250	29.500	23.37	683.5	4.74649	79.43	296.2
		10	– –	10S	0.312	29.376	29.10	677.8	4.70667	98.93	293.7
		STD	– –	– –	0.375	29.250	34.90	672.0	4.66638	118.65	291.2
		XS	20	– –	0.500	29.000	46.34	660.5	4.58695	157.53	286.2
		– –	30	– –	0.625	28.750	57.68	649.2	4.50821	196.08	281.3
32	32.000	– –	10	– –	0.312	31.376	31.06	773.2	5.36937	105.59	335.0
		STD	– –	– –	0.375	31.250	37.26	767.0	5.32633	126.66	332.4
		XS	20	– –	0.500	31.000	49.48	754.8	5.24145	168.21	327.1
		– –	30	– –	0.625	30.750	61.60	742.6	5.15726	209.43	321.8
		– –	40	– –	0.688	30.624	67.68	736.6	5.11508	230.08	319.2
34	34.000	– –	10	– –	0.312	33.376	33.02	874.9	6.07571	112.25	379.1
		STD	– –	– –	0.375	33.250	39.61	868.3	6.02992	134.67	376.3
		XS	20	– –	0.500	33.000	52.62	855.3	5.93959	178.89	370.6
		– –	30	– –	0.625	32.750	65.53	842.4	5.84993	222.78	365.0
		– –	40	– –	0.688	32.624	72.00	835.9	5.80501	244.77	362.2
36	36.000	– –	10	– –	0.312	35.376	34.98	982.9	6.82568	118.92	425.9
		STD	– –	– –	0.375	35.250	41.97	975.9	6.77714	142.68	422.9
		XS	20	– –	0.500	35.000	55.76	962.1	6.68135	189.57	416.9
		– –	30	– –	0.625	34.750	69.46	948.4	6.58625	236.13	411.0
		– –	40	– –	0.750	34.500	83.06	934.8	6.49182	282.35	405.1

Extracted from Technical Paper No. 410, *Flow of Fluids*, with permission of Crane Co.

American Pipe Flange Dimensions
Diameter of Bolt Circle—Inches
Per ASME B16.1, B16.5, and B16.24

Nominal Pipe Size	Class[1] 125 (Cast Iron)[2] or Class 150 (Steel)	Class[3] 250 (Cast Iron)[2] or Class 300 (Steel)	Class 600	Class 900	Class 1500	Class 2500
1	3.12	3.50	3.50	4.00	4.00	4.25
1–1/4	3.50	3.88	3.88	4.38	4.38	5.12
1–1/2	3.88	4.50	4.50	4.88	4.88	5.75
2	4.75	5.00	5.00	6.50	6.50	6.75
2–1/2	5.50	5.88	5.88	7.50	7.50	7.75
3	6.00	6.62	6.62	7.50	8.00	9.00
4	7.50	7.88	8.50	9.25	9.50	10.75
5	8.50	9.25	10.50	11.00	11.50	12.75
6	9.50	10.62	11.50	12.50	12.50	14.50
8	11.75	13.00	13.75	15.50	15.50	17.25
10	14.25	15.25	17.00	18.50	19.00	21.75
12	17.00	17.75	19.25	21.00	22.50	24.38
14	18.75	20.25	20.75	22.00	25.00	– – –
16	21.25	22.50	23.75	24.25	27.75	– – –
18	22.75	24.75	25.75	27.00	30.50	– – –
20	25.00	27.00	28.50	29.50	32.75	– – –
24	29.50	32.00	33.00	35.50	39.00	– – –
30	36.00	39.25	– – –	– – –	– – –	– – –
36	42.75	46.00	– – –	– – –	– – –	– – –
42	49.50	52.75	– – –	– – –	– – –	– – –
48	56.00	60.75	– – –	– – –	– – –	– – –

1. Nominal pipe sizes 1 through 12 also apply to Class 150 cast copper alloy flanges.
2. These diameters apply to steel valves for nominal pipe sizes 1 through 24.
3. Nominal pipe sizes 1 thorough 8 also apply to Class 300 cast copper alloy flanges.

American Pipe Flange Dimensions
Number of Stud Bolts and Diameter in Inches
Per ASME B16.1, B16.5, and B16.24

NOMINAL PIPE SIZE	CLASS[1] 125 (CAST IRON) OR CLASS 150 (STEEL)[2]		CLASS[3] 250 (CAST IRON) OR CLASS 300 (STEEL)[2]		CLASS 600		CLASS 900		CLASS 1500		CLASS 2500	
	No.	Dia.	No.	Dia.	No.	Dia.	No.	Dia.	No.	Dia.	No.	Dia.
1	4	0.50	4	0.62	4	0.62	4	0.88	4	0.88	4	0.88
1-1/4	4	0.50	4	0.62	4	0.62	4	0.88	4	0.88	4	1.00
1-1/2	4	0.50	4	0.75	4	0.75	4	1.00	4	1.00	4	1.12
2	4	0.62	8	0.62	8	0.62	8	0.88	8	0.88	8	1.00
2-1/2	4	0.62	8	0.75	8	0.75	8	1.00	8	1.00	8	1.12
3	4	0.62	8	0.75	8	0.75	8	0.88	8	1.12	8	1.25
4	8	0.62	8	0.75	8	0.88	8	1.12	8	1.25	8	1.50
5	8	0.75	8	0.75	8	1.00	8	1.25	8	1.50	8	1.75
6	8	0.75	12	0.75	12	1.00	12	1.12	12	1.38	8	2.00
8	8	0.75	12	0.88	12	1.12	12	1.38	12	1.62	12	2.00
10	12	0.88	16	1.00	16	1.25	16	1.38	12	1.88	12	2.50
12	12	0.88	16	1.12	20	1.25	20	1.38	16	2.00	12	2.75
14	12	1.00	20	1.12	20	1.38	20	1.50	16	2.25	...	...
16	16	1.00	20	1.25	20	1.50	20	1.62	16	2.50	...	...
18	16	1.12	24	1.25	20	1.62	20	1.88	16	2.75	...	...
20	20	1.12	24	1.25	24	1.62	20	2.00	16	3.00	...	...
24	20	1.25	24	1.50	24	1.88	20	2.50	16	3.50	...	...
30	28	1.25	28	1.75	...	...	...	...	...	...	...	...
36	32	1.50	32	2.00	...	...	...	...	...	...	...	...
42	36	1.50	36	2.00	...	...	...	...	...	...	...	...
48	44	1.50	40	2.00	...	...	...	...	...	...	...	...

1. Nominal pipe sizes 1 through 12 also apply to Class 150 cast copper alloy flanges.
2. These diameters apply to steel valves for nominal pipe sizes 1 through 24.
3. Nominal pipe sizes 1 through 8 also apply to Class 300 cast copper alloy flanges.

American Pipe Flange Dimensions
Flange Diameter—Inches
Per ASME B16.1, B16.5, and B16.24

Nominal Pipe Size	Class[1] 125 (Cast Iron) or Class 150 (Steel)	Class[2] 250 (Cast Iron) or Class 300 (Steel)	Class 600	Class 900	Class 1500	Class 2500
1	4.25	4.88	4.88	5.88	5.88	6.25
1-1/4	4.62	5.25	5.25	6.25	6.25	7.25
1-1/2	5.00	6.12	6.12	7.00	7.00	8.00
2	6.00	6.50	6.50	8.50	8.50	9.25
2-1/2	7.00	7.50	7.50	9.62	9.62	10.50
3	7.50	8.25	8.25	9.50	10.50	12.00
4	9.00	10.00	10.75	11.50	12.25	14.00
5	10.00	11.00	13.00	13.75	14.75	16.50
6	11.00	12.50	14.00	15.00	15.50	19.00
8	13.50	15.00	16.50	18.50	19.00	21.75
10	16.00	17.50	20.00	21.50	23.00	26.50
12	19.00	20.50	22.00	24.00	26.50	30.00
14	21.00	23.00	23.75	25.25	29.50	---
16	23.50	25.50	27.00	27.75	32.50	---
18	25.00	28.00	29.25	31.00	36.00	---
20	27.50	30.50	32.00	33.75	38.75	---
24	32.00	36.00	37.00	41.00	46.00	---
30	38.75	43.00	---	---	---	---
36	46.00	50.00	---	---	---	---
42	53.00	57.00	---	---	---	---
48	59.50	65.00	---	---	---	---

1. Nominal pipe sizes 1 through 12 also apply to Class 150 cast copper alloy flanges.
2. Nominal pipe sizes 1 through 8 also apply to Class 300 cast copper alloy flanges.

DIN Standards
DIN Cast Steel Valve Ratings[1]

PN	PERMISSIBLE WORKING PRESSURE (BAR) AT TEMP. SHOWN					
	−10°C to 120°C	200°C	250°C	300°C	350°C	400°C
16	16	14	13	11	10	8
25	25	22	20	17	16	13
40	40	35	32	28	24	21
63	64	50	45	40	36	32
100	100	80	70	60	56	50
160	160	130	112	96	90	80
250	250	200	175	150	140	125
320	320	250	225	192	180	160
400	400	320	280	240	225	200

1. Hydrostatic test pressure: 1.5 times rating at 20°C.

American Pipe Flange Dimensions
Flange Thickness for Flange Fittings—Inches
Per ASME B16.1, B16.5 and B16.24

NOMINAL PIPE SIZE	CLASS 150 (CI) FF CLASS 150 (STL) RF	CLASS 150 (STL) RTJ	CLASS 150 CAST COPPER ALLOY	CLASS 250 (CI) AND CLASS 300 (STL)(1) RF	CLASS 300 (STL) RTJ	CLASS 300 CAST COPPER ALLOY	CLASS 600 RF	CLASS 600 RTJ	CLASS 900 RF	CLASS 900 RTJ	CLASS 1500 RF	CLASS 1500 RTJ	CLASS 2500 RF	CLASS 2500 RTJ
1	0.44	0.69	0.38	0.69	0.94	0.59	0.69	0.94	1.12	1.37	1.12	1.37	1.38	1.63
1-1/4	0.50	0.75	0.41	0.75	1.00	0.62	0.81	1.06	1.12	1.37	1.12	1.37	1.50	1.81
1-1/2	0.56	0.81	0.44	0.81	1.06	0.69	0.88	1.13	1.25	1.50	1.25	1.50	1.75	2.06
2	0.62	0.87	0.50	0.88	1.19	0.75	1.00	1.31	1.50	1.81	1.50	1.81	2.00	2.31
2-1/2	0.69	0.94	0.56	1.00	1.31	0.81	1.12	1.43	1.62	1.93	1.62	1.93	2.25	2.62
3	0.75	1.00	0.62	1.12	1.43	0.91	1.25	1.56	1.50	1.81	2.12	2.43	2.62	3.00
4	0.94	1.19	0.69	1.25	1.56	1.06	1.50	1.81	1.75	2.06	2.12	2.43	3.00	3.44
5	0.94	1.19	0.75	1.38	1.69	1.12	1.75	2.03	2.00	2.31	2.88	3.19	3.62	4.12
6	1.00	1.25	0.81	1.44	1.75	1.19	1.88	2.19	2.19	2.50	3.25	3.62	4.25	4.75
8	1.12	1.37	0.94	1.62	1.93	1.38	2.19	2.50	2.50	2.81	3.62	4.06	5.00	5.56
10	1.19	1.44	1.00	1.88	2.19	—	2.50	2.81	2.75	3.06	4.25	4.69	6.50	7.19
12	1.25	1.50	1.06	2.00	2.31	—	2.62	2.93	3.12	3.43	4.88	5.44	7.25	7.94
14	1.38	1.63	—	2.12	2.43	—	2.75	3.06	3.38	3.82	5.25	5.88	—	—
16	1.44	1.69	—	2.25	2.56	—	3.00	3.31	3.50	3.94	5.75	6.44	—	—
18	1.56	1.81	—	2.38	2.69	—	3.25	3.56	4.00	4.50	6.38	7.07	—	—
20	1.69	1.94	—	2.50	2.88	—	3.50	3.88	4.25	4.75	7.00	7.69	—	—
24	1.88	2.13	—	2.75	3.19	—	4.00	4.44	5.50	6.12	8.00	8.81	—	—
30	2.12	—	—	3.00	—	—	—	—	—	—	—	—	—	—
36	2.38	—	—	3.38	—	—	—	—	—	—	—	—	—	—
42	2.62	—	—	3.69	—	—	—	—	—	—	—	—	—	—
48	2.75	—	—	4.00	—	—	—	—	—	—	—	—	—	—

1. These dimensions apply to steel valves for nominal pipe sizes 1 through 24.

DIN Cast Steel Flange Standard for PN 16

DN	PIPE THICK-NESS	FLANGE			BOLTING		
		Outside Diameter	Thickness	Bolt Circle Diameter	Number of Bolts	Thread	Bolt Hole Diameter
10	6	90	16	60	4	M12	14
15	6	95	16	65	4	M12	14
20	6.5	105	18	75	4	M12	14
25	7	115	18	85	4	M12	14
32	7	140	18	100	4	M16	18
40	7.5	150	18	110	4	M16	18
50	8	165	20	125	4	M16	18
65	8	185	18	145	4	M16	18
80	8.5	200	20	160	8	M16	18
100	9.5	220	20	180	8	M16	18
125	10	250	22	210	8	M16	18
150	11	285	22	240	8	M20	22
175	12	315	24	270	8	M20	22
200	12	340	24	295	12	M20	22
250	14	405	26	355	12	M24	26
300	15	460	28	410	12	M24	26
350	16	520	30	470	16	M24	26
400	18	580	32	525	16	M27	30
500	21	715	36	650	20	M30	33
600	23	840	40	770	20	M33	36
700	24	910	42	840	24	M33	36
800	26	1025	42	950	24	M36	39
900	27	1125	44	1050	28	M36	39
1000	29	1255	46	1170	28	M39	42
1200	32	1485	52	1390	32	M45	48
1400	34	1685	58	1590	36	M45	48
1600	36	1930	64	1820	40	M52	56
1800	39	2130	68	2020	44	M52	56
2000	41	2345	70	2230	48	M56	62
2200	43	2555	74	2440	52	M56	62

All dimensions in mm.

DIN Cast Steel Flange Standard for PN 25

DN	PIPE THICK–NESS	FLANGE			BOLTING		
		Outside Diameter	Thickness	Bolt Circle Diameter	Number of Bolts	Thread	Bolt Hole Diameter
10	6	90	16	60	4	M12	14
15	6	95	16	65	4	M12	14
20	6.5	105	18	75	4	M12	14
25	7	115	18	85	4	M12	14
32	7	140	18	100	4	M16	18
40	7.5	150	18	110	4	M16	18
50	8	165	20	125	4	M16	18
65	8.5	185	22	145	8	M16	18
80	9	200	24	160	8	M16	18
100	10	235	24	190	8	M20	22
125	11	270	26	220	8	M24	26
150	12	300	28	250	8	M24	26
175	12	330	28	280	12	M24	26
200	12	360	30	310	12	M24	26
250	14	425	32	370	12	M27	30
300	15	485	34	430	16	M27	30
350	16	555	38	490	16	M30	33
400	18	620	40	550	16	M33	36
500	21	730	44	660	20	M33	36
600	23	845	46	770	20	M36	39
700	24	960	50	875	24	M39	42
800	26	1085	54	990	24	M45	48
900	27	1185	58	1090	28	M45	48
1000	29	1320	62	1210	28	M52	56
1200	32	1530	70	1420	32	M52	56
1400	34	1755	76	1640	36	M56	62
1600	37	1975	84	1860	40	M56	62
1800	40	2195	90	2070	44	M64	70
2000	43	2425	96	2300	48	M64	70

All dimensions in mm.

DIN Cast Steel Flange Standard for PN 40

DN	PIPE THICK-NESS	FLANGE			BOLTING		
		Outside Diameter	Thickness	Bolt Circle Diameter	Number of Bolts	Thread	Bolt Hole Diameter
10	6	90	16	60	4	M12	14
15	6	95	16	65	4	M12	14
20	6.5	105	18	75	4	M12	14
25	7	115	18	85	4	M12	14
32	7	140	18	100	4	M16	18
40	7.5	150	18	110	4	M16	18
50	8	165	20	125	4	M16	18
65	8.5	185	22	145	8	M16	18
80	9	200	24	160	8	M16	18
100	10	235	24	190	8	M20	22
125	11	270	26	220	8	M24	26
150	12	300	28	250	8	M24	26
175	13	350	32	295	12	M27	30
200	14	375	34	320	12	M27	30
250	16	450	38	385	12	M30	33
300	17	515	42	450	16	M30	33
350	19	580	46	510	16	M33	36
400	21	660	50	585	16	M36	39
450	21	685	50	610	20	M36	39
500	21	755	52	670	20	M39	42
600	24	890	60	795	20	M45	48
700	27	995	64	900	24	M45	48
800	30	1140	72	1030	24	M52	56
900	33	1250	76	1140	28	M52	56
1000	36	1360	80	1250	28	M52	56
1200	42	1575	88	1460	32	M56	62
1400	47	1795	98	1680	36	M56	62
1600	54	2025	108	1900	40	M64	70

All dimensions in mm.

DIN Cast Steel Flange Standard for PN 63

DN	PIPE THICK–NESS	FLANGE			BOLTING		
		Outside Diameter	Thickness	Bolt Circle Diameter	Number of Bolts	Thread	Bolt Hole Diameter
10	10	100	20	70	4	M12	14
15	10	105	20	75	4	M12	14
25	10	140	24	100	4	M16	18
32	12	155	24	110	4	M20	22
40	10	170	28	125	4	M20	22
50	10	180	26	135	4	M20	22
65	10	205	26	160	8	M20	22
80	11	215	28	170	8	M20	22
100	12	250	30	200	8	M24	26
125	13	295	34	240	8	M27	30
150	14	345	36	280	8	M30	33
175	15	375	40	310	12	M30	33
200	16	415	42	345	12	M33	36
250	19	470	46	400	12	M33	36
300	21	530	52	460	16	M33	36
350	23	600	56	525	16	M36	39
400	26	670	60	585	16	M39	42
500	31	800	68	705	20	M45	48
600	35	930	76	820	20	M52	56
700	40	1045	84	935	24	M52	56
800	45	1165	92	1050	24	M56	62
900	50	1285	98	1170	28	M56	62
1000	55	1415	108	1290	28	M64	70
1200	64	1665	126	1530	32	M72X6	78

All dimensions in mm.

DIN Cast Steel Flange Standard for PN 100

DN	PIPE THICK-NESS	FLANGE			BOLTING		
		Outside Diameter	Thickness	Bolt Circle Diameter	Number of Bolts	Thread	Bolt Hole Diameter
10	10	100	20	70	4	M12	14
15	10	105	20	75	4	M12	14
25	10	140	24	100	4	M16	18
32	12	155	24	110	4	M20	22
40	10	170	28	125	4	M20	22
50	10	195	30	145	4	M24	26
65	11	220	34	170	8	M24	26
80	12	230	36	180	8	M24	26
100	14	265	40	210	8	M27	30
125	16	315	40	250	8	M30	33
150	18	355	44	290	12	M30	33
175	20	385	48	320	12	M30	33
200	21	430	52	360	12	M33	36
250	25	505	60	430	12	M36	39
300	29	585	68	500	16	M39	42
350	32	655	74	560	16	M45	48
400	36	715	78	620	16	M45	48
500	44	870	94	760	20	M52	56
600	51	990	104	875	20	M56	62
700	59	1145	120	1020	24	M64	70

All dimensions in mm.

DIN Cast Steel Flange Standard for PN 160

DN	PIPE THICK-NESS	FLANGE			BOLTING		
		Outside Diameter	Thickness	Bolt Circle Diameter	Number of Bolts	Thread	Bolt Hole Diameter
10	10	100	20	70	4	M12	14
15	10	105	20	75	4	M12	14
25	10	140	24	100	4	M16	18
40	10	170	28	125	4	M20	22
50	10	195	30	145	4	M24	26
65	11	220	34	170	8	M24	26
80	12	230	36	180	8	M24	26
100	14	265	40	210	8	M27	30
125	16	315	44	250	8	M30	33
150	18	355	50	290	12	M30	33
175	19	390	54	320	12	M33	36
200	21	430	60	360	12	M33	36
250	31	515	68	430	12	M39	42
300	36	585	78	500	16	M39	42

All dimensions in mm.

DIN Cast Steel Flange Standard for PN 250

DN	PIPE THICK- NESS	FLANGE			BOLTING		
		Outside Diameter	Thickness	Bolt Circle Diameter	Number of Bolts	Thread	Bolt Hole Diameter
10	10	125	24	85	4	M16	18
15	10	130	26	90	4	M16	18
25	11	150	28	105	4	M20	22
40	13	185	34	135	4	M24	26
50	13	200	38	150	8	M24	26
65	14	230	42	180	8	M24	26
80	16	255	46	200	8	M27	30
100	19	300	54	235	8	M30	33
125	22	340	60	275	12	M30	33
150	25	390	68	320	12	M33	36
175	29	430	74	355	12	M36	39
200	32	485	82	400	12	M39	42
250	38	585	100	490	16	M45	48
300	47	690	120	590	16	M48	52

All dimensions in mm.

DIN Cast Steel Flange Standard for PN 320

DN	PIPE THICK- NESS	FLANGE			BOLTING		
		Outside Diameter	Thickness	Bolt Circle Diameter	Number of Bolts	Thread	Bolt Hole Diameter
10	11	125	24	85	4	M16	18
15	11	130	26	90	4	M16	18
25	11	160	34	115	4	M20	22
40	14	195	38	145	4	M24	26
50	15	210	42	160	8	M24	26
65	18	255	51	200	8	M27	30
80	19	275	55	220	8	M27	30
100	24	335	65	265	8	M33	36
125	27	380	75	310	12	M33	36
150	32	425	84	350	12	M36	39
175	35	485	95	400	12	M39	42
200	38	525	103	440	16	M39	42
250	49	640	125	540	16	M48	52

All dimensions in mm.

DIN Cast Steel Flange Standard for PN 400

DN	PIPE THICK– NESS	FLANGE			BOLTING		
		Outside Diameter	Thickness	Bolt Circle Diameter	Number of Bolts	Thread	Bolt Hole Diameter
10	11	125	28	85	4	M16	18
15	11	145	30	100	4	M20	22
25	12	180	38	130	4	M24	26
40	15	220	48	165	4	M27	30
50	18	235	52	180	8	M27	30
65	22	290	64	225	8	M30	33
80	25	305	68	240	8	M30	33
100	30	370	80	295	8	M36	39
125	36	415	92	340	12	M36	39
150	41	475	105	390	12	M39	42
175	47	545	120	450	12	M45	48
200	53	585	130	490	16	M45	48

All dimensions in mm.

Chapter 12

Conversions and Equivalents

Length Equivalents

Note: Use Multiplier at Convergence of Row and Column	Meters	Inches	Feet	Millimeters	Miles	Kilometers
Meters	1	39.37	3.2808	1000	0.0006214	0.001
Inches	0.0254	1	0.0833	25.4	0.00001578	0.0000254
Feet	0.3048	12	1	304.8	0.0001894	0.0003048
Millimeters	0.001	0.03937	0.0032808	1	0.0000006214	0.000001
Miles	1609.35	63,360	5,280	1,609,350	1	1.60935
Kilometers	1,000	39,370	3280.83	1,000,000	0.62137	1

1 meter = 100 centimeters = 1000 millimeters = 0.001 kilometers = 1,000,000 micrometers
To convert metric units, merely adjust the decimal point
1 millimeter = 1000 microns = 0.03937 inches = 39.37 mils.

Whole Inch–Millimeter Equivalents

In.	0	1	2	3	4	5	6	7	8	9
	mm									
0	0.0	25.4	50.8	76.2	101.6	127.0	152.4	177.8	203.2	228.6
10	254.0	279.4	304.8	330.2	355.6	381.0	406.4	431.8	457.2	482.6
20	508.0	533.4	558.8	584.2	609.6	635.0	660.4	685.8	711.2	736.6
30	762.0	787.4	812.8	838.2	863.6	889.0	914.4	939.8	965.2	990.6
40	1016.0	1041.4	1066.8	1092.2	1117.6	1143.0	1168.4	1193.8	1219.2	1244.6
50	1270.0	1295.4	1320.8	1346.2	1371.6	1397.0	1422.4	1447.8	1473.2	1498.6
60	1524.0	1549.4	1574.8	1600.2	1625.6	1651.0	1676.4	1701.8	1727.2	1752.6
70	1778.0	1803.4	1828.8	1854.2	1879.6	1905.0	1930.4	1955.8	1981.2	2006.6
80	2032.0	2057.4	2082.8	2108.2	2133.6	2159.0	2184.4	2209.8	2235.2	2260.6
90	2286.0	2311.4	2336.8	2362.2	2387.6	2413.0	2438.4	2463.8	2489.2	2514.6
100	2540.0	2565.4	2590.8	2616.2	2641.6	2667.0	2692.4	2717.8	2743.2	2768.6

Note: All values in this table are exact, based on the relation 1 in = 25.4 mm. By manipulation of the decimal point any decimal value or multiple of an inch may be converted to its exact equivalent in millimeters.

Fractional Inches To Millimeters
(1 Inch = 25.4 Millimeters)

In.	0	1/16	1/8	3/16	1/4	5/16	3/8	7/16
					mm			
0	0.0	1.6	3.2	4.8	6.4	7.9	9.5	11.1
1	25.4	27.0	28.6	30.2	31.8	33.3	34.9	36.5
2	50.8	52.4	54.0	55.6	57.2	58.7	60.3	61.9
3	76.2	77.8	79.4	81.0	82.6	84.1	85.7	87.3
4	101.6	103.2	104.8	106.4	108.0	109.5	111.1	112.7
5	127.0	128.6	130.2	131.8	133.4	134.9	136.5	138.1
6	152.4	154.0	155.6	157.2	158.8	160.3	161.9	163.5
7	177.8	179.4	181.0	182.6	184.2	185.7	187.3	188.9
8	203.2	204.8	206.4	208.0	209.6	211.1	212.7	214.3
9	228.6	230.2	231.8	233.4	235.0	236.5	238.1	239.7
10	254.0	255.6	257.2	258.8	260.4	261.9	263.5	265.1

Fractional Inches To Millimeters (continued)
(1 Inch = 25.4 Millimeters)

In.	1/2	9/16	5/8	11/16	3/4	13/16	7/8	15/16
					mm			
0	12.7	14.3	15.9	17.5	19.1	20.6	22.2	23.8
1	38.1	39.7	41.3	42.9	44.5	46.0	47.6	49.2
2	63.5	65.1	66.7	68.3	69.9	71.4	73.0	74.6
3	88.9	90.5	92.1	93.7	95.3	96.8	98.4	100.0
4	114.3	115.9	117.5	119.1	120.7	122.2	123.8	125.4
5	139.7	141.3	142.9	144.5	146.1	147.6	149.2	150.8
6	165.1	166.7	168.3	169.9	171.5	173.0	174.6	176.2
7	190.5	192.1	193.7	195.3	196.9	198.4	200.0	201.6
8	215.9	217.5	219.1	220.7	222.3	223.8	225.4	227.0
9	241.3	242.9	244.5	246.1	247.7	249.2	250.8	252.4
10	266.7	268.3	269.9	271.5	273.1	274.6	276.2	277.8

Additional Fractional/Decimal Inch—Millimeter Equivalents

INCHES		MILLI–METERS	INCHES		MILLI–METERS	INCHES		MILLI–METERS
Frac–tions	Decimals		Frac–tions	Decimals		Frac–tions	Decimals	
	.00394	.1		.2	5.08		.44	11.176
	.00787	.2	13/64	.203125	5.1594		.45	11.430
	.01	.254		.21	5.334	29/64	.453125	11.5094
	.01181	.3	7/32	.21875	5.5562		.46	11.684
1/64	.015625	.3969		.22	5.588	15/32	.46875	11.9062
	.01575	.4		.23	5.842		.47	11.938
	.01969	.5	15/64	.234375	5.9531		.47244	12.0
	.02	.508		.23622	6.0		.48	12.192
	.02362	.6		.24	6.096	31/64	.484375	12.3031
	.02756	.7	1/4	.25	6.35		.49	12.446
	.03	.762		.26	6.604	1/2	.50	12.7
1/32	.03125	.7938	17/64	.265625	6.7469		.51	12.954
	.0315	.8		.27	6.858		.51181	13.0
	.03543	.9		.27559	7.0	33/64	.515625	13.0969
	.03937	1.0		.28	7.112		.52	13.208

(continued)

Additional Fractional/Decimal Inch—Millimeter Equivalents (continued)

INCHES Fractions	Decimals	MILLIMETERS	INCHES Fractions	Decimals	MILLIMETERS	INCHES Fractions	Decimals	MILLIMETERS
	.04	1.016	9/32	.28125	7.1438		.53	13.462
3/64	.046875	1.1906		.29	7.366	17/32	.53125	13.4938
	.05	1.27	19/64	.296875	7.5406		.54	13.716
	.06	1.524		.30	7.62	35/64	.546875	13.8906
1/16	.0625	1.5875		.31	7.874		.55	13.970
	.07	1.778	5/16	.3125	7.9375		.55118	14.0
5/64	.078125	1.9844		.31496	8.0		.56	14.224
	.07874	2.0		.32	8.128	9/16	.5625	14.2875
	.08	2.032	21/64	.328125	8.3344		.57	14.478
	.09	2.286		.33	8.382	37/64	.578125	14.6844
3/32	.09375	2.3812		.34	8.636		.58	14.732
	.1	2.54	11/32	.34375	8.7312		.59	14.986
7/64	.109375	2.7781		.35	8.89		.59055	15.0
	.11	2.794		.35433	9.0	19/32	.59375	15.0812
	.11811	3.0	23/64	.359375	9.1281		.60	15.24
	.12	3.048		.36	9.144	39/64	.609375	15.4781
1/8	.125	3.175		.37	9.398		.61	15.494
	.13	3.302	3/8	.375	9.525		.62	15.748
	.14	3.556		.38	9.652	5/8	.625	15.875
9/64	.140625	3.5719		.39	9.906		.62992	16.0
	.15	3.810	25/64	.390625	9.9219		.63	16.002
5/32	.15625	3.9688		.39370	10.0		.64	16.256
	.15748	4.0	13/32	.40	10.16	41/64	.640625	16.2719
	.16	4.064		.40625	10.3188		.65	16.510
	.17	4.318		.41	10.414	21/32	.65625	16.6688
11/64	.171875	4.3656		.42	10.668		.66	16.764
	.18	4.572	27/64	.421875	10.7156		.66929	17.0
3/16	.1875	4.7625		.43	10.922		.67	17.018
	.19	4.826		.43307	11.0	43/64	.671875	17.0656
	.19685	5.0	7/16	.4375	11.1125		.68	17.272
11/16	.6875	17.4625	51/64	.796875	20.2406		.90551	23.0
	.69	17.526		.80	20.320	29/32	.90625	23.0188
	.70	17.78		.81	20.574		.91	23.114
45/64	.703125	17.8594	13/16	.8125	20.6375		.92	23.368
	.70866	18.0		.82	20.828	59/64	.921875	23.4156
	.71	18.034		.82677	21.0		.93	23.622
23/32	.71875	18.2562	53/64	.828125	21.0344	15/16	.9375	23.8125
	.72	18.288		.83	21.082		.94	23.876
	.73	18.542		.84	21.336		.94488	24.0
47/64	.734375	18.6531	27/32	.84375	21.4312		.95	24.130
	.74	18.796		.85	21.590	61/64	.953125	24.2094
	.74803	19.0	55/64	.859375	21.8281		.96	24.384
3/4	.75	19.050		.86	21.844	31/32	.96875	24.6062
	.76	19.304		.86614	22.0		.97	24.638
49/64	.765625	19.4469		.87	22.098		.98	24.892
	.77	19.558	7/8	.875	22.225		.98425	25.0
	.78	19.812		.88	22.352	63/64	.984375	25.0031
25/32	.78125	19.8438		.89	22.606		.99	25.146
	.78740	20.0	57/64	.890625	22.6219	1	1.00000	25.4000
	.79	20.066		.90	22.860			

Round off decimal points to provide no more than the desired degree of accuracy.

Area Equivalents

Note: Use Multiplier at Convergence of Row and Column	Square Meters	Square Inches	Square Feet	Square Miles	Square Kilometers
Square Meters	1	1549.99	10.7639	3.861×10^{-7}	1×10^{-6}
Square Inches	0.0006452	1	6.944×10^{-3}	2.491×10^{-10}	6.452×10^{-10}
Square Feet	0.0929	144	1	3.587×10^{-8}	9.29×10^{-8}
Square Miles	2,,589,999	– – –	27,878,400	1	2.59
Square Kilometers	1,000,000	– – –	10,763,867	0.3861	1

1 square meter = 10,000 square centimeters.
1 square millimeter = 0.01 square centimeter = 0.00155 square inches.

Volume Equivalents

Note: Use Multiplier at Convergence of Row and Column	Cubic Decimeters (Liters)	Cubic Inches	Cubic Feet	U.S. Quart	U.S. Gallon	Imperial Gallon	U.S. Barrel (Petroleum)
Cubic Decimeters (Liters)	1	61.0234	0.03531	1.05668	0.264178	0.220083	0.00629
Cubic Inches	0.01639	1	5.787×10^{-4}	0.01732	0.004329	0.003606	0.000103
Cubic Feet	28.317	1728	1	29.9221	7.48055	6.22888	0.1781
U.S. Quart	0.94636	57.75	0.03342	1	0.25	0.2082	0.00595
U.S. Gallon	3.78543	231	0.13368	4	1	0.833	0.02381
Imperial Gallon	4.54374	277.274	0.16054	4.80128	1.20032	1	0.02877
U.S. Barrel (Petroleum)	158.98	9702	5.6146	168	42	34.973	1

1 cubic meter = 1,000,000 cubic centimeters.
1 liter = 1000 milliliters = 1000 cubic centimeters.

Volume Rate Equivalents

Note: Use Multiplier at Convergence of Row and Column	Liters Per Minute	Cubic Meters Per Hour	Cubic Feet Per Hour	Liters Per Hour	U.S. Gallon Per Minute.	U.S. Barrel Per Day
Liters Per Minute	1	0.06	2.1189	60	0.264178	9.057
Cubic Meters Per Hour	16.667	1	35.314	1000	4.403	151
Cubic Feet Per Hour	0.4719	0.028317	1	28.317	0.1247	4.2746
Liters Per Hour	0.016667	0.001	0.035314	1	0.004403	0.151
U.S. Gallon Per Minute	3.785	0.2273	8.0208	227.3	1	34.28
U.S. Barrel Per Day	0.1104	0.006624	0.23394	6.624	0.02917	1

Mass Conversion—Pounds to Kilograms
(1 pound = 0.4536 kilogram)

Pounds	0	1	2	3	4	5	6	7	8	9
	Kilograms									
0	0.00	0.45	0.91	1.36	1.81	2.27	2.72	3.18	3.63	4.08
10	4.54	4.99	5.44	5.90	6.35	6.80	7.26	7.71	8.16	8.62
20	9.07	9.53	9.98	10.43	10.89	11.34	11.79	12.25	12.70	13.15
30	13.61	14.06	14.52	14.97	15.42	15.88	16.33	16.78	17.24	17.69
40	18.14	18.60	19.05	19.50	19.96	20.41	20.87	21.32	21.77	22.23
50	22.68	23.13	23.59	24.04	24.49	24.95	25.40	25.86	26.31	26.76
60	27.22	27.67	28.12	28.58	29.03	29.48	29.94	30.39	30.84	31.30
70	31.75	32.21	32.66	33.11	33.57	34.02	34.47	34.93	35.38	35.83
80	36.29	36.74	37.20	37.65	38.10	38.56	39.01	39.46	39.92	40.37
90	40.82	41.28	41.73	42.18	42.64	43.09	43.55	44.00	44.45	44.91

Pressure Equivalents

Note: Use Multiplier at Convergence of Row and Column	Kg. Per Sq. Cm.	Lb. Per Sq. In.	Atm.	Bar	In. of Hg.	Kilopascals	In. of Water	Ft. of water
Kg. Per Sq. Cm.	1	14.22	0.9678	0.98067	28.96	98.067	394.05	32.84
Lb. Per Sq. In.	0.07031	1	0.06804	0.06895	2.036	6.895	27.7	2.309
Atm.	1.0332	14.696	1	1.01325	29.92	101.325	407.14	33.93
Bar	1.01972	14.5038	0.98692	1	29.53	100	402.156	33.513
In. of Hg.	0.03453	0.4912	0.03342	0.033864	1	3.3864	13.61	11.134
Kilopascals	0.0101972	0.145038	0.0098696	0.01	0.2953	1	4.02156	0.33513
In. of Water	0.002538	0.0361	0.002456	0.00249	0.07349	0.249	1	0.0833
Ft. of Water	0.03045	0.4332	0.02947	0.029839	0.8819	2.9839	12	1

1 ounce/sq. inch = 0.0625 lbs./sq. inch

Pressure Conversion—Pounds per Square Inch to Bar*

Pounds Per Square Inch	Bar									
	0	1	2	3	4	5	6	7	8	9
0	0.000000	0.068948	0.137895	0.206843	0.275790	0.344738	0.413685	0.482633	0.551581	0.620528
10	0.689476	0.758423	0.827371	0.896318	0.965266	1.034214	1.103161	1.172109	1.241056	1.310004
20	1.378951	1.447899	1.516847	1.585794	1.654742	1.723689	1.792637	1.861584	1.930532	1.999480
30	2.068427	2.137375	2.206322	2.275270	2.344217	2.413165	2.482113	2.551060	2.620008	2.688955
40	2.757903	2.826850	2.895798	2.964746	3.033693	3.102641	3.171588	3.240536	3.309484	3.378431
50	3.447379	3.516326	3.585274	3.654221	3.723169	3.792117	3.861064	3.930012	3.998959	4.067907
60	4.136854	4.205802	4.274750	4.343697	4.412645	4.481592	4.550540	4.619487	4.688435	4.757383
70	4.826330	4.895278	4.964225	5.033173	5.102120	5.171068	5.240016	5.308963	5.377911	5.446858
80	5.515806	5.584753	5.653701	5.722649	5.791596	5.860544	5.929491	5.998439	6.067386	6.136334
90	6.205282	6.274229	6.343177	6.412124	6.481072	6.550019	6.618967	6.687915	6.756862	6.825810
100	6.894757	6.963705	7.032652	7.101600	7.170548	7.239495	7.308443	7.377390	7.446338	7.515285

Note: To convert to kilopascals, move decimal point two positions to right; to convert to Megapascals, move decimal point one position to left. For example, 30 psi = 2.068427 bar = 206.8427 kPa = 0.2068427 MPa.
Note: Round off decimal points to provide no more than the desired degree of accuracy.

Temperature Conversion Formulas

To Convert From	To	Substitute in Formula
Degrees Celsius	Degrees Fahrenheit	$(°C \times 9/5) + 32$
Degrees Celsius	Kelvin	$(°C + 273.16)$
Degrees Fahrenheit	Degrees Celsius	$(°F{-}32) \times 5/9$
Degrees Fahrenheit	Degrees Rankin	$(°F + 459.69)$

Temperature Conversions

°C	Temp. in °C or °F to be Converted	°F	°C	Temp. in °C or °F to be Converted	°F	°C	Temp. in °C or °F to be Converted	°F
−273.16	−459.69		−90.00	−130	−202.0	−17.8	0	32.0
−267.78	−450		−84.44	−120	−184.0	−16.7	2	35.6
−262.22	−440		−78.89	−110	−166.0	−15.6	4	39.2
−256.67	−430		−73.33	−100	−148.0	−14.4	6	42.8
−251.11	−420		−70.56	−95	−139.0	−13.3	8	46.4
−245.56	−410		−67.78	−90	−130.0	−12.2	10	50.0
−240.00	−400		−65.00	−85	−121.0	−11.1	12	53.6
−234.44	−390		−62.22	−80	−112.0	−10.0	14	57.2
−228.89	−380		−59.45	−75	−103.0	−8.89	16	60.8
−223.33	−370		−56.67	−70	−94.0	−7.78	18	64.4
−217.78	−360		−53.89	−65	−85.0	−6.67	20	68.0
−212.22	−350		−51.11	−60	−76.0	−5.56	22	71.6
−206.67	−340		−48.34	−55	−67.0	−4.44	24	75.2
−201.11	−330		−45.56	−50	−58.0	−3.33	26	78.8
−195.56	−320		−42.78	−45	−49.0	−2.22	28	82.4
−190.00	−310		−40.00	−40	−40.0	−1.11	30	86.0
−184.44	−300		−38.89	−38	−36.4	0	32	89.6
−178.89	−290		−37.78	−36	−32.8	1.11	34	93.2
−173.33	−280		−36.67	−34	−29.2	2.22	36	96.8
−169.53	−273.16	−459.69	−35.56	−32	−25.6	3.33	38	100.4
−168.89	−272	−457.6	−34.44	−30	−22.0	4.44	40	104.0
−167.78	−270	−454.0	−33.33	−28	−18.4	5.56	42	107.6
−162.22	−260	−436.0	−32.22	−26	−14.8	6.67	44	111.2
−156.67	−250	−418.0	−31.11	−24	−11.2	7.78	46	114.8
−151.11	−240	−400.0	−30.00	−22	−7.6	8.89	48	118.4
−145.56	−230	−382.0	−28.89	−20	−4.0	10.0	50	122.0
−140.00	−220	−364.0	−27.78	−18	−0.4	11.1	52	125.6
−134.44	−210	−346.0	−26.67	−16	3.2	12.2	54	129.2
−128.89	−200	−328.0	−25.56	−14	6.8	13.3	56	132.8
−123.33	−190	−310.0	−24.44	−12	10.4	14.4	58	136.4
−117.78	−180	−292.0	−23.33	−10	14.0	15.6	60	140.0
−112.22	−170	−274.0	−22.22	−8	17.6	16.7	62	143.6
−106.67	−160	−256.0	−21.11	−6	21.2	17.8	64	147.2
−101.11	−150	−238.0	−20.00	−4	24.8	18.9	66	150.8
−95.56	−140	−220.0	−18.89	−2	28.4	20.0	68	154.4

(continued)

Temperature Conversions (continued)

°C	Temp. in °C or °F to be Converted	°F	°C	Temp. in °C or °F to be Converted	°F	°C	Temp. in °C or °F to be Converted	°F
21.1	70	158.0	204.4	400	752.0	454.4	850	1562.0
22.2	72	161.6	210.0	410	770.0	460.0	860	1580.0
23.3	74	165.2	215.6	420	788.0	465.6	870	1598.0
24.4	76	168.8	221.1	430	806.0	471.1	880	1616.0
25.6	78	172.4	226.7	440	824.0	476.7	890	1634.0
26.7	80	176.0	232.2	450	842.0	482.2	900	1652.0
27.8	82	179.6	237.8	460	860.0	487.8	910	1670.0
28.9	84	183.2	243.3	470	878.0	493.3	920	1688.0
30.0	86	186.8	248.9	480	896.0	498.9	930	1706.0
31.1	88	190.4	254.4	490	914.0	504.4	940	1724.0
32.2	90	194.0	260.0	500	932.0	510.0	950	1742.0
33.3	92	197.6	265.6	510	950.0	515.6	960	1760.0
34.4	94	201.2	271.1	520	968.0	521.1	970	1778.0
35.6	96	204.8	276.7	530	986.0	526.7	980	1796.0
36.7	98	208.4	282.2	540	1004.0	532.2	990	1814.0
37.8	100	212.0	287.8	550	1022.0	537.8	1000	1832.0
43.3	110	230.0	293.3	560	1040.0	543.3	1010	1850.0
48.9	120	248.0	298.9	570	1058.0	548.9	1020	1868.0
54.4	130	266.0	304.4	580	1076.0	554.4	1030	1886.0
60.0	140	284.0	310.0	590	1094.0	560.0	1040	1904.0
65.6	150	302.0	315.6	600	1112.0	565.6	1050	1922.0
71.1	160	320.0	321.1	610	1130.0	571.1	1060	1940.0
76.7	170	338.0	326.7	620	1148.0	576.7	1070	1958.0
82.2	180	356.0	332.2	630	1166.0	582.2	1080	1976.0
87.8	190	374.0	337.8	640	1184.0	587.8	1090	1994.0
93.3	200	392.0	343.3	650	1202.0	593.3	1100	2012.0
98.9	210	410.0	348.9	660	1220.0	598.9	1110	2030.0
104.4	220	428.0	354.4	670	1238.0	604.4	1120	2048.0
110.0	230	446.0	360.0	680	1256.0	610.0	1130	2066.0
115.6	240	464.0	365.6	690	1274.0	615.6	1140	2084.0
121.1	250	482.0	371.1	700	1292.0	621.1	1150	2102.0
126.7	260	500.0	376.7	710	1310.0	626.7	1160	2120.0
132.2	270	518.0	382.2	720	1328.0	632.2	1170	2138.0
137.8	280	536.0	387.8	730	1346.0	637.8	1180	2156.0
143.3	290	554.0	393.3	740	1364.0	643.3	1190	2174.0
148.9	300	572.0	398.9	750	1382.0	648.9	1200	2192.0
154.4	310	590.0	404.4	760	1400.0	654.4	1210	2210.0
160.0	320	608.0	410.0	770	1418.0	660.0	1220	2228.0
165.6	330	626.0	415.6	780	1436.0	665.6	1230	2246.0
171.1	340	644.0	421.1	790	1454.0	671.1	1240	2264.0
176.7	350	662.0	426.7	800	1472.0	676.7	1250	2282.0
182.2	360	680.0	432.2	810	1490.0	682.2	1260	2300.0
187.8	370	698.0	437.8	820	1508.0	687.8	1270	2318.0
193.3	380	716.0	443.3	830	1526.0	693.3	1280	2336.0
198.9	390	734.0	448.9	840	1544.0	698.9	1290	2354.0

(continued)

Temperature Conversions (continued)

°C	Temp. in °C or °F to be Converted	°F	°C	Temp. in °C or °F to be Converted	°F	°C	Temp. in °C or °F to be Converted	°F
704.4	1300	2372.0	760.0	1400	2552.0	815.6	1500	2732.0
710.0	1310	2390.0	765.6	1410	2570.0			
715.6	1320	2408.0	771.1	1420	2588.0			
721.1	1330	2426.0	776.7	1430	2606.0			
726.7	1340	2444.0	782.2	1440	2624.0			
732.2	1350	2462.0	787.0	1450	2642.0			
737.8	1360	2480.0	793.3	1460	2660.0			
743.3	1370	2498.0	798.9	1470	2678.0			
748.9	1380	2516.0	804.4	1480	2696.0			
754.4	1390	2534.0	810.0	1490	2714.0			

A.P.I. and Baumé Gravity Tables and Weight Factors

A.P.I. Gravity	Baumé Gravity	Specific Gravity	Lb/ U.S. Gal	U.S. Gal/Lb	A.P.I. Gravity	Baumé Gravity	Specific Gravity	Lb/ U.S. Gal	U.S. Gal/Lb
0	10.247	1.0760	8.962	0.1116					
1	9.223	1.0679	8.895	0.1124	31	30.78	0.8708	7.251	0.1379
2	8.198	1.0599	8.828	0.1133	32	31.77	0.8654	7.206	0.1388
3	7.173	1.0520	8.762	0.1141	33	32.76	0.8602	7.163	0.1396
4	6.148	1.0443	8.698	0.1150	34	33.75	0.8550	7.119	0.1405
5	5.124	1.0366	8.634	0.1158	35	34.73	0.8498	7.076	0.1413
6	4.099	1.0291	8.571	0.1167	36	35.72	0.8448	7.034	0.1422
7	3.074	1.0217	8.509	0.1175	37	36.71	0.8398	6.993	0.1430
8	2.049	1.0143	8.448	0.1184	38	37.70	0.8348	6.951	0.1439
9	1.025	1.0071	8.388	0.1192	39	38.69	0.8299	6.910	0.1447
10	10.00	1.0000	8.328	0.1201	40	39.68	0.8251	6.870	0.1456
11	10.99	0.9930	8.270	0.1209	41	40.67	0.8203	6.830	0.1464
12	11.98	0.9861	8.212	0.1218	42	41.66	0.8155	6.790	0.1473
13	12.97	0.9792	8.155	0.1226	43	42.65	0.8109	6.752	0.1481
14	13.96	0.9725	8.099	0.1235	44	43.64	0.8063	6.713	0.1490
15	14.95	0.9659	8.044	0.1243	45	44.63	0.8017	6.675	0.1498
16	15.94	0.9593	7.989	0.1252	46	45.62	0.7972	6.637	0.1507
17	16.93	0.9529	7.935	0.1260	47	50.61	0.7927	6.600	0.1515
18	17.92	0.9465	7.882	0.1269	48	50.60	0.7883	6.563	0.1524
19	18.90	0.9402	7.830	0.1277	49	50.59	0.7839	6.526	0.1532
20	19.89	0.9340	7.778	0.1286	50	50.58	0.7796	6.490	0.1541
21	20.88	0.9279	7.727	0.1294	51	50.57	0.7753	6.455	0.1549
22	21.87	0.9218	7.676	0.1303	52	51.55	0.7711	6.420	0.1558
23	22.86	0.9159	7.627	0.1311	53	52.54	0.7669	6.385	0.1566
24	23.85	0.9100	7.578	0.1320	54	53.53	0.7628	6.350	0.1575
25	24.84	0.9042	7.529	0.1328	55	54.52	0.7587	6.316	0.1583
26	25.83	0.8984	7.481	0.1337	56	55.51	0.7547	6.283	0.1592
27	26.82	0.8927	7.434	0.1345	57	56.50	0.7507	6.249	0.1600
28	27.81	0.8871	7.387	0.1354	58	57.49	0.7467	6.216	0.1609
29	28.80	0.8816	7.341	0.1362	59	58.48	0.7428	6.184	0.1617
30	29.79	0.8762	7.296	0.1371	60	59.47	0.7389	6.151	0.1626

(continued)

A.P.I. and Baumé Gravity Tables and Weight Factors (continued)

A.P.I. Gravity	Baumé Gravity	Specific Gravity	Lb/ U.S. Gal	U.S. Gal/Lb	A.P.I. Gravity	Baumé Gravity	Specific Gravity	Lb/ U.S. Gal	U.S. Gal/Lb
61	60.46	0.7351	6.119	0.1634	81	80.25	0.6659	5.542	0.1804
62	61.45	0.7313	6.087	0.1643	82	81.24	0.6628	5.516	0.1813
63	62.44	0.7275	6.056	0.1651	83	82.23	0.6597	5.491	0.1821
64	63.43	0.7238	6.025	0.1660	84	83.22	0.6566	5.465	0.1830
65	64.42	0.7201	5.994	0.1668	85	84.20	0.6536	5.440	0.1838
66	65.41	0.7165	5.964	0.1677	86	85.19	0.6506	5.415	0.1847
67	66.40	0.7128	5.934	0.1685	87	86.18	0.6476	5.390	0.1855
68	67.39	0.7093	5.904	0.1694	88	87.17	0.6446	5.365	0.1864
69	68.37	0.7057	5.874	0.1702	89	88.16	0.6417	5.341	0.1872
70	69.36	0.7022	5.845	0.1711	90	89.15	0.6388	5.316	0.1881
71	70.35	0.6988	5.817	0.1719	91	90.14	0.6360	5.293	0.1889
72	71.34	0.6953	5.788	0.1728	92	91.13	0.6331	5.269	0.1898
73	72.33	0.6919	5.759	0.1736	93	92.12	0.6303	5.246	0.1906
74	73.32	0.6886	5.731	0.1745	94	93.11	0.6275	5.222	0.1915
75	74.31	0.6852	5.703	0.1753	95	94.10	0.6247	5.199	0.1924
76	75.30	0.6819	5.676	0.1762	96	95.09	0.6220	5.176	0.1932
77	76.29	0.6787	5.649	0.1770	97	96.08	0.6193	5.154	0.1940
78	77.28	0.6754	5.622	0.1779	98	97.07	0.6166	5.131	0.1949
79	78.27	0.6722	5.595	0.1787	99	98.06	0.6139	5.109	0.1957
80	79.26	0.6690	5.568	0.1796	100	99.05	0.6112	5.086	0.1966

The relation of Degrees Baumé or A.P.I. to Specific Gravity is expressed by the following formulas:

For liquids lighter than water:

$$\text{Degrees Baumé} = \frac{140}{G} - 130, \qquad G = \frac{140}{130 + \text{Degrees Baume}}$$

$$\text{Degrees A.P.I.} = \frac{141.5}{G} - 131.5, \qquad G = \frac{141.5}{131.5 + \text{Degrees A.P.I.}}$$

For liquids heavier than water:

$$\text{Degrees Baumé} = 145 - \frac{145}{G} \qquad G = \frac{145}{145 - \text{Degrees Baume}}$$

G = Specific Gravity = ratio of the weight of a given volume of oil at 60° Fahrenheit to the weight of the same volume of water at 60° Fahrenheit.

The above tables are based on the weight of 1 gallon (U.S.) of oil with a volume of 231 cubic inches at 60° Fahrenheit in air at 760 mm pressure and 50% humidity. Assumed weight of 1 gallon of water at 60° Fahrenheit in air is 8.32828 pounds.

To determine the resulting gravity by mixing oils of different gravities:

$$D = \frac{md_1 + nd_2}{m + n}$$

D = Density or Specific Gravity of mixture
m = Proportion of oil of d_1 density
n = Proportion of oil of d_2 density
d_1 = Specific Gravity of m oil
d_2 = Specific Gravity of n oil

Equivalent Volume and Weight
Flow Rates of Compressible Fluids

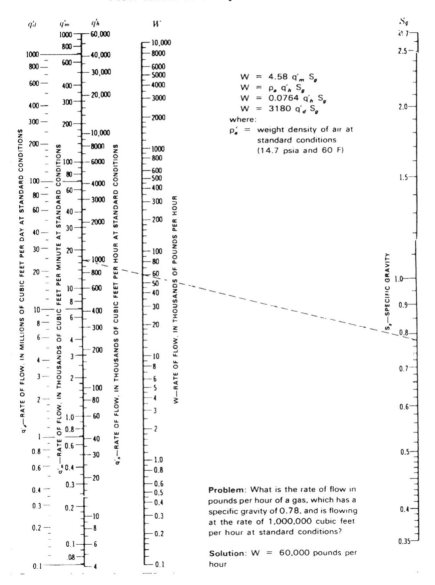

$$W = 4.58\ q'_m\ S_g$$
$$W = \rho'_a\ q'_h\ S_g$$
$$W = 0.0764\ q'_h\ S_g$$
$$W = 3180\ q'_d\ S_g$$

where:

ρ'_a = weight density of air at standard conditions (14.7 psia and 60 F)

Problem: What is the rate of flow in pounds per hour of a gas, which has a specific gravity of 0.78, and is flowing at the rate of 1,000,000 cubic feet per hour at standard conditions?

Solution: W = 60,000 pounds per hour

Extracted from Technical Paper No. 410, *Flow of Fluids*, with permission of Crane Co.

Viscosity Conversion Nomograph

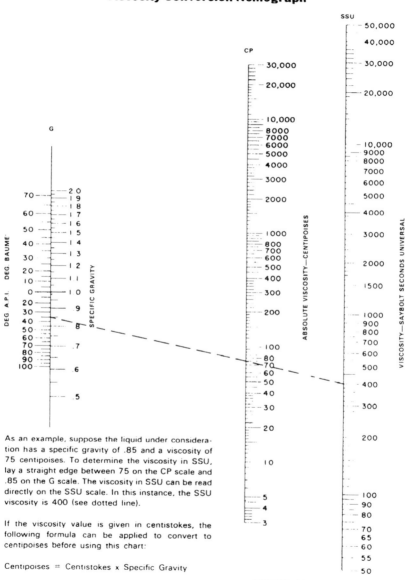

As an example, suppose the liquid under consideration has a specific gravity of .85 and a viscosity of 75 centipoises. To determine the viscosity in SSU, lay a straight edge between 75 on the CP scale and .85 on the G scale. The viscosity in SSU can be read directly on the SSU scale. In this instance, the SSU viscosity is 400 (see dotted line).

If the viscosity value is given in centistokes, the following formula can be applied to convert to centipoises before using this chart:

Centipoises = Centistokes x Specific Gravity

VISCOSITY CONVERSION NOMOGRAPH

Other Useful Conversions

To Convert From	To	Multiply By
Cu Ft (Methane)	B.T.U.	1000 (approx.)
Cu Ft of Water	Lbs of Water	62.4
Degrees	Radians	0.01745
Gals	Lbs of Water	8.336
Grams	Ounces	0.0352
Horsepower (mech.)	Ft Lbs per Min	33,000
Horsepower (elec.)	Watts	746
Kg	Lbs	2.205
Kg per Cu Meter	Lbs per Cu Ft	0.06243
Kilowatts	Horsepower	1.341
Lbs	Kg	0.4536
Lbs of Air (14.7 psia and 60°F)	Cu Ft of Air	13.1
Lbs per Cu Ft	Kg per Cu Meter	16.0184
Lbs per Hr (Gas)	Std Cu Ft per Hr	13.1/Specific Gravity
Lbs per Hr (Water)	Gals per Min	0.002
Lbs per Sec (Gas)	Std Cu Ft per Hr	46,160/Specific Gravity
Radians	Degrees	57.3
Scfh Air	Scfh Propane	0.81
Scfh Air	Scfh Butane	0.71
Scfh Air	Scfh 0.6 Natural Gas	1.29
Scfh	Cu Meters per Hr	0.028317

Metric Prefixes and Symbols

Multiplication Factor	Prefix	Symbol
$1\ 000\ 000\ 000\ 000\ 000\ 000 = 10^{18}$	exa	E
$1\ 000\ 000\ 000\ 000\ 000 = 10^{15}$	peta	P
$1\ 000\ 000\ 000\ 000 = 10^{12}$	tera	T
$1\ 000\ 000\ 000 = 10^{9}$	giga	G
$1\ 000\ 000 = 10^{6}$	mega	M
$1\ 000 = 10^{3}$	kilo	k
$100 = 10^{2}$	hecto	h
$10 = 10^{1}$	deka	da
$0.1 = 10^{-1}$	deci	d
$0.01 = 10^{-2}$	centi	c
$0.001 = 10^{-3}$	milli	m
$0.000\ 001 = 10^{-6}$	micro	μ
$0.000\ 000\ 001 = 10^{-9}$	nano	n
$0.000\ 000\ 000\ 001 = 10^{-12}$	pico	p
$0.000\ 000\ 000\ 000\ 001 = 10^{-15}$	femto	f
$0.000\ 000\ 000\ 000\ 000\ 001 = 10^{-18}$	atto	a

Subject Index